THE NEURAL CONTROL OF BEHAVIOR

CONTRIBUTORS

PER ANDERSEN

J. BUREŠ

O. BUREŠOVÁ

FREDERICK CRESCITELLI

S. EDWARDS

J. P. FLYNN

W. FOOTE

GABRIEL HORN

E. ROY JOHN

TERJE LØMO

J. OLDS

W. W. ROBERTS

RICHARD F. THOMPSON

H. VANEGAS

M. VERZEANO

NORMAN M. WEINBERGER

L. WEISKRANTZ

THE NEURAL CONTROL OF BEHAVIOR

Edited by

RICHARD E. WHALEN, RICHARD F. THOMPSON,

MARCEL VERZEANO, and NORMAN M. WEINBERGER
Department of Psychobiology
University of California
Irvine, California

 ACADEMIC PRESS   New York and London

WL 102
N 40 N
1970

ACADEMIC PRESS, INC.
111 Fifth Avenue, New York, New York 10003

United Kingdom Edition published by
ACADEMIC PRESS, INC. (LONDON) LTD.
Berkeley Square House, London W1X 6BA

LIBRARY OF CONGRESS CATALOG CARD NUMBER: 72-117097

PRINTED IN THE UNITED STATES OF AMERICA

CONTENTS

Section I. NEURAL MECHANISMS

Mode of Control of Hippocampal Pyramidal Cell Discharges

PER ANDERSEN AND TERJE LØMO

Evoked Responses and Network Dynamics

M. VERZEANO

v

Hypothalamic Mechanisms for Motivational and Species-Typical Behavior

W. W. ROBERTS

Section IV. LEARNING AND MEMORY

The Reunified Split Brain

J. BUREŠ AND O. BUREŠOVÁ

Visual Memory and the Temporal Lobe of the Monkey

L. WEISKRANTZ

The Behavior of Hippocampal Neurons during Conditioning Experiments

J. OLDS

LIST OF CONTRIBUTORS

Numbers in parentheses indicate the pages on which the authors' contributions begin.

Per Andersen (3), Institute of Neurophysiology, University of Oslo, Oslo

J. Bureš (211), Institute of Physiology, Czechoslovak Academy of Sciences, Prague

O. Burešová (211), Institute of Physiology, Czechoslovak Academy of Sciences, Prague

Frederick Crescitelli (77), Department of Zoology, University of California, Los Angeles

S. Edwards (135), Departments of Psychiatry and Anatomy, Yale University School of Medicine, New Haven

J. P. Flynn (135), Departments of Psychiatry and Anatomy, Yale University School of Medicine, New Haven

W. Foote (135), Departments of Psychiatry and Anatomy, Yale University School of Medicine, New Haven

Gabriel Horn (103), Department of Anatomy, Cambridge University, Cambridge

E. Roy John (295), Brain Research Laboratories, New York Medical College, New York

Terje Lømo (3), Insititute of Neurophysiology, University of Oslo, Oslo

J. Olds (257), Department of Psychology, University of Michigan, Ann Arbor

W. W. Roberts (175), Department of Psychology, University of Minnesota, Minneapolis

Richard F. Thompson (55), Department of Psychobiology, University of California, Irvine

H. Vanegas (135), Departments of Psychiatry and Anatomy, Yale University School of Medicine, New Haven

M. Verzeano (27), Department of Psychobiology, University of California, Irvine

Norman M. Weinberger (63), Department of Psychobiology, University of California, Irvine

L. Weiskrantz (239), Institute of Experimental Psychology, Oxford

PREFACE

On June 9–June 13, 1968 the Department of Psychobiology of the University of California, Irvine had the great pleasure of serving as host to eminent scholars from throughout the world. The occasion was the department's first interdisciplinary conference on the neural control of behavior. This conference was coordinated with the overall Centennial Year Program of the University of California, yet remained a local event designed primarily to facilitate research level discussions between the faculty and students of the department and scientists from a variety of disciplines that touch upon the primary concerns of psychobiology. We feel that our goal was fulfilled. Our five days together proved to be a delightfully enriching experience.

This volume contains some of the material presented and discussed at the conference. The chapters represent a distillation of the topics covered. In no way do they capture the excitement of the communications or the flavor of the interchanges that took place. Nonetheless, we felt it worthwhile to bring these discussions together in book form because these presentations do provide a foundation for future research on neurobiology and behavior.

Since this conference represented the combined efforts of faculty members, graduate students, and staff of the Department of Psychobiology, we decided that the author of this book is properly "The Department of Psychobiology" rather than any one member of the department. Nonetheless, special contributions were made by a few and these should be recognized. Richard F. Thompson, Marcel Verzeano, Norman M. Weinberger, and Richard E. Whalen served as focal points for organizing sections of the book. Their efforts have led to this publication. The most important person, however, was our Departmental Administrative Assistant, Mrs. Ruth Lerner, who coordinated the vast array of details and arrangements which made our first conference successful.

GUESTS OF THE DEPARTMENT

PER ANDERSEN
Institute of Neurophysiology
  University of Oslo

JAN BUREŠ
Institute of Physiology
  Czechoslovak Academy of Sciences

FREDERICK CRESCITELLI
Department of Zoology
  University of California at Los Angeles

RUSSELL DeVALOIS
Department of Psychology
  Indiana University

JOHN P. FLYNN
Departments of Psychiatry and
  Anatomy
  Yale University

RALPH W. GERARD
School of Biological Sciences
  University of California at Irvine

GABRIEL HORN
Department of Anatomy
  Cambridge University

E. ROY JOHN
Brain Research Laboratories
  New York Medical College

JAMES OLDS
Department of Psychology
  University of Michigan

KARL PRIBRAM
Department of Psychiatry
  Standford University

WARREN W. ROBERTS
Department of Psychology
  University of Minnesota

EVELYN SATINOFF
Medical School
  University of Pennsylvania

JOSÉ SEGUNDO
Department of Anatomy
  University of California at Los Angeles

FELIX STRUMWASSER
Division of Biology
  California Institute of Technology

GUNNAR SVAETICHEN
Department of Neurobiology
  IVIC, Caracas

PHILIP TEITELBAUM
Department of Psychology
  University of Pennsylvania

THE DEPARTMENT OF PSYCHOBIOLOGY: 1968

Faculty

CARL COTMAN	*Assistant Professor*
JAMES L. McGAUGH	*Professor and Dean of the School of Biological Sciences*
VINCENT J. POLIDORA	*Visiting Associate Professor*
ROGER W. RUSSELL	*Professor and Vice Chancellor of Academic Affairs*
GWEN STEPHENS	*Research Associate*
ARTHUR SUMMERFIELD	*Visiting Professor*
RICHARD F. THOMPSON	*Professor*
EDMUNDO VALLECALLE	*Visiting Professor*
MARCEL VERZEANO	*Professor*
DAVID WARBURTON	*Assistant Professor*
NORMAN M. WEINBERGER	*Associate Professor*
RICHARD E. WHALEN	*Associate Professor and Chairman of the Department*

Graduate and Postdoctoral Students of the Department

HERBERT ALPERN   DONNA HARDY

LEWIS BETTINGER   THOMAS IMIG

HERMAN BIRCH   LEONARD KITZES

JOEL DAVIS   PHILIP LANDFIELD

RONALD DAWSON   WILLIAM LUTTGE

RONALD DILL   MARVIN LUTTGES

DAVID EDWARDS   KATHLEEN MAYERS

DAVID GOODMAN   RICHARD T. ROBERTSON

PHILIP GROVES   DAVID SEGAL

JONATHAN HART   RICHARD SWANSON

STEVEN ZORNETZER

NEURAL MECHANISMS

MODE OF CONTROL OF HIPPOCAMPAL PYRAMIDAL CELL DISCHARGES

PER ANDERSEN AND TERJE LØMO

INSTITUTE OF NEUROPHYSIOLOGY, UNIVERSITY OF OSLO, OSLO, NORWAY

The available evidence indicates that the substrate for control of behavior must be located within a variety of sites in the central nervous system. Because the limbic system seems to be involved in a variety of behavioral conditions, it may be of interest to study the modes by which one of the main parts of this system—the hippocampus—controls its cellular discharges. This is particularly so since the mode of activation of the individual pyramidal cells, as well as their modulation by neighboring neurons, differ considerably from the classical pattern of activation, largely derived from studies on motoneurons.

The study of activation pattern in the hippocampus is greatly facilitated by the orderly arrangement of the participating elements, both the neurons and the afferent paths. In particular, the afferent pathways are known to terminate within discrete strata, parallel to the surface of the structure. Since the majority of the cellular elements is oriented vertically to the ventricular surface, it follows that the pathways end on restricted territories of the dendrites and cell bodies. In this way, it is possible to activate synaptically a restricted and defined part of the dendritic tree or the cell body.

From histological observation by Ramón y Cajal (1911), Lorente de Nó (1934), and Blackstad (1956, 1958), it is known that one of the main sources of afferent information to the hippocampus is the entorhinal area. The ordinary activation path of the hippocampal structures from the entorhinal area appears as in Fig. 1 (Andersen, Holmqvist, & Voorhoeve, 1966b). The entorhinal cells emit axons which assemble in the perforant path (p.p.) which traverse the hippocampal fissure to end with synapses in the middle

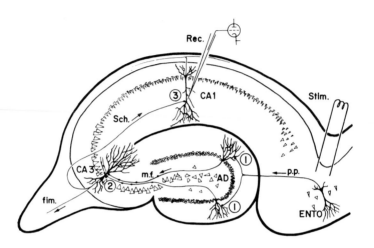

Fig. 1. *Diagram of the hippocampal formation with the different cell types activated from the entorhinal area.* The encircled numbers ①, ②, and ③, give the successive synaptic stations activated. AD—dentate area; ENTO—entorhinal area; fim.—fimbria; m.f.—mossy fibers; p.p.—perforant path; Sch.—Schaffer collateral.

third of the dendritic tree of the granule cells of the dentate area (AD). This synaptic connection is marked with ①. The axons of the granule cells are called mossy fibers (m.f.). These penetrate the hilus of the dentate fascia and end with synapses on CA3 pyramids on the proximal part of the apical dendrite ②. The CA3 pyramids send their impulses out of the hippocampus through the fimbria and fornix to hypothalamic structures. A thick myelinated collateral is diverted and reenters the hippocampus to end in a restricted area of the apical dendritic tree of the CA1 neurons ③. The axons of the CA1 cells bifurcate in the alveus, the white matter just under the ventricle. One branch runs forward to the fimbria and joins the axons of the CA3 cells to septal and hypothalamic areas. The other branch courses in a caudal direction. The exact termination of this branch is still not known.

In addition to this activation system, afferent fibers enter the hippocampus through the fornix in a caudal direction. However, the exact termination and the physiology of these fibers are not fully known. We shall omit this type of afferent information from the present discussion.

I. Methods

Experiments were conducted in adult rabbits, anaesthetized with a mixture of urethane and chloralose (.75 g and 40 mg/kg, respectively) given intravenously in the marginal vein of the ear. The electrodes were placed at the appropriate places under visual control after the neocortex was removed by suction, exposing the ventricular surface of the hippocampal formation. The stimulation electrodes were fine tungsten electrodes, electrolytically polished and insulated with a varnish. They measured from 2 to 20 μ at their tips. Current pulses from 40 μA to .4 mA were applied. The recording electrodes were glass pipettes, filled with 4 M NaCl for extracellular recording, and with 2 M potassium citrate for intracellular recording. Their resistance ranged from 1 to 4 MΩ for extracellular work, and from 4 to 15 MΩ for intracellular recording.

II. Results

A. LOCATION OF EXCITATORY SYNAPSES

Through a combination of physiological and histological methods, all identified excitatory paths have been found to terminate by synapses located on the dendritic tree (Andersen, Blackstad, & Lømo, 1966a). A particularly useful illustration of this principle is the Schaffer collateral pathway. This can conveniently be activated by stimulating the entorhinal area and recording from the CA1 pyramidal cells. In Fig. 2A are extracellular responses recorded at the indicated depths below the ventricular surface in response to a single entorhinal shock. At a depth of .3 mm, a large negative spike occurred after a latency of about 20 msec (+). When the electrode was moved further down, the spike diminished in amplitude and was located on top of a large negative wave (PCN □). The spike had a distinct maximum at .3–.4 mm corresponding to the level of the pyramidal cell bodies (Fig. 2B). The negative wave had its maximum at a level of about .8 mm, corresponding to the layer of Schaffer collateral afferents (Figs. 2B and C). Comparing the firing pattern of individual cells and the results of various lesion experiments, the large negative wave at .8 mm depth may be regarded as the extracellular counterpart of a dendritic EPSP created by the volley along the Schaffer collaterals.

B. MODE OF ACTIVATION OF PYRAMIDAL CELLS

A striking finding with intracellular recording from hippocampal pyramidal cells is the rare presence of EPSP's in response to synaptic excitation

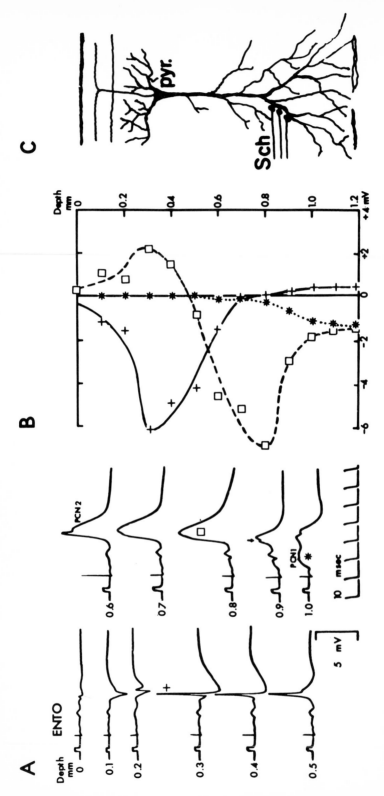

Fig. 2. A: Extracellular potentials in response to a single entorhinal volley recorded with an electrode penetrating the CA1 layer. Recording depths indicated to the left of each trace. B: Plot of the size of the spike ($+$) and of the Schaffer collateral synaptic wave ($\square$) against recording depth. C: A pyramidal cell drawn to scale to facilitate comparison with the graph in B. pyr.—pyramidal cell; Sch.—Schaffer collateral fibers with their synapses.

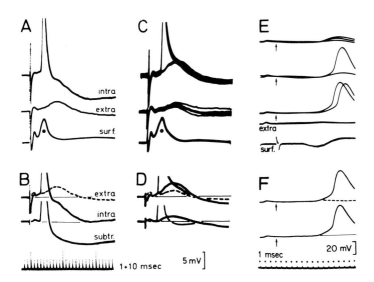

Fig. 3. Upper trace is an intracellular recording from a CA1 neuron in response to fimbrial stimulation at 1/sec. Middle and lower traces are extracellular and surface records, respectively. In B, the extracellular wave is drawn with a broken line superimposed upon the fully drawn intracellular record. The geometrical subtraction is shown in the lower tracing. C and D are similar to B—but the records were taken at 10/sec stimulation. E: Upper line gives intracellular records from a postcruciate pyramidal cell in response to three successive ulnar volleys showing discrete unitary EPSP's. The second and third lines give responses to slightly stronger ulnar volleys with spikes emerging from the EPSP. The fourth and fifth lines give the extracellular and surface records, respectively. F: Upper trace shows the extra- and intracellular records superimposed, lower trace gives the subtracted records, showing a definite EPSP.

in spite of the ability to discharge the cell. In Fig. 3A, the records were taken from a CA3 pyramidal cell in response to fimbrial stimulation. With low rates of stimulation (A), the spike is seen superimposed on a positive wave, similar to an EPSP. However, in the hippocampal formation, the extracellular field potentials are very large, due to the close packing of the cells. Therefore, to obtain the true transmembrane potential change, one must subtract the intracellular from the extracellular record. This procedure (B) shows that the spike takes off from the baseline without any prepotential. Similarly if the cell is driven at higher rates of stimulation (C), the spike seems to take off from a slow depolarizing potential. With the subtraction technique, however, the spike was found to start from the baseline level of the membrane potential. There was a small EPSP, but the onset of the spike occurred before any appreciable depolarization due to the EPSP.

In conclusion, the majority of discharges of these cells occur without an EPSP being detected by an intrasomatic electrode.

C. DETONATOR SYNAPSES

The behavior of the hippocampal pyramidal cells to afferent stimulation is very different from that of neocortical cells in response to a thalamocortical volley. Figure 3E shows unitary EPSP's from a postcruciate cell in response to an ulnar volley. When four or five unitary EPSP's summate, the cell is brought to discharge. This kind of synapse clearly differs from the one prevailing in the hippocampal formation. The histological substrate for the large EPSP's is presumably the horsetail synapse described by Colonnier (1966), whereas the histological substrate for the weaker synaptic effect is the en passage boutons with their parent fibers passing through the dendritic tree at right angles.

D. DENDRITIC CONDUCTION

In Fig. 4, the microelectrode has recorded the CA1 response to single entorhinal volleys. In each assemblage, the upper trace is the microelectrode record and the two lower records are microelectrode and surface record, respectively, shown on expanded sweep. The intensified portion of the upper trace is expanded. The surface record was used as a reference mark to avoid any mistakes caused by spontaneous excitability changes.

The peak of the negative dendritic spike is indicated by arrows. Both the onset and the peak latency increased as the electrode was moved in the direction of the soma. The graph in Fig. 4B gives the conduction speed along the apical dendritic shaft to about .5 m/sec, whereas the conduction along the thinner basal dendritic branches is only .2 m/sec. This evidence clearly points to a dendritic location of the spike initiation. By comparing the size of the synaptic extracellular wave, which corresponds to the dendritic EPSP and the spike size, the largest negative spike occurs in regions slightly removed from that of the synaptic territory (Fig. 2B). In fact, the activated synaptic regions apparently act as shunts for the sodium current associated with propagation of the spike along the dendritic tree.

E. CONDUCTING AND SYNAPTIC DENDRITES

Trying to find a histological correlate for the dendritic synaptic locations and the site of origin of the dendritic spike, several methods have been employed. First, by a comparison of normal electron micrographs with micrographs after degeneration of specific excitatory afferent paths, it can be ascertained that the excitatory synapses are exclusively located in the dendritic territory. For the major part, the afferent fibers make synaptic contact

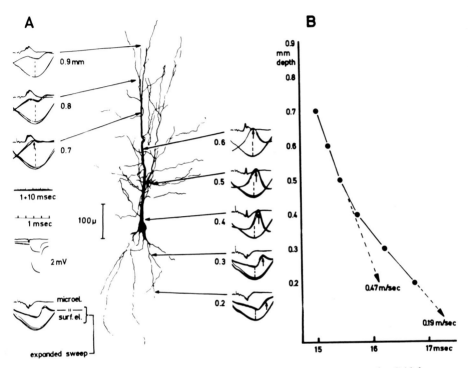

Fig. 4. *Extracellular records taken with a microelectrode penetrating the CA1 layer*
The recording depth has been correlated to a Golgi drawing of a typical CA1 pyramid.
Further explanation in text. B: Graph showing dendritic site of CA1 spike initiation, and
dendritic conduction and its velocity.

with the heads of the dendritic spines (Andersen *et al.*, 1966a). Since excitatory
synapses very rarely occur on the smooth parts on dendrites, and almost
never on the thicker dendrites, the spine portions of the dendritic tree may be
regarded as the synaptic region. Figure 5 shows a Golgi section with impregnation of the spines. There are two types of dendrites present. First, there
are the smooth and relatively thick apical dendrites with their main branches,
the surface of which is covered with glial membranes only. In contrast to
these primary dendrites, the secondary dendrites are very much thinner, only
about 1 μ. The initial portion of the secondary dendrites is smooth. After a
stretch of 5 to 15 μ, the secondary dendrites suddenly become very densely
covered with spines. Since this is the position of excitatory synapses we have
called this region the synaptic dendrites. The remaining smooth portions of
the dendrites, that is the apical dendrite and the initial portion of the secondary dendrites are suitably arranged to conduct spikes. During excitatory
synaptic action, current will flow into the cell under the synaptic membrane

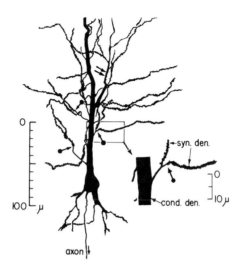

Fig. 5. Part of a CA1 neuron with Golgi impregnation. There is a large difference between the diameter of the apical dendritic shaft and its main branches on one hand and of the thin secondary branches on the other. Furthermore, note the difference between the initial smooth and the more peripheral spine-invested parts of the secondary dendrites.

and leave the neuron by the nearby nonsynaptic dendrites. The outward current will initiate the spike which travels along the smooth dendritic membrane of the apical dendrite and its main branches. Because of the very dense packing of excitatory synapses on the synaptic dendrites, the likelihood of spike production here is small, due to the conductance shunt each activated synapse will produce for the neighboring synapses. The situation in the smooth dendrites is quite different. Contrary to what is often indicated, the main apical dendritic branch is very much thicker than the majority of secondary branches. Therefore, the probability of a block of conduction is presumably smaller than ordinarily anticipated.

As a preliminary conclusion, an afferent volley exciting hippocampal pyramidal cells sets up a local dendritic EPSP which give rise to large extracellular negative potentials at the synaptic sites. These sites correspond to the thin secondary dendrites stuffed with dendritic spines. The action potential is presumably created in the neighboring part of the dendritic tree, that is, the initial smooth part of secondary dendrites and the neighboring part of the apical or basal thick smooth dendrites. From this site of initiation, the spikes are conducted along the dendrites toward the soma where, in the ordinary condition, it appears without any prepotential. During this dendritic conduction, the safety factor may be relatively low. However, by adding depolarization from several adjoining secondary dendrites, the cell may have a new facility for integrating activity coming from several sources.

F. RECURRENT INHIBITION

By far the most common response of hippocampal pyramidal cells to both orthodromic and antidromic activation is the large hyperpolarizing response which has been shown to be an IPSP (Kandel, Spencer, & Brinley, 1961). The extracellular counterpart of the IPSP is a positive wave due to the current leaving the hyperpolarized area of the cell. By plotting the size of the extra-cellular positive wave and relating it to the architecture of the cell (Fig. 6), the inhibitory synapses have been located on the soma (Andersen, Eccles, & Løyning, 1964). There was always a delay of 1.2 to 2.5 msec between the onset of synaptic or antidromic activation and the onset of the IPSP. Furthermore, the IPSP's were found in a large number of cells, even with a relatively small input volley. Therefore, it was presumed that an inhibitory interneuron with axonal ramifications was interposed in the pathway. By a chronic deafferenta-tion procedure, Kandel et al. (1961) showed that a pure antidromic activation of pyramidal cells led to the same type of IPSP's. Therefore, the inhibition in question operates by way of axon collaterals and may be termed a recurrent inhibition.

By applying the criteria listed above, the only histological candidate for an inhibitory interneuron is the basket cell described by Ramón y Cajal (1911, p. 739) and Lorente de Nó (1934). The basket cells have wide axonal ramifications, and are most likely activated by recurrent collaterals of the pyramidal cells and distribute their terminals exclusively to the somata of the pyramidal cells.

In addition to the wide distribution, another important feature of the recurrent inhibition is the long duration and large size of the hyperpolariza-tion and the corresponding profound reduction of the excitability of the pyramidal neurons to direct or synaptic activation. The recurrent inhibitory system is also capable of transmitting impulses at relatively high frequencies. Figure 7 shows recordings from a CA3 pyramidal cell in response to fimbrial stimulation at the indicated rates of stimulation. The time base is very slow, so that the IPSP's appear as nearly vertical lines only. During tetanic stimula-tion, the cell was kept at a fixed maximal membrane potential, corresponding to the membrane potential attained by a single IPSP. This level of the mem-brane potential is most likely identical with the equilibrium potential for the IPSP, indicating the great power of this inhibitory system. Furthermore, it is evident that the inhibitory system may maintain its activity for prolonged periods of time.

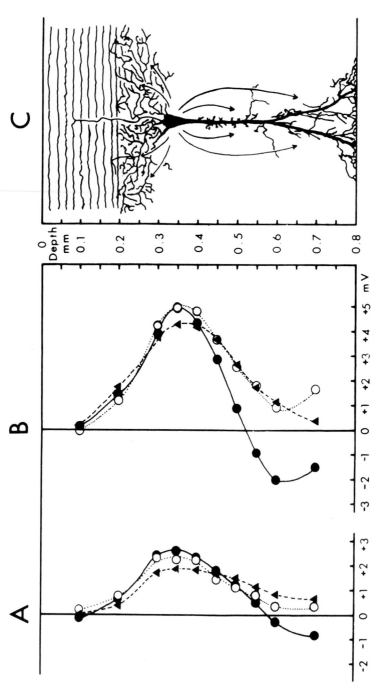

Fig. 6. A and B show the size of the extracellular positive wave associated with inhibition in response to stimulation of three afferent paths: commissural (●), septal (▲), and local (○) at two different strengths, respectively. The maximum positivity corresponds to the level of the pyramidal cell bodies (C). C: The arrows indicate the current flowing during the rise time of the IPSP showing that the inhibitory synapses are located to the soma.

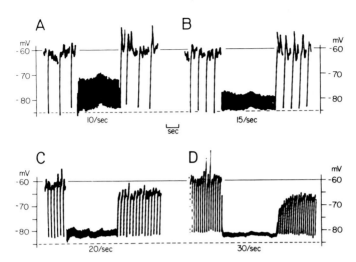

Fig. 7. *Records from a CA3 pyramidal cell in response to fimbrial stimulation at the indicated rate.* Time base is slow so that the IPSP appears as nearly vertical lines. Repetitive stimulation gives a virtual "clamping" of the cell at a fixed membrane potential of about −83 mV.

G. Synaptic Location

The diagram in Fig. 8 indicates the localization pattern of excitatory synapses (E syn: ○) on dendritic spines and inhibitory synapses (I syn: ●) on the soma of a hippocampal pyramidal cell. The basket cell (Bc) is inhibitory and is activated by recurrent collaterals of the pyramidal cell axon (a coll).

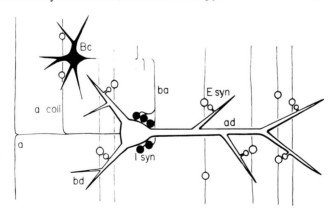

Fig. 8. *Diagrammatic representation of the localization of excitatory and inhibitory synapses on hippocampal pyramidal cells.* Inhibitory cells and synapses are drawn in black. a—pyramidal cell axon; a coll—axon collateral; ad—apical dendrite; ba—basket cell axon; Bc—basket cell; bd—basal dendrite; E syn—excitatory synapse; I syn—inhibitory synapse.

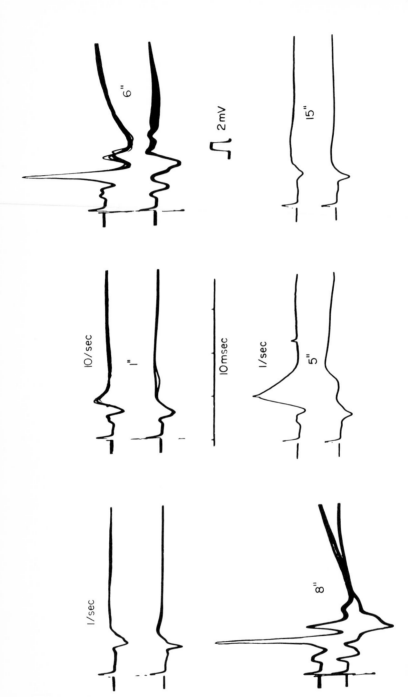

Fig. 9. Extracellular record from the CA3 pyramidal layer (upper trace) and surface record from the CA3 region (lower trace) in response to different rates of stimulation. After a few seconds, 10/sec stimulation produces a large recruitment of pyramidal cell discharges as shown by the big population spikes.

H. Interaction of Excitatory and Inhibitory Processes

In view of the data given above, it is difficult to see how the excitation of pyramidal cells may overcome the powerful and efficient inhibition. This is possible by the process of frequency potentiation.

In a cortical chain of neurons, the synaptic efficiency of tetanic stimulation is much larger than that of a single shock. Figure 9 shows extracellular responses from the CA3 region to a single entorhinal volley. At 1/sec there were discharges of the dentate granule cells but no activity of the CA3 cells. If the simulus rate were raised to 10/sec, however, an excitatory process was built up, giving a large population spike after 6 and 8 sec. Single unit recording has shown that the population spike is composed of the discharges of many individual pyramidal cells. A comparison between the smallest and the largest population spikes indicates that the recruitment must be formidable, from a few to several thousand cells.

The mechanism of this powerful frequency potentiation may be studied by intracellular recording. With single volleys (Fig. 10A), the ordinary response was an IPSP. However, on repetitive stimulation, there was a gradual buildup of a large and prolonged EPSP (B–E). The initial part of this EPSP was monosynaptic. With stronger stimuli (K–O), the same sequence was repeated but the cell was discharged both antidromically and synaptically. A study with different excitability tests showed that the postsynaptic excitability changed little during the frequency potentiation. Therefore, the frequency potentiation process may be largely explained by an increased output of transmitter with successive stimuli in the tetanic period.

In the hippocampal system, it is possible to study the effect of frequency potentiation in a chain of neurons, starting in the entrohinal area and involving the dentate granule cells and CA3 and CA1 pyramids. With simultaneous recording from these three stations and with low rates of stimulation (Fig. 11A), the volley does not penetrate beyond the first synaptic stage. Only the dentate granule cells (▲) were discharged by the stimulus. Keeping the stimulus strength constant, but increasing the rate of stimulation, frequency potentiation occurred as indicated by an increased size of the dentate granule population spike. On successive increase of the rate of stimulation (B–F), the other stations of this chain were also brought into action. With an interval of 1.75 sec, the CA3 pyramidal cells (○) were brought into action first after 55 sec of tetanic stimulation. With 1.4-sec interval, the CA1 cells were activated as well (●). By playing upon the tetanic stimulation rate and duration, it is, therefore, possible to activate larger or smaller areas of the cortical matrix. This appears as a new process for the control of cortical pyramidal discharges. In this connection, it is relevant to recall that the average discharge rate of cortical neurons range from 5 to 15/sec, which also are the best frequencies for frequency potentiation.

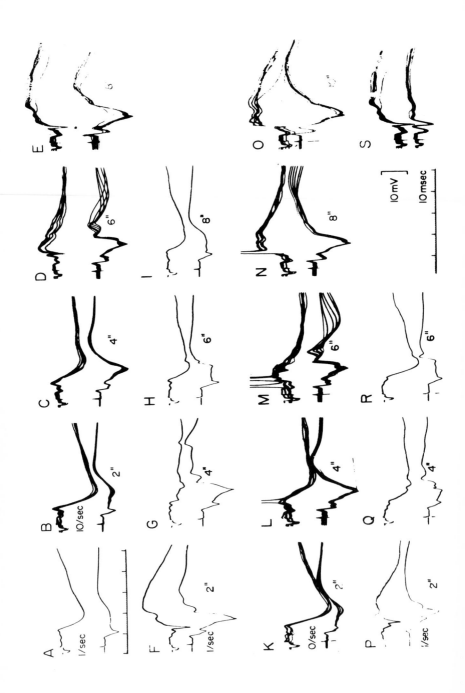

I. Integrative Mechanisms of Individual Cortical Pyramidal Cells

A synthesis of some of the data given above, with a possible scheme for integrative behavior of the pyramidal cells, is given by the diagram in Fig. 12. An afferent input which activates synapses either close to the cell body or with extended synaptic contacts so as to provide a massive synaptic activation of the cell, will be called a detonator line. The physiological response of a cell to such activation, would be a large and distinct EPSP as seen by an intrasomatic electrode. Even with a small convergence of afferent impulses, the EPSP would be sufficiently large to discharge the cell. Therefore, the cell would faithfully follow the afferent volley frequency. This arrangement is ideally suited for automatic activity such as reflexes of various kinds.

The other afferent line is called an integrator line. These synapses are located further away from the cell body. The depolarization caused by an individual synapse is so small that a considerable degree of summation is needed in order to discharge the cell. In fact, since the individual EPSP's are very small, the probability for discharge from a single volley is similarly small. However, if this line is repetitively activated, the successive volleys release increased amounts of transmitter, building up an EPSP which eventually gets large enough to discharge the cell. The integrator line is ideally suited for summating and comparing mechanisms, such as presumably operate when pyramidal cells are used for more elaborate functions like learning and memory. It should be stressed that the large majority of cortical synapses belong to the last type.

In Fig. 13, another component is added to this scheme. When the pyramidal cell discharges, both hippocampal and neocortical cells operate a powerful recurrent inhibitory system through basket or Golgi II cells, respectively. This system will inhibit the response of all cells not being sufficiently excited. An integrator line may activate a focus of cells and there overcome the inhibition produced by the recurrent pathway. However, in a fringe around this focus of activation, the excitation will be lower whereas the recurrent inhibition will be powerful because it is much wider distributed than the excitation. Consequently, the cells in this fringe will be kept below the excitatory level. In this way, the cell discharges will be limited to a much smaller number of cells than otherwise would have been the case.

Fig. 10. A: Intracellular record from a CA3 neuron (upper trace) and surface CA3 record (lower trace) in response to entorhinal stimulation at 1/sec. B–E: As A, but stimulation at 10/sec for 2, 4, 6, and 8 sec, respectively. F–I: Responses obtained after returning to 1/sec stimulation. K–O: As B–E, but with stronger stimulus. The cell was discharged synaptically (L–N) by the developing EPSP. P–R: Recovery after returning to 1/sec stimulation. In S, the upper record is the intracellular record, corresponding to E, whereas the lower trace is the extracellular record obtained just outside the cell during a similar train.

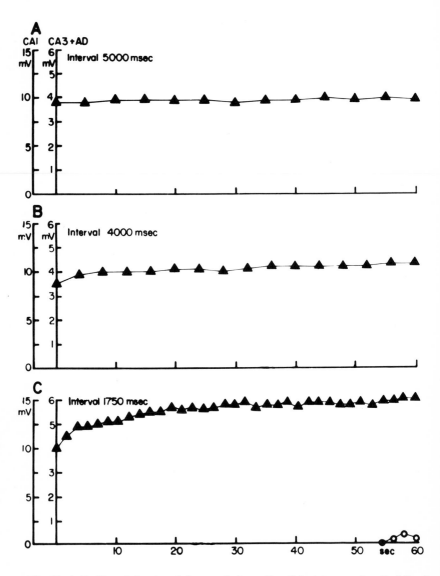

Fig. 11. A–F: Plot of the size of the population spike of dentate granule cells (▲), of CA3 pyramidal cells (○), and of CA1 pyramidal cells (●), as a function of the stimulus rate given by the indicated intervals and duration of the tetanic stimulation. Further description in text.

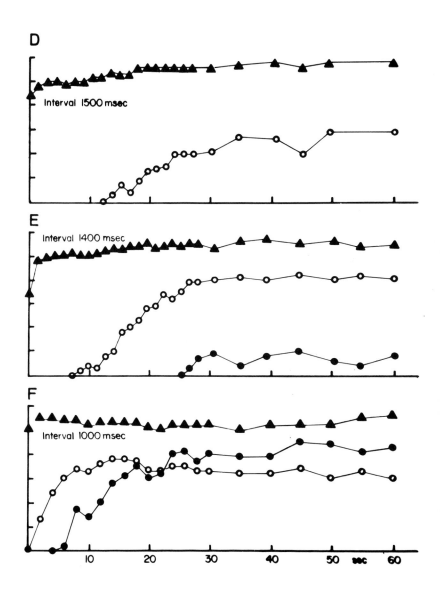

D

Interval 1500 msec

E

Interval 1400 msec

F

Interval 1000 msec

10   20   30   40   50   sec   60

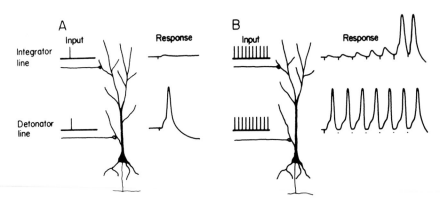

Fig. 12. Schematic diagram of the property of the proposed integrator and detonator lines with their respective synapses. Further description in text.

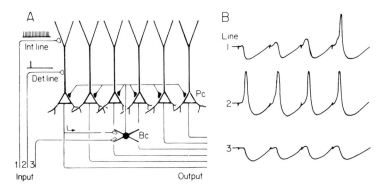

Fig. 13. Schematic diagram of the different output patterns resulting from different types of input along the integrator, detonator, or inhibitory lines. Further description in text.

Repetitive volleys along an integrator line are better suited to break through this inhibition than the detonator line because of the large facility for potentiation of the excitatory synaptic effect. Control of pyramidal cell output may, therefore, be exercised partly by choice of line, and partly by frequency modulation of the afferent volleys. For plasticity in the nervous system, the integrator line seems the most suitable.

REFERENCES

Andersen, P., Blackstad, T. W., & Lømo, T. Location and identification of excitatory synapses on hippocampal pyramidal cells. *Experimental Brain Research*, 1966, **1**, 236–248. (a)

Andersen, P., Eccles, J. C., & Løyning, Y. Location of postsynaptic inhibitory synapses on hippocampal pyramids. *Journal of Neurophysiology*, 1964, **27**, 592–607.

Andersen, P., Holmqvist, B., & Voorhoeve, P. E. Excitatory synapses on hippocampal apical dendrites activated by entorhinal stimulation. *Acta Physiologica Scandinavica*, 1966, **66**, 461–472. (b)

Blackstad, T. W. Commissural connections of the hippocampal region in the rat, with special reference to their mode of termination. *Journal of Comparative Neurology*, 1956, **105**, 417–536.

Blackstad, T. W. On the termination of some afferents to the hippocampus and fascia dentata. *Acta Anatomica*, 1958, **35**, 202–214.

Colonnier, M. L. The structural design of the neocortex. In J. C. Eccles (Ed.), *Brain and conscious experience*. New York: Springer Verlag, 1966. Pp. 1–29.

Kandel, E. R., Spencer, W. A., & Brinley, F. J., Jr. Electrophysiology of hippocampal neurons. I. Sequential invasion and synaptic organization. *Journal of Neurophysiology*, 1961, **24**, 225–242.

Lorente de Nó, R. Studies on the structure of the cerebral cortex. II. Continuation of the study of the Ammonic system. *Journal für Psychologie und Neurologie*, 1934, **46**, 113–117.

Ramón y Cajal, S. *Histologie du système nerveux de l'homme et des vertébrés*. Vol. 2. Paris: Maloine, 1911.

Discussion

OLDS: When you talked about the interaction of excitation and inhibition, you used a model of posttetanic potentiation to build up the transmitter. I presume that the message you postulated on those dendritic spines began and was transmitted down the dendrite to the soma where it first met the inhibitory process. Now it's not clear to me how a buildup of drive on those spines, which would have to turn into one spike moving down the dendrite, could get around the inhibitory process if a smaller amount of drive didn't. And, therefore, I don't see how the buildup could counteract the inhibition.

ANDERSEN: That is because a first depolarization on a spine is so small that it will decay electrotonically without being felt by the soma. But, with successive messages, the depolarization will increase until a spike is fired, which will travel down the dendritic tree. During conditions in which inhibition is there beforehand, we have seen a lot of cases in which the dendritic spike does not pass to the soma. Now, if you add depolarization through the regions lying closer to the cell body, you can assist the transmission of the spike down to the soma. The other point is that hyperpolarization on the cell body does not necessarily cause a block, because there is a great difference between initiating a spike and conducting a spike. In addition I can tell you that when you stimulate at 10/sec you see a large beautiful spike with a little AB break. When you go back to 1/sec stimulation you see a small spike, 4–5 mV in amplitude. And if you step up the frequency again, then it suddenly comes back with full power.

JOHN: I wonder if I could ask Dr. Andersen to speculate about how the following phenomenon could take place.

We've been studying the evoked potential and unit activity in different structures in the same paths, using chronically implanted microelectrodes which can be moved. One of the things that we found, which, in particular, is striking, is that if you present to a trained animal a known signal, the evoked potential wave shape in the geniculate and in the hippocampus are almost identical. That is, if you identify peaks and troughs at various points in time and determine the latency of these peaks and troughs, you find that each peak in the geniculate corresponds to one in the hippocampus. But there is usually a delay of a few milliseconds between the appearance of a peak in the geniculate and the appearance of the same peak in the hippocampus.

If you present a different stimulus to an animal who is differentially trained, the evoked potential wave shapes in the two places change, so there is one evoked potential for one signal, and another evoked potential for a different signal. Now if you present (that holds as long as the animal is performing correctly, as long as he is differentiating correctly) stimuli toward which the animal behaves inappropriately, the correspondence of wave shapes between geniculate and hippocampus degrades. The geniculate retains the wave shape which it had, the evoked potential wave shape in the hippocampus simply changes to a new species, which one hasn't seen before. Now, having made this observation, we've been moving these microelectrodes down through the structures, so that we've mapped very large regions, staying in each region perhaps a week or so, and studying the characteristics of multiple unit activity, and then moving a few hundred microns, and mapping again. What we find is that the fields are remarkably homogeneous. The wave shape is very constant, and you have a gradient which gradually falls off. And as you look at the activity of the units through this field you find that the pattern of the response is the same throughout the field. So you get the impression that there is enormous homogeneity, that the homogeneity is dynamic, that it's not wired in, because whenever the behavior decomposes, the homogeneity decomposes.

The purpose of this diatribe was to ask you if you could speculate, on the basis of the very interesting work you've just been discussing, about the way in which this kind of, if you like, correspondence between hippocampal and geniculate activity could be established in a dynamic way?

ANDERSEN: It is a very difficult question. The conditions are very different. You have used unanesthetized animals, whereas we have used anesthetized animals in order to try to find the simple hook-up, with the idea of starting from the simple pathways and building up from there.

Number two, we have used very fine, rather nonphysiological inputs, stimulating a little bundle of fibers. We have no reason to believe that this happens in real life, whereas I'm sure you have used stimuli which are much closer to the normal situation. So that is one reason that I think it's not easy to answer your question. I might say only one thing though; that is, if I understood you right, you say that the wave forms changed little as you went through the tissues for long distances. This, I would be very afraid of, I must say. Because this means, you see, that the generator of the field potential is located away from your electrode.

GERARD: I am intrigued by the increased potential in summated impulses on the dendrite. It's your privilege in not dealing with the accumulation of transmitter, but with the release each time of a larger amount of transmitter. And that intrigues me because I would have expected, with a constant input, in terms of stimulating impulse and in terms of a supply which is not replenished very rapidly, that successive releases would be smaller rather than larger.

ANDERSEN: There are a lot of synaptic connections where this happens. The main one, as you know, is the autonomic nervous system, where you have a successive increase of junction potentials in response to a series of constant afferent volleys. Eventually the cell is fired. And you know well that in the sympathetic, you have to do 5/sec stimulation to do anything at all.

Then you have the pyramidal tract connection with cervical motor neurons (the Phillips papers), showing that each pyramidal volley, being measured as it goes down, to be constant, releases an increased EPSP, which acts as an efficient stimulus. And then you have the Ia EPSP's on respiratory motor neurons. This too increases very nicely on repetitive stimulation, and is coupled to the increased force which must be applied during inspiration. So, there are lots of instances where we do not have the motor neuron pattern of Eccles. With regard to transmitter supply I think it is quite evident that there is very large supply of transmitter present in many synapses, particularly these ones. I might add that Dr. Lømo in my laboratory has applied short tetanic periods, and afterwards tested the system with occasional single shocks, and shown that there remains for quite a considerable time an increased release of transmitter. In fact, the latency to the first discharge, which we may take as a kind of indication of the transmitting power, is markedly decreased.

GERARD: I suppose what I'm really asking you is to explain the phenomena: What transmitter is coming out and why? I am not questioning your findings.

ANDERSEN: No, I cannot explain that. In analogy with the autonomic system, the mobilization of the transmitter may be so slow that several volleys are required to produce a maximal release.

SVAETICHIN: I would like more evidence about this dendritic spike; to me, it is strange that you thought this envelope of the spike very local, as to the cell body. Now there is an enormous number of large dendrites, and they have an area which is much bigger than the soma. Why don't you get these spikes there, by extra stimuli?

ANDERSEN: Well, you have. You can record spikes both from the soma and from the dendritic regions.

SVAETICHIN: But the amplitude is bigger in the soma. Why don't you have the big amplitude where the dendrites are?

ANDERSEN: Because the current density per tissue area is much smaller. When the action potential passes the soma region, where the cells are packed together 200 Å apart, the inward current is passing through this dense area. So per unit space of the tissue, the current will cause a large voltage drop across the tissue resistor, and make the large extracellular spike potentials. Out in the dendritic area, although the dendrites are thick and numerous, the bulk of the matter is composed of thin profiles. So the inward current here is much smaller per unit area. The current density will be much smaller, and therefore, your extracellular potential, which you record as a spike, has to be small.

SVAETICHIN: Do you get intracellular recordings easily from the dendrites?

ANDERSEN: We have done, I think, only one which I believe in. In that record we saw an EPSP. The reason for my belief is that the cell was penetrated 200 μ below the cell body layer. Further, we had an input which should be in the correct place, and we saw an EPSP with a small dendritic or local spike on top.

SVAETICHIN: We have studied the cerebellum of the fish and we can get very easily intercellular recordings from the dendrites. You get enormous, full-size spikes from the cell body. From the dendrites you only get something if you are close to the cell body; you'll get the spike there, but when you go farther, you get no spike at all.

ANDERSEN: In that case, of course, it depends very much upon whether you have simultaneous synaptic activation or not. Are these synaptically activated spikes?

SVAETICHIN: These were spontaneous.

ANDERSEN: Then, I would presume that they are synaptically activated. And of course then you have a complex situation, even in a fish cerebellum, because you have your electrode inside the dendrite recording the voltage changes across the membrane. But, at the same time you will have a leaky membrane because of the synaptic activation. So your spike *must* be reduced. It is impossible to have a full-sized spike under these conditions.

SVAETICHIN: That would mean that, during normal activity, there are no spikes in the dendrites. You have to stimulate them in an artificial way to get spikes, is that what you say?

ANDERSEN: Yes. Full-sized dendritic spikes I think are only acceptable if you can secure that you have no synaptic conductance shunt. This is the requirement.

BUREŠ: I want to make two points: One is whether the assumption of the increase of the output of the transmitter is necessary at all?

Wouldn't it be possible to assume that there is an increased accumulation of transmitter around the synapse resulting in a lingering depolarization and that, when you get more excitatory input on the dendrite, the level of depolarization reached by the membrane would prevent conduction? What you get then is just a play of depolarization at the dendritic tree and hyperpolarization in the soma; and when these things subtract from each other you might get, at the axon hillock, a situation which would start an axon spike? So I think that it is reasonable to assume that with a small depolarization at the dendritic tree you first get a conducted dendritic spike, but with more depolarization you will get the other massive depolarization of the dendrites, which will preclude the possibility of having a conducted dendritic spike. My second point: It's the possibility that separating the excitatory and inhibitory synapses has made it possible to confirm some of the claims as to the differences in the morphology of the excitatory and inhibitory synapses.

ANDERSEN: Yes, your suggestion is reasonable. It is highly possible that these increased EPSP's are due to lingering of transmitter. However, if that were true, then you would require that the membrane potential should be reduced. Now this is not the case. The EPSP, if it's there at all, goes back to the original level very fast. And it's a long stretch of time after recovery before the start of another EPSP. But, your idea cannot be completely disproved. We'll keep your suggestion in mind. It is true that sodium inactivation of the spike occurs when it tries to cross a depolarized soma. In fact, if you keep on stimulating with a high stimulus rate, the sodium carrier is decoupled. But, this happens only after you have recruited the cells. Therefore, first, we get a local depolarization, then spike discharge, and then sodium inactivation because of the large depolarization.

With regard to the identification of inhibitory and excitatory synapses, using criteria other than localization the situation on the hippocampus is not clear. Blackstad is trying to work on it at the moment. I don't know what he has found as yet.

THOMPSON: Over what frequency do you have the potentiation?

ANDERSEN: It depends. With anesthesia, it ranges from about 3 to 4/sec, to a maximum of 10 to 12/sec. You see very few long lasting effects beyond 15/sec. If you apply, say, 50/sec, you get a spurt of activity, but after less than 2 sec, you get nothing out of the hippocampus. This, I think, has practical value. If you want to have a hippocampal output, you should keep to 5 to 10/sec and not above that. The best, of course, is to monitor the discharge of the output cells.

EVOKED RESPONSES AND NETWORK DYNAMICS

M. VERZEANO
DEPARTMENT OF PSYCHOBIOLOGY, UNIVERSITY OF CALIFORNIA, IRVINE

I. Introduction

During the last two decades, the investigation of central sensory processes has been based, to a large extent, on the study of the responses evoked, by sensory stimulation, in the various sensory regions of the brain. Much attention has been given to the "gross" evoked response, and a great deal of controversy has developed with respect to its relations to incoming sensory information. Since information is transmitted from the periphery to the sensory regions of the brain by neural elements, it was expected that, if the gross evoked response recorded from a sensory region was related to incoming information, some correlations should be found between its characteristics and the activity of neurons in that region. A number of studies, based on the recording of the activity of *single* neurons, did indicate that such correlations existed (Jung & Baumgartner, 1955; Grusser & Grutzner, 1958; Fox & O'Brien, 1965; Kondratyeva, 1967, 1968; Kondratyeva & Polyansky, 1968). However, the nature, the consistency and the extent of the correlations remained unclear.

Previous studies of the relations between gross waves and neuronal activity, conducted in this and other laboratories have shown that the development of *spontaneous* gross waves is related to the complex interactions

Aided by grant NB 07145 from the National Institutes of Health.

27

between the activities of many neurons and groups of neurons, within and between large neuronal networks, and that, in order to elucidate the mechanism involved in the development of gross waves, as well as their physiological significance, it was necessary to study not only the activity of single neurons, but also the dynamics of network activity, by viewing, simultaneously, the activity of many neurons within one or several networks (Verzeano & Calma, 1954; Verzeano, Naquet, & King, 1955; Verzeano, 1956, 1961, 1963; Verzeano & Negishi, 1960, 1961; Negishi & Verzeano, 1961; Verzeano, Laufer, Spear, & McDonald, 1965; Laufer & Verzeano, 1967; Andersen & Andersson, 1968). Because of the fruitful results obtained by the application of these concepts of network analysis to the study of spontaneous activity, the same methods have been applied, recently, to the study of evoked activity.

It has been shown (Verzeano, Groves, & Thomas, 1968; John & Morgades, 1969) that the *average* gross evoked response to visual stimulation, recorded by a microelectrode in the lateral geniculate body, shows great similarity to the post-stimulus histogram of the *multineuronal* discharge, simultaneously recorded at the same point, by the same microelectrode. Further study (Dill, Vallecalle, & Verzeano, 1968; Verzeano, Dill, Vallecalle, Groves, & Thomas, 1968) has provided a more precise relation between the time course and waveform of the gross evoked response and the multineuronal activity recorded from the same region: The maximum probability of multineuronal discharge is highest at the times which correspond to the steepest negative slopes, and lowest at the times which correspond to the steepest positive slopes of the gross response. These relations obtain in the visual cortex as well as in the lateral geniculate body and remain consistent whatever the magnitude or the polarity of the gross response. More recently, Thompson, Bettinger, Birch, and Groves (1969), have indicated that similar relations between the slope of the gross response and the probability of neuronal discharge are found in the visual association cortex, while Weinberger *et al.* (personal communication, 1968), have shown that they are found in the auditory system.

The remarkable consistency of these relations, under many different conditions and in several regions of the brain, suggests that they may be implicated in some of the basic mechanisms of sensory perception. The purpose of this report is to summarize these results and discuss their physiological significance.

II. Methods

Single or multiple microelectrodes made of platinum–iridium wire, sharpened electrolytically to diameters of 1 to 5 μ and insulated with glass (Wolbarsht, MacNichol, & Wagner, 1960), were stereotaxically implanted in the brain of cats. The animals were maintained for periods of up to ten months, and the gross and neuronal responses were studied in wakefulness, in the unanesthetized, unrestrained state. In a few cases, experiments were conducted in animals immobilized with Flaxedil and maintained with artificial respiration or under barbiturate anesthesia.

1. *Technique of Implantation*

The animals were anesthetized with a fast-acting barbiturate (sodium thiamylal, 2.5%), administered intravenously, in repeated doses, sufficient to maintain anesthesia, but small enough to allow very rapid recovery after implantation.

The device used for implantation is illustrated in Fig. 1. The microelectrodes (μE, 1, 2, 3) were connected to a bakelite piston (B), which could travel downwards within a lucite cylinder, 8 mm in diameter, under the command of a screw (S); the lower extremity of the lucite cylinder was

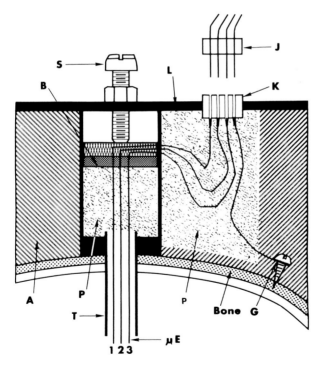

Fig. 1. *Device for implantation of microelectrodes.* A: acrylic cement; B: bakelite piston; G: "ground" connection; J: jack; K: plug; L: lucite cap; P: paraffin; S: screw; T: teflon tube; 1–2–3–μE: microelectrodes. For operation, see text. (Reproduced from Thomas, Groves, & Verzeano, *Experientia*, 1968, **24**, 360–362.)

connected to a thin teflon tube (T) which penetrated a short distance into the brain and served to maintain the microelectrodes in the proper direction. The base of the cylinder, containing the upper part of the teflon tube, was attached to the skull by means of an acrylic cement and remained permanently fixed so that, as the piston moved down, the microelectrodes were lowered to the desired location in the brain.

The upper extremities of the microelectrodes, which were fixed to the bakelite piston, were connected by means of flexible wires to a plug (K), completely separated from the cylinder structure, so that inserting the jack (J) into the plug, in order to make connections with the amplifiers, would cause no change in the position of the microelectrodes. The interior of the cylinder and the space between the cylinder and the connecting plug were partially filled with paraffin (P). A longitudinal slit in the wall of the cylinder allowed the flexible wires to move down with the piston and the excess of paraffin to escape into the space between the cylinder and the plug.

The whole assembly was enclosed in a block of acrylic cement (A) attached to the skull. Because the piston fitted into the cylinder very tightly and because of the presence of paraffin inside the cylinder, the downward movement of the piston and the microelectrodes was made against considerable resistance and, when the desired location was reached, with the piston tightly held inside the cylinder, supported by the paraffin below and the screw above, great stability of electrode positioning was achieved (Thomas, Groves, & Verzeano, 1968).

In later models of the device it was found that the bakelite piston could be fitted into the cylinder so tightly that great stability of positioning could be insured, without the addition of paraffin.

2. Electronic Devices

Binocular stimulation was performed with brief flashes of light generated by a "Grass" photostimulator, modified in such a way as to allow the production of a wider range of stimulus intensities. The flash-producing element was set at a distance of 2 ft from the animal's eyes and the illumination, measured at the level of the eyes, could be varied from 255 to 138,000 lux. All stimulation was conducted in darkness. The output of the stimulator, provided a pulse, synchronous with the flash of light, which was recorded on a separate channel of the magnetic tape and, subsequently, served as a trigger for the computer analysis of the time-dependent data.

The microelectrodes were connected to amplifiers with adequate input impedance and low grid currents (Verzeano & Negishi, 1960). They recorded, simultaneously, the gross as well as the neuronal responses. The output of the amplifiers was stored on magnetic tape and the pertinent data were analyzed subsequently. Permanent recordings were made by means of a

" Honeywell-Visicorder " oscillograph. The overall frequency response of the system, amplifiers—magnetic tape recorders—oscillograph, was from 3 to 5000 Hz (3 dB).

In most cases, each microelectrode could detect the activity of several neurons or groups of neurons and, accordingly, recorded spike discharges of several amplitudes. The different amplitudes were separated by means of a pulse-height analyzer (Verzeano *et al.*, 1965) and their number and distribution gave an indication of the number of active neurons and the distribution of neuronal activity within the territory surveyed by the microelectrodes.

By using appropriate low pass and high pass filters, the gross and the neuronal responses could be separated when desired. The construction of the high pass filter required particular care: Some of the gross responses contain fast components, of the order of 100 to 250 Hz. Should such components go through the high pass filter, they might trigger the pulse height analyzer and, thereby, cause errors in the determination of the time histograms of the neuronal responses by the computers. For this reason a specially designed high pass filter was used, which eliminated all undesirable components (Fig. 2).

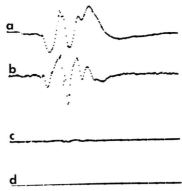

Fig. 2. *Action of high pass filter*. a: average evoked response; b: average first derivative of a; c: output of high pass filter showing the complete elimination of a; d: time histogram obtained by processing the output of the high pass filter (c) through the computer, showing no spurious counts.

The average gross response, its average first derivative (dV/dt = rate of change of amplitude with respect to time = slope), and the " time histogram " (the probability of occurrence of the spikes in the neuronal response), in one or several amplitude categories, were obtained by means of analog and digital computers (Fig. 3).

3. *Recordings from Single Neurons*

Recordings from single neurons were obtained either by using a very fine microelectrode, which detected the activity of only one neuron, or by using a larger microelectrode, which would detect the activity of several neurons,

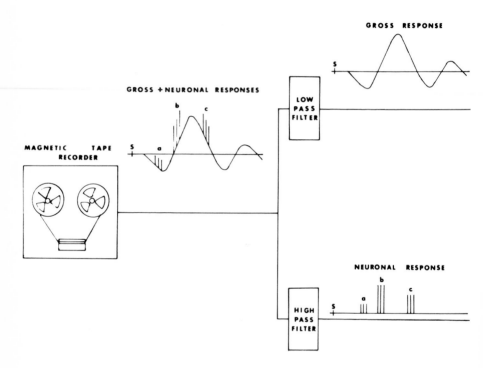

Fig. 3. *Arrangement of filters, pulse height analyzer, analog and digital computers,* for the determination of the average gross evoked response, its average first derivative, and the probabilities of neuronal discharge in several spike amplitude ranges.

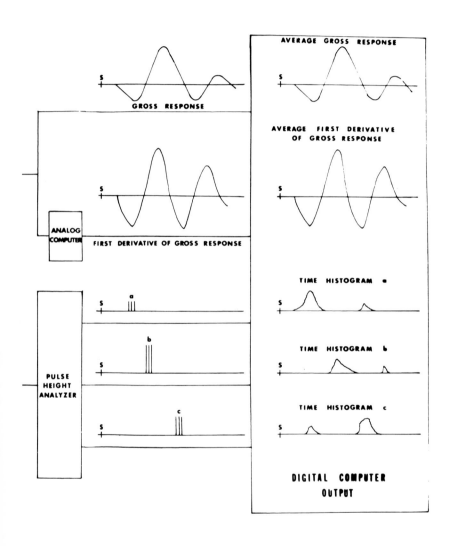

AVERAGE GROSS RESPONSE

GROSS RESPONSE

AVERAGE FIRST DERIVATIVE
OF GROSS RESPONSE

ANALOG
COMPUTER

FIRST DERIVATIVE OF GROSS RESPONSE

TIME HISTOGRAM a

TIME HISTOGRAM b

PULSE
HEIGHT
ANALYZER

TIME HISTOGRAM c

DIGITAL COMPUTER
OUTPUT

and extracting from it, by means of the pulse height analyzer, the spikes generated by a single neuron. In all cases, the criteria used to define single neuronal spikes, were their waveform as well as their amplitude. The time histograms of single neuronal discharges were obtained in the same way and by means of the same computers as those of the multineuronal discharge.

III. Results

A. Lateral Geniculate Body

Recordings from the lateral geniculate body were obtained from: (a) unanesthetized, unrestrained animals, with permanently implanted microelectrodes; (b) unanesthetized animals paralyzed with Flaxedil and maintained with artificial respiration or animals under barbiturate anesthesia.

1. *Results Obtained in the Unanesthetized, Unrestrained State*

Recordings obtained under these conditions, show that the probability of occurrence of neuronal discharge is highest at the times which correspond to the steepest negative slopes (the negative peaks of the first derivative) and lowest at the times which correspond to the steepest positive slopes (the positive peaks of the first derivative), of the gross response. This is illustrated in Figs. 4, 5, and 14. Figure 4 shows a section of an original recording, containing both neuronal spikes as well as gross waves (a); the first derivative of the gross waves (b); the output of the high pass filter, containing only neuronal spikes (c); and five outputs of the pulse height analyzer, classifying these spikes into five different ranges of amplitude. It can be seen on line ">60," which contains all the spikes larger than 60 μV, that the highest frequency of neuronal discharge occurs at a time x, which corresponds to the negative peak of the first derivative (the steepest negative slope) of the gross response; on lines 60–80, 80–100, etc., which contain spikes of selected amplitudes, it can be seen that high frequencies of neuronal discharge occur at progressively later times, and decrease progressively in density in the progressively higher amplitude ranges (x_1, y, z, t).

Figure 5 shows the relations between gross response and neuronal discharge computed from 200 evoked responses taken from the same original recording as that shown in Fig. 4: a is the average gross response; b is its average first derivative; c–f are time histograms of neuronal spikes, classified in four different amplitude ranges. The greatest probability of neuronal discharge in the lowest amplitude range f corresponds to the first negative peak of the first derivative of the gross response (at x); the greatest probability of

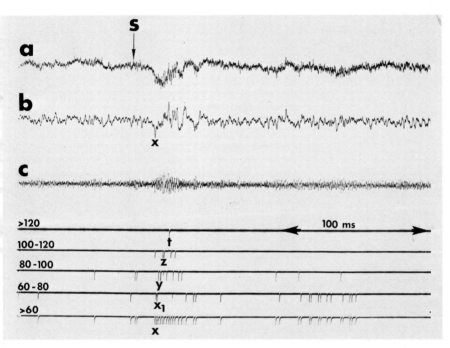

Fig. 4. *Amplitude spectrum of neuronal spikes in the lateral geniculate body of unrestrained, unanesthetized cat.* a: gross evoked response; b: its first derivative with respect to time; c: output of highpass filter, eliminating gross response and passing only neuronal spikes; >60: output of pulse height analyzer, showing all neuronal spikes higher than 60 μV, with maximum density of discharge x corresponding to the negative peak of the first derivative and the steepest negative slope of the gross response; 60–80, 80–100, etc.: output of pulse height analyzer showing neuronal spikes in progressively higher amplitude ranges; >120: output of pulse height analyzer showing all spikes higher than 120 μV; s: stimulus. Note that high densities of neuronal discharge (x_1, y, z, t) occur at progressively later times in the progressively higher spike amplitude ranges.

neuronal discharge in the next higher amplitude range e, occurs a few milliseconds later and is of smaller magnitude (at y); the delay increases and the magnitude decreases, gradually, in progressively higher amplitude ranges d and c until, in the highest amplitude range, the greatest probability of neuronal discharge corresponds to the positive peak of the first derivative and its magnitude is much smaller than in the low ranges (at t). It can, thus, be seen that the first negative and the first positive slope of the gross response (the first negative and the first positive peaks of its first derivative) correspond to the discharge of two different groups of neurons, one group which produces many spikes of low amplitude x, and another group which produces fewer spikes, of high amplitude t.

When all spike amplitudes are lumped together, the highest peaks of the

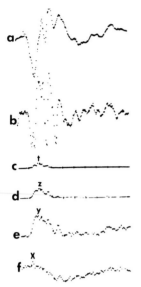

Fig. 5. *Relations between gross response and neuronal discharge in the lateral geniculate body of the unrestrained, unanesthetized cat,* computed from 200 evoked responses taken from the same original record as the response shown in Fig. 4. a: average gross response; b: its average first derivative with respect to time; f : time histogram of neuronal spikes in the amplitude range 30–60 μV, showing the greatest probability of discharge x, corresponding to the negative peak of the average first derivative; e, d, c: time histograms of neuronal spikes in the ranges 60–100, 100–140, and >140μ, respectively, showing that the greatest probability of neuronal discharge occurs at progressively later times in progressively higher amplitude ranges (y, z, t). Duration of sweep: 125 msec.

time histogram correspond to the negative peaks of the first derivative. This is illustrated in section 8 of Fig. 14, which shows the relations between gross response and neuronal discharge computed from 200 evoked responses, in which the time histogram was computed on the totality of the neuronal discharge, containing all the spikes of amplitudes higher than 20 μV. To every negative peak of the average first derivative of the gross response there corresponds a high probability of neuronal discharge; to every positive peak of the average first derivative there corresponds a low probability of neuronal discharge, so that total time distribution of the probability of neuronal discharge is a mirror image of the average first derivative of the gross response.

2. *Results Obtained under Flaxedil or under Barbiturate Anesthesia*

Recordings obtained under these conditions show the same relations between the slope of the gross response and the probability of neuronal discharge, as those obtained in the unanesthetized, unrestrained state. This is illustrated in Figs. 6, 7, and 8. Figure 6 shows a section of an original recording containing neuronal spikes as well as gross waves (a), the first derivative of the gross waves (b), the output of the high pass filter, containing only neuronal spikes (c), and three outputs of the pulse height analyzer, classifying these spikes into three different ranges of amplitude. High frequencies of neuronal discharge, within the ranges 70–150 μV, occur at times

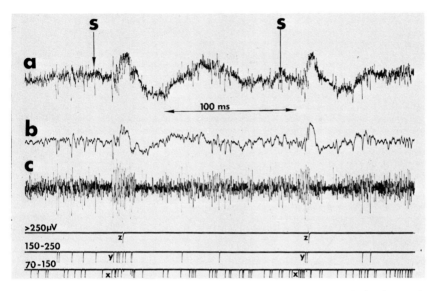

Fig. 6. *Amplitude spectrum of neuronal spikes in the lateral geniculate body of cat under Flaxedil.* a: average gross response; b: its first derivative; c: output of high pass filter, showing only neuronal spikes; 70–150: output of pulse height analyzer, showing all neuronal spikes in the range 70–150 μV, and maximum density of discharge x corresponding to a negative peak of the first derivative of the gross response; 150–250 and >250: outputs of pulse height analyzer showing high densities of neuronal discharge occurring at progressively later times in progressively higher amplitude ranges (y, z).

which correspond to the negative peaks of the first derivative of the gross response x; they occur at progressively later times and decrease in density, in progressively higher ranges (y, z).

Figure 7 shows the relations between gross response and neuronal discharge computed from 58 evoked responses taken from the same original recording as that shown in Fig. 6: a is the average gross response, b its average first derivative; c–e are time histograms of neuronal spikes, classified into three different amplitude ranges. The greatest probability of neuronal discharge in the lowest amplitude range e corresponds to the first negative peak of the first derivative of the gross response (at x); the greatest probability of neuronal discharge in the next higher amplitude range d occurs a few milliseconds later and is of smaller magnitude (at y); in the highest amplitude range c, the greatest probability of neuronal discharge occurs still later, is of still smaller magnitude, and corresponds to the positive peak of the first derivative (at z). It can, thus, be seen that in this case, just as in the unrestrained animal, the first negative slope and the first positive slope of the gross response (the first negative and the first positive peaks of its first derivative) correspond to the discharge of two different groups of neurons, one which produces

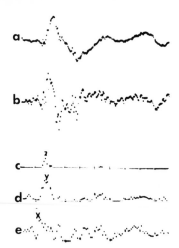

Fig. 7. *Relations between gross response and neuronal discharge in the lateral geniculate body of the cat, under Flaxedil,* computed from 58 evoked responses taken from the same original record as the responses shown in Fig. 6. a: average gross response; b: its average first derivative; e: time histogram of neuronal spikes in the amplitude range 70–150 μV, showing the greatest probability of discharge *x*, corresponding to the negative peak of the average first derivative; d, c: time histograms of neuronal spikes in the ranges 150–250 and >250μ, respectively, showing that the greatest probability of neuronal discharge occurs at progressively later times in progressively higher amplitude ranges (*y*, *z*). Duration of sweep: 125 msec.

many spikes of low amplitude *x* and another which produces fewer spikes, of high amplitude *z*.

Figure 8 shows the relations between gross response and neuronal discharge, computed from 158 evoked responses obtained from an animal under barbiturate anesthesia: (a) is the average gross response, (b) is its average first derivative, (c) is the time histogram of the spikes produced by a single cell in the neuronal response, and (d) is the time histogram of the multineuronal discharge. The highest probability of discharge corresponds to the negative peak of the first derivative of the gross response, in both the single and multineuronal time histograms.

Fig. 8. *Relations between gross response and neuronal discharge in lateral geniculate body of cat under barbiturate anesthesia*: a: average gross response; b: its first derivative with respect to time; c: time histogram of discharge of single neuron, spike amplitude 300 μV; d: time histogram of multineuronal discharge, including all spikes above 40 μV. In this case, the greatest probability of both, multineuronal and single neuronal discharge, corresponds to the negative peak of the average first derivative of the gross response.

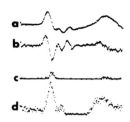

B. CORTEX

Recordings from the lateral gyrus were obtained from: (a) unanesthetized, unrestrained animals, with permanently implanted microelectrodes; (b) unanesthetized animals paralyzed with Flaxedil and maintained with artificial respiration. Under both of these conditions, the results obtained were quite similar to those obtained from the lateral geniculate body. This is illustrated in Fig. 9 which shows: the average gross evoked response (a); its average first derivative, (b); and the time histograms of neuronal discharges, in two different amplitude ranges (c, d); computed from recordings obtained from an unanesthetized, unrestrained animal (sections 1, 2, and 3) and from an animal under Flaxedil (sections 4, 5, and 6). It can be seen that in the low spike-amplitude ranges, the probability of neuronal discharge is highest at the times which correspond to the negative peaks, and lowest at the times which correspond to the positive peaks, of the average first derivative z, and that its time course approximates a mirror image of the average first derivative.

When the neuronal spikes are separated into several amplitude ranges, it is found that, as in the lateral geniculate, the greatest frequencies and the greatest probabilities of discharge occur at progressively later times for spikes of progressively higher amplitudes. This is illustrated in Figs. 10 and 11. Figure 10 shows: (a) a section of an original recording obtained from the lateral gyrus of an unanesthetized animal maintained under Flaxedil; (b) the first derivative of the gross waves; (c) the output of the high pass filter containing only neuronal spikes; and four outputs of the pulse height analyzer classifying these spikes into four amplitude ranges. High frequencies of neuronal discharge are seen to occur at progressively later times (at x, y, z, t). Figure 11 shows the relations between gross response and neuronal discharge computed from 370 evoked responses taken from the same original recording as that shown in Fig. 10: (a) is the average gross response; (b) is its average first derivative; (c, d, e and f) are time histograms of neuronal spikes, classified into four different amplitude ranges. The greatest probability of neuronal discharge in the lowest amplitude range (f) corresponds to the first negative peak of the first derivative of the gross response (at x); the greatest probability of neuronal discharge in the next higher amplitude range (e) occurs a few milliseconds later and is of smaller magnitude (at y); the delay increases and the magnitude decreases, gradually, in progressively higher amplitude ranges, until, in the highest amplitude range (c), the greatest probability of neuronal discharge corresponds to the positive peak of the first derivative and its magnitude is much smaller than in the low ranges (at t). A similar progression in the peaks of the time histogram can be seen in the later part of the response (at p, q, r, s). In the first progression (x, y, z, t), the peak in the lowest time histogram x corresponds to a negative slope of the gross response (a negative peak of its first derivative) while the peak in the highest time histogram t corresponds to a positive slope (a positive peak of the first derivative). Similar relations between the peaks of the time histogram and the slopes of the gross response obtain in the later progression (p, q, r, s). It can, thus, be

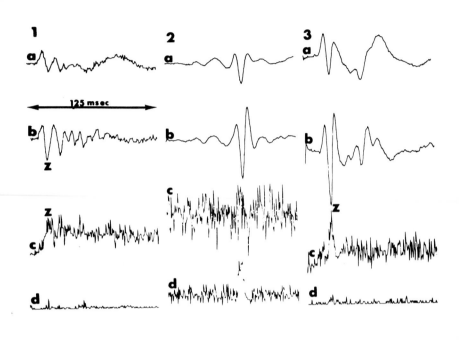

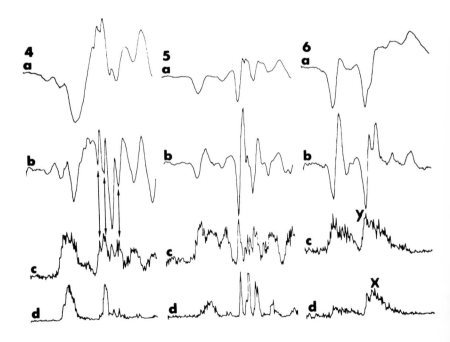

seen that the deflections of the gross response which correspond to these two progressions, are related to the alternating activities of two groups of neurons: one group which produces many spikes of low amplitude (such as *x*), and another group which produces fewer spikes of high amplitude (such as *t*).

C. Recordings from Single Cells

Recordings of the activity of single cells were obtained from the lateral gyrus and from the lateral geniculate body. In both structures, the single neuronal discharge shows greater variability than the multineuronal discharge. It may appear in the earlier or in the later part of the response and its latency and duration may vary considerably from one evoked response to the next. This is illustrated in Fig. 12, which shows two evoked responses obtained from the lateral gyrus of an animal under Flaxedil: one at a depth of 0.75 mm (trace 1) and the other at a depth of 1.5 mm below the surface of the cortex (trace 2). The discharge of the neuron in trace 1 appears more than 100 msec after the stimulus and consists of several bursts separated by various intervals; the discharge of the neuron in the lower tracing appears about 30 msec after the stimulus and consists of three shorter bursts separated by different intervals.

However, the statistical study of single cell responses indicates that, in spite of the apparent variability which appears in the isolated sweeps, the highest probability of their discharge still maintains a relation with the slope of the gross response: in some cases with the negative slope, in others with

Fig. 9. *Relations between gross responses and neuronal discharge, in the visual cortex of the cat.* a: average gross evoked responses; b: their average first derivatives; and c, d: time histograms of simultaneous neuronal responses obtained from the visual cortex and computed from 200 responses. Section 1 shows responses obtained from an unanesthetized, unrestrained animal, at a depth of 0.5 mm below the surface of the cortex. Sections 2 and 3 show responses obtained from the same animal, with the same microelectrode, at a depth of 1 mm below the surface of the cortex, with stimulus intensities of 600 and 1600 lux, respectively. Sections 4, 5, and 6 show responses obtained from the visual cortex of an animal immobilized with Flaxedil, at depths of 0.75, 1.5, and 2.25 mm below the surface of the cortex, respectively, with stimulus intensities of 825 lux. Tracings c represent time histograms of neuronal spikes of low amplitude (20–25 μV in sections 1, 2, and 3; 60–100 μV in sections 4, 5, and 6). Tracings d represent time histograms of neuronal spikes of higher amplitudes (all spikes above 25 μV in sections 1, 2, and 3; all spikes above 120 μV in sections 4, 5, and 6). The arrows in section 4 show examples of correlation between high probabilities of neuronal discharge and negative peaks of the first derivative of the gross response. The *x* in section 6 shows an example of maximum probability of discharge of higher amplitude spikes, occurring later than the maximum probability of discharge of lower amplitude spikes (*y*). (Reproduced from Dill *et al.*, 1968.)

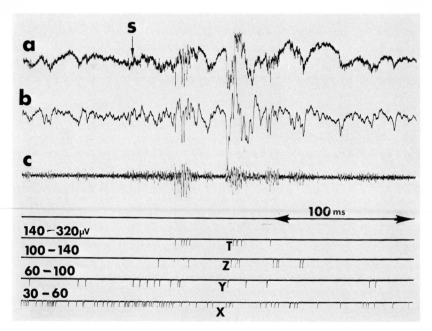

Fig. 10. *Amplitude spectrum of neuronal spikes in the visual cortex of the cat, under Flaxedil.* a: gross evoked response; b: its first derivative; c: output of high pass filter showing only neuronal spikes; 30–60, 60–100, etc.: output of the pulse height analyzer, showing neuronal spikes in progressively higher amplitude ranges. Note that the higher densities of neuronal discharge (x, y, z, t) occur at progressively later times in the progressively higher amplitude ranges.

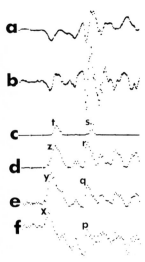

Fig. 11. *Relations between gross response and neuronal discharge in visual cortex of the cat under Flaxedil,* computed from 370 responses obtained from the same original tracing as the response of Fig. 10. a: average gross response; b: its average first derivative; f: time histogram of neuronal spikes in the amplitude range 30–60 μV, showing the greatest probabilities of discharge (x, p) at times corresponding to negative peaks of the average first derivative; e, d: time histograms of neuronal spikes in the ranges 60–100 and 100–140 μV, respectively, showing that the greatest probabilities of neuronal discharge (y, z, q, r) occur at progressively later times in progressively higher amplitude ranges; c: time histogram of discharge of single neuron (spike amplitude >320 μV), showing greatest probabilities of discharge (t and s) occurring later than z and r, in the amplitude range immediately below. Note that when the activity is at a maximum in the lowest amplitude range, it is either zero or at a minimum in the higher amplitude ranges, and vice versa. Duration of sweep: 125 msec.

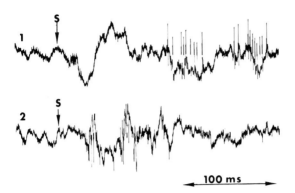

Fig. 12. *Activity of single neurons.* Evoked responses obtained from the lateral gyrus of cat under Flaxedil; 1: at 0.75 mm below the surface; 2: at 1.5 mm below the surface. Note the variability of occurrence of single neuronal activity in relation to the gross response.

the positive slope. This is illustrated in Fig. 13. The left and right sections of this figure, show the relations between gross response and neuronal discharge computed from 400 responses taken from the same tracings as the upper and lower parts of Fig. 12, respectively. In both sections, A is the average gross response, B is its average first derivative, C is the time histogram of the single neuronal response, and D is the time histogram of the multineuronal response. It can be seen that the highest probabilities of discharge of the single neuron in the left side correspond to the negative peaks (at y) of the average first derivative of the gross response, while those of the single neuron in the right side correspond to its positive peaks (at x). However, the highest probabilities of multineuronal discharge, in both sections, still correspond to the negative peaks of the average first derivative of the gross response.

Single neurons in the lateral geniculate discharge in a similar way, with similar variabilities, the highest probability of discharge corresponding, in some cases, to the negative peaks of the average first derivative of the gross response (as in the example of Fig. 8), in others to its positive peaks.

D. Effects of Changes in the Intensity of the Stimulus

Changes in the intensity of stimulation cause changes in the latency, the magnitude, and the configuration of the gross response, with concomitant changes in the neuronal response. It has been found that whatever these changes may be, the basic relation between the gross response and the multi-neuronal response remain the same: the highest probabilities of discharge correspond to the steepest negative slopes of the gross response. This is illustrated in Fig. 9 for the cortex, and in Fig. 14 for the lateral geniculate.

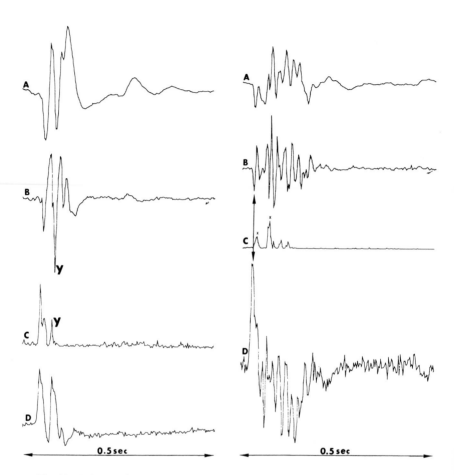

Fig. 13. *Relations between gross response and single neuronal response, in the visual cortex of the cat,* computed from 400 responses taken from the same original records as the responses of Fig. 12. Left side of this figure corresponds to upper tracing and right side to lower tracing of Fig. 12. A: average gross response; B: its average first derivative; C: time histogram of single neuronal activity; D: time histogram of multineuronal activity (all neuronal spikes in the range 40–100 μV). Note that in spite of the variability of single neuronal activity *in individual responses,* its time histogram computed from a large number of responses does relate to the gross response: on the left side, the time histogram (C) shows the greatest probability of discharge corresponding to the negative peaks of the first derivative *y,* on the right side to its positive peaks *x;* the time histograms of the multineuronal response (D) show the greatest probability of neuronal discharge corresponding to the negative peaks of the first derivative, in both cases.

Sections 2 and 3 of Fig. 9 show the results obtained from the lateral gyrus of an unanesthetized, unrestrained animal, with stimuli giving illuminations, at the level of the animal's eyes, of 600 and 1600 lux, respectively. It can be seen that in spite of the changes in the gross and neuronal responses caused by the increased stimulus intensity, the highest probabilities of neuronal discharge still correspond to the negative peaks of the average first derivative of the gross response (at z). Figure 14, sections 1–9, shows: the average gross

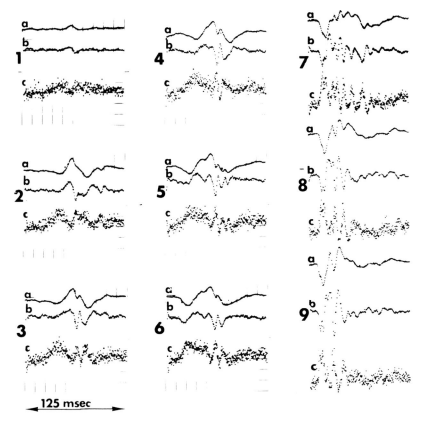

Fig. 14. *Effects of changes in stimulus intensity on gross and neuronal responses.* a: average gross responses; b: their average first derivatives; and c: time histograms of simultaneous multineuronal responses including all spikes larger than 20 μV obtained from the lateral geniculate body and computed from 200 responses. Sections 1–9 show the changes induced by increasing the intensity of the visual stimulus: 1 = 255 lux; 2 = 360 lux; 3 = 600 lux; 4 = 1000 lux; 5 = 1600 lux; 6 = 3300 lux; 7 = 4300 lux; 8 = 34,500 lux; 9 = 138,000 lux. Note that the relations between the slope of the gross response (b) and the probability of occurrence of neuronal discharge (c) remain consistent at all stimulus intensities, and that, in all sections, the time histogram (c) is a mirror image of the first derivative (b).

responses (a); their average first derivative (b); and the time histograms of the multineuronal discharge (c), obtained from the lateral geniculate body of an unanesthetized, unrestrained animal, with increasing stimulus intensities, varying from 255 to 138,000 lux illumination at the level of the animal's eyes. It can be seen that the changes in the stimulus intensity cause marked changes in the gross and neuronal responses, but the consistency of the relations between the average first derivative of the gross response and the probability of multineuronal discharge is maintained.

E. EFFECTS OF CHANGES IN THE LOCATION OF THE RECORDING POINT

In lowering the microelectrode through the cortex or the lateral geniculate body, the configuration and the polarity of the gross response change. When the neuronal response is recorded, simultaneously with this changed gross response, by the same microelectrode, at this new location, the relations between the slope of the gross response and the probability of occurrence of neuronal discharge still hold. This is illustrated in Figs. 9 and 15. In Fig. 9, sections 1 and 2 show responses obtained from the visual cortex of an unanesthetized, unrestrained animal at depths of 0.5 and 1 mm, respectively; sections 4, 5, and 6 show the responses obtained from the visual cortex of an animal immobilized with Flaxedil, at depths of 0.75, 1.5, and 2.25 mm below the surface, respectively. In Fig. 15, sections 1 and 2 show the responses obtained from the lateral geniculate body of an unanesthetized, unrestrained

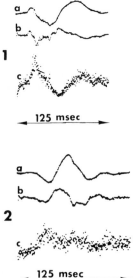

Fig. 15. *Effects of changes in the location of the recording point.* a: average gross evoked response recorded from the lateral geniculate body; b: its average first derivative; and c: the time histogram of the simultaneous neuronal response, computed from 200 responses. Section 1: control; section 2: after 2-mm-downward displacement of the microelectrode through the lateral geniculate. (Reproduced from Dill *et al.*, 1968.)

animal, before and after lowering the microelectrode through this nucleus by 2 mm. It can be seen that, both in the cortex and in the lateral geniculate body, the configuration and the polarity of the gross responses as well as the configuration and the magnitude of the neuronal responses have changed with the displacement of the microelectrode, but the relations between the slopes of the gross response and the probability of neuronal discharge have remained the same: the steepest negative slopes, as indicated by the highest negative peaks of the first derivative, still correspond to the highest probability of occurrence of neuronal discharge, as indicated by the highest peaks of the time histogram.

IV. Discussion

The investigations described in this report have provided experimental evidence which leads to the following conclusions: (1) the existence of the relations between gross waves and neuronal discharge, which has been demonstrated in the past for spontaneous activity, is, now, clearly demonstrated for evoked activity as well; (2) the relations between gross waves and neuronal discharge are based on rates of change; (3) these relations have an important significance in the *multineuronal* coding and transmission of information in the central nervous system.

A. Gross Waves and Neuronal Activity

The relations between *spontaneous* gross waves and neuronal discharge have been demonstrated many years ago, starting with Verzeano and Calma (1954), and confirmed through many subsequent studies, by Verzeano and his collaborators. Their existence has been, again, reconfirmed, and their statistical study has been advanced, by Fox and Norman (1968). The demonstration, in this study, of the presence of relations between *evoked* gross waves and neuronal discharge, gives additional emphasis to the generality of the relations between the two phenomena.

However, in spite of these many confirmations, some doubts are still being expressed on the existence and consistency of these relations. These doubts are based on the finding that, when gross waves and *single* neuronal discharge are recorded simultaneously, consistent relations between the two phenomena cannot always be detected. On these grounds, the conclusion is drawn that there is an irreconcilable contradiction between the results obtained in studies involving multineuronal discharge and those obtained in studies involving single neuronal discharge and that, for reasons which are never explained, only the studies based on single neuronal discharge have any validity.

The results presented in this report may contribute to the resolution of this apparent contradiction, by providing the observation that different neurons behave in different ways in relation to the slow waves. As has been shown in these investigations, the largest majority of neurons, which produce spikes of low amplitudes, discharge in consistent relation to the negative slopes of the gross response. A small minority of neurons, which produce spikes of high amplitudes, discharge in a more variable fashion: in some instances in relation to the negative, in other instances in relation to the positive slopes of the gross responses (Figs. 8, 11, 12 and 13).

A microelectrode of small diameter and high impedance, such as is used, most frequently, in studies of single neuronal discharge, produces a relatively large amount of " noise," which masks the neuronal spikes of lower amplitudes. Such a microelectrode may, therefore, "select" the higher amplitude spikes, produced by some neurons, and may miss altogether the discharge of the many neurons which produce the far more numerous spikes of low amplitudes, consistently related to the gross response. Furthermore, when the activity of a single neuron is observed in isolation, regardless of the amplitude of its spikes, its behavior in relation to the gross waves or to the characteristics of a peripheral stimulus, shows much greater variability than that of a large group of neurons studied under the same conditions.

These considerations lead to the conclusion that there is no real contradiction between the findings obtained with single neuronal recording and those obtained with multineuronal recording, and that the explanation for their being sometimes at variance, resides in the different sets of neurons which are observed by means of the two different techniques, and in the greater variability of the behavior of single neurons as compared to the statistical behavior of networks of neurons.

B. Rates of Change and Brain Function

The importance of rates of change in several aspects of nervous function has been emphasized by other authors. As early as 1945, Campbell has shown that the potential recorded from the ventral root of a spinal nerve in response to afferent stimulation, closely resembles the first derivative of the potential simultaneously evoked, by the same stimulus, in the ventral horn of the spinal cord (Campbell, 1945). More recently, Clynes (1961, 1962) and Clynes, Kohn and Lifshitz (1964), have provided theoretical and experimental evidence which demonstrates that a number of processes that occur in the nervous system are sensitive to rates of change. The findings obtained in the series of investigations described in this and in previous reports (Dill *et al.*, 1968; Verzeano, Groves, & Thomas 1968) demonstrate that rates of change are involved in the relations between gross waves and neuronal activity in the brain.

One of the most remarkable of these findings is the consistency of the relations between the first derivative of the gross response (the rate of change of amplitude with respect to time) and the probability of neuronal discharge, in so many locations and under so many different conditions: in the lateral geniculate body, the primary and secondary visual cortex, the auditory system; in wakefulness or sleep; at low or high intensities of stimulation. This widespread distribution and this remarkable consistency, suggest that these relations are based on fundamental neural processes and have an important physiological significance.

Another remarkable finding is that the relations between the first derivative of the gross response and the probability of neuronal discharge still hold, even when the magnitude, the configuration, or the polarity of the gross response change, with the displacement of the microelectrode through the tissue. Since the tip of a microelectrode of the type used in these experiments surveys a territory approximately 200 μ in diameter and since the same tip records *both* the gross waves and the neuronal activity from the very same territory, it may be concluded that the relations between the two are based on processes which occur *locally*, in the immediate vicinity of the tip, and not on processes which occur at large distances from one another, some at the surface of the tissue, some within its depth.

The fact that the greatest probabilities of discharge, in the time histograms of neuronal activity occur at progressively later times and decrease progressively in magnitude for spikes of progressively higher amplitudes (Figs. 5, 7, and 11), suggests that a convergence of activity over neural elements of progressively increasing size and decreasing number may be involved in these processes; and the fact that consecutive phases of the gross response correspond, alternately, to consecutive periods of enhanced and reduced neuronal activity (Fig. 11), suggests that a chain of successive phases of excitation and inhibition develop within the neuronal territory from which these phenomena are recorded. The data available at present do not allow the identification of the neural events responsible for each particular phase. It is evident, however, that the activity of synaptic, dendritic, somatic, and perhaps other neural elements must participate in the development of this convergence and in the distribution of excitation and inhibition through the neuronal territory, and it is probable that the interactions between these activities result in relations involving rates of change.

C. MULTINEURONAL CODING

The events of the outside world are not described by the nervous system in terms of the activity of single, isolated neurons. No matter how simple, no matter how limited in time and in space a peripheral stimulus may be, the response in the pertinent sensory receiving region of the brain, implicates a widespread distribution of excitation and inhibition over a large neuronal territory. The question arises, therefore, whether this multineuronal response, viewed in its totality, bears any relation to the characteristics of the peripheral stimulus. The analysis of the data presented in this report indicates that such a relation does indeed exist. This is illustrated in Figs. 11, 13, and 14.

Figure 11, tracing f, shows a time histogram, obtained from the lateral gyrus, which represents a large part of the neuronal response in the territory surveyed by the microelectrode. The section of the tracing which represents the latency of the response corresponds to the level of spontaneous neuronal activity in the territory (activity which occurs before the arrival of information from the retina). As soon as this information arrives, the activity is enhanced and depressed in a series of fluctuations which take it way above (x) and way below the spontaneous level. Similar modifications of the spontaneous activity can be seen in Fig. 13, tracings D. Figure 14 shows a series of time histograms (c), obtained from the lateral geniculate body, with progressively increasing intensities of stimulation, and representing a very large part of the neuronal response in the territory surveyed by the microelectrode (all neuronal spikes above 20 μV). It can be seen that, with increasing intensities of stimulation, there is an increasing complexity in the time histograms which corresponds to increasing complexities in the gross evoked response (a) and its first derivative (b).

These findings indicate that the incoming information *modulates* the neuronal activity of the territory into which it arrives, in such a way that the total spatial and temporal distribution of excitation and inhibition within the territory corresponds to the characteristics of the peripheral stimulus.

As has been shown in previous work (Verzeano & Negishi, 1960; Negishi & Verzeano, 1961; Verzeano, 1963) this distribution of excitation and inhibition in the neuronal territory results from the interaction between the neuronal activity engendered by the incoming sensory information and the neuronal activity which is present, at all times, in thalamic and cortical networks, in the form of periodic circulation of neuronal impulses. The time histograms presented in this report provide a statistical picture of these interactions, over large segments of neuronal territories.

The conclusion can be drawn, therefore, that the cortical or thalamic activity related to sensation and perception can be viewed, significantly, in statistical terms, by considering the dynamics of large neuronal networks.

This does not diminish in any way the importance of the study of these phenomena at the single neuronal level. It only points out that the two different methods, single neuronal and multineuronal recording, survey the same events from different viewpoints, that each method has its advantages and its limitations, and that both are essential in the investigation of cerebral function.

In order to understand certain physical phenomena, it is necessary to view them from the point of view of single particle physics, as well as from the point of view of statistical mechanics and quantum mechanics. By analogy (Walter, 1968; Wechsler, 1960), in order to understand certain neurophysiological and psychological phenomena it is necessary to study them from the point of view of single neuronal activity as well as from the point of view of the statistical aspects of multineuronal activity.

The findings presented in this report give additional support to these concepts of nervous function, and lead to the conclusion that the statistical study of network dynamics should prove a valuable method of neurophysiological and psychological investigation.

V. Summary

Gross evoked responses as well as evoked neuronal responses, obtained by stimulation with brief flashes of light, were recorded from the lateral geniculate body and the visual cortex of the cat, under three different sets of conditions: (a) unanesthetized, unrestrained animals with chronically implanted microelectrodes; (b) in "acute" experiments, in animals maintained under Flaxedil and artificial respiration; (c) under barbiturate anesthesia.

Each microelectrode could detect the activity of several neurons or groups of neurons and, accordingly, recorded spike discharges of several amplitudes. The different amplitudes were separated by means of a pulse height analyzer and their number and distribution gave, at any time after the stimulus, an indication of the number of active neurons and the distribution of neuronal activity within the territory surveyed by the microelectrode.

The average gross evoked response, its average first derivative with respect to time, and the time histogram of the spike discharges of the neuronal response, in one or several amplitude categories, were obtained by means of analog and digital computers. Thus it was possible to study the time and phase relations between the gross evoked response, its first derivative (the rate of change of amplitude with respect to time, or slope) and the probability of neuronal discharge at any time after the stimulus.

It has been found that, in the lateral geniculate body as well as in the visual cortex, and under all three sets of experimental conditions:

(1)   The probability of neuronal discharge is greatest at the times which correspond to the steepest negative slopes, and smallest at the times which correspond to the steepest positive slopes of the gross response.

(2)   These relations between neuronal activity and the slope of the gross response still obtain after the microelectrode has been lowered through the

lateral geniculate body or through the cortex and the polarity and configuration of the gross response have changed. This indicates that these relations are based on processes which occur *locally*, in the vicinity of the microelectrode tip, and not on processes which occur at large distances from one another, some at the surface of the tissue, some within its depth.

(3)   As the intensity of the stimulus is increased, the amplitude of the gross response increases and its slope becomes steeper; simultaneously the level of neuronal activity increases and its maxima and minima continue to correspond to the steepest negative and the steepest positive slopes of the gross response, respectively.

(4)   Consecutive deflections of the gross response correspond to consecutive phases of excitation and inhibition of different groups of neural elements located within the same territory.

(5)   Within each phase of excitation, neuronal spikes of different amplitudes are sequentially distributed in time, progressively higher amplitudes appearing at intervals of a few milliseconds, and indicating the sequential activation of elements of progressively increasing size.

(6)   The distribution of the consecutive phases of excitation and inhibition changes with the intensity of stimulation and results in a " modulation " of the spontaneous neuronal activity of the region, providing a pattern of multineuronal coding for the incoming sensory information.

REFERENCES

Andersen, P., & Andersson, S. *Physiological basis of the alpha rhythm.* New York: Appleton-Century-Crofts, 1968.

Campbell, B. The distribution of potential fields within the spinal cord. *Anatomical Record,* 1945, **91**, 77–88.

Clynes, M. Unidirectional rate sensitivity: A biocybernetic law of reflex and humoral systems as physiologic channels of control and communication. *Annals of the New York Academy of Sciences,* 1961, **92**(3), 946–969.

Clynes, M. The nonlinear biological dynamics of unidirectional rate sensitivity illustrated by analog computer analysis, pupillary reflex to light and sound, and heart rate behavior. *Annals of the New York Academy of Sciences,* 1962, **98**(4), 806–845.

Clynes, M., Kohn, M., & Lifshitz, K. Dynamics and spatial behavior of light evoked potentials, their modification under hypnosis, and online correlation in relation to rhythmic components. *Annals of the New York Academy of Sciences,* 1964, **112**(1), 468–508.

Dill, R. C., Vallecalle, E., & Verzeano, M. Evoked potentials, neuronal activity and stimulus intensity in the visual system. *Physiology and Behavior,* 1968, **3**, 797–802.

Fox, S. S., & Norman, R. J. A new measure of brain activity: functional congruence; an index of neural homogeneity. *Proceedings of the 24th International Congress of Physiological Sciences,* 1968, **7**, 142.

Fox, S. S., & O'Brien, J. H. Duplication of evoked potential waveform by curve of probability of firing of a single cell. *Science,* 1965, **147**, 888.

Grusser, O. J., & Grutzner, A. Neurophysiologische Grundlagen der periodischen Nach-bildphasen nach kurzen Lichtreizen. *Archiv für Ophthalmologie*, 1958, **160**, 65–93.

John, E. R., & Morgades, P. P. Neural correlates of conditioned responses, studied with multiple chronically implanted moving microelectrodes, *Experimental Neurology*, 1969, **23**, 412–425.

Jung, R., & Baumgartner, G. Hemmungsmechanismen und bremsende Stabilisierung an einzelnen Neuronen des optischen Cortex. Ein Beitrag zur Koordination corticaler Erregungsvorgange. *Archiv für die Gesamte Physiologie*, 1955, **261**, 434–456.

Kondratyeva, I. N. Cyclic changes in activity of cortical neurons, after short lasting stimuli. *Contemporary problems in the electrophysiology of the central nervous system*. Moscow: Nauka, 1967. Pp. 148–159.

Kondratyeva, I. N. Investigation of unit responses in the visual cortex to a light of growing intensity. *Pavlov Journal of Higher Nervous Activity, English Translation*, 1968, **18**(1), 157–159.

Kondratyeva, I. N., & Polyansky, V. B. Inhibition in the neuronal systems of the visual cortex. *Activitas Nervosa Superior*, 1968, **10**(1), 1–11.

Laufer, M., & Verzeano, M. Periodic activity in the visual system of the cat. *Vision Research*, 1967, **7**, 215–229.

Negishi, K., & Verzeano, M. Recordings with multiple microelectrodes, from the lateral geniculate and the visual cortex of the cat. In R. Jung & H. Kornhuber (Eds.), *The visual system*. Berlin: Springer, 1961. Pp. 288–295.

Thomas, J., Groves, P., & Verzeano, M. The activity of neurons in the lateral geniculate body during wakefulness and natural sleep. *Experientia*, 1968, **24**, 360–362.

Thompson, R. F., Bettinger, L. A., Birch, H., & Groves, P. M. Comparison of evoked gross and unit responses in association cortex of waking cat. *Electroencephalography and EEG Clinical Neurophysiology*, 1969, **27**, 146–151.

Verzeano, M. Activity of cerebral neurons in the transition from wakefulness to sleep. *Science*, 1956, **124**, 366–367.

Verzeano, M. Neuronal interaction and synchronization of the EEG. Fifth International Congress of Electroencephalography and Clinical Neurophysiology, Rome, September, 1961. *Excerpta Medica, International Congress Series*, 1961, **37**, 49–54. (Abstract)

Verzeano, M. The synchronization of brain waves. *Acta Neurologica Latinoamericana*, 1963, **9**, 297–307.

Verzeano, M., & Calma, I. Unit-activity in spindle bursts. *Journal of Neurophysiology*, 1954, **17**, 417–428.

Verzeano, M., Dill, R. C., Vallecalle, E., Groves, P., & Thomas, J. Evoked responses and neuronal activity in the lateral geniculate. *Experientia*, 1968, **24**, 696–698.

Verzeano, M., Groves, P., & Thomas, J. Relations between evoked response and neuronal activity in the lateral geniculate body. *Biophysical Journal*, 1968, **8**, A–152.

Verzeano, M., Laufer, M., Spear, P., & McDonald, S. L'activitié des reseaux neuroniques dans le thalamus du singe. In A. Monnier (Ed.), *Actualités neurophysiologiques*. Vol. 6. Paris: Masson, 1965. Pp. 223–252.

Verzeano, M., Naquet, R., & King, E. E. Action of barbiturates and convulsants in the unit-activity of the diffusely projecting nuclei of the thalamus. *Journal of Neurophysiology*, 1955, **18**, 502–512.

Verzeano, M., & Negishi, K. Neuronal activity in cortical and thalamic networks. A study with multiple microelectrodes. *Journal of General Physiology*, 1960, **43**(Suppl.), 177–195.

Verzeano, M., & Negishi, K. Neuronal activity in wakefulness and in sleep. In G. E. W. Wolstenholme & M. O'Connor (Eds.), *The nature of sleep*. Ciba Symposium. London: Churchill, 1961. Pp. 108–126.

Walter, D. O. The indeterminacies of the brain. *Perspectives in Biology and Medicine*, 1968. **11**, 203–207.

Wechsler, D. Intelligence, quantum resonance and thinking machines. *Transactions of New York Academy of Sciences*, 1960, **22**, 259–266.

Wolbarsht, M. L., MacNichol, E. F., & Wagner, H. G. Glass insulated platinum micro-electrode. *Science*, 1960, **132**, 1309–1310.

RELATIONS BETWEEN EVOKED GROSS AND UNIT ACTIVITY IN ASSOCIATION CORTEX OF WAKING CAT

RICHARD F. THOMPSON
UNIVERSITY OF CALIFORNIA, IRVINE

For the past several years, we have been interested in neuronal activity in nonspecific polysensory evoked association response areas of the cerebral cortex. In terms of gross evoked responses there appears to be a close relationship between response amplitude and behavioral state.

The data shown in Fig. 1 illustrate the effect of presentation of novel stimuli on nonspecific evoked association responses recorded from the posterior middle suprasylvian association area in normal waking cats (chronically implanted gross bipolar surface to depth electrodes). Control responses on the left are to repeated synchronous peripheral probe stimuli. Effects of presentations of novel stimuli on the evoked association responses are shown on the right. In all cases there is a marked depression of responses to the repeated probe stimulus during novel stimulation, regardless of modality.

A recent study by Goldring, Sheptak, and Karahashi (1967) suggests a rather unfortunate explanation for the decrement of association responses during attention in the waking cat: They were unable to record association responses in normal waking cats under any conditions using computer averaging techniques. In order to investigate this question further we have completed a series of experiments on normal waking animals recording both

CONTROL   TEST

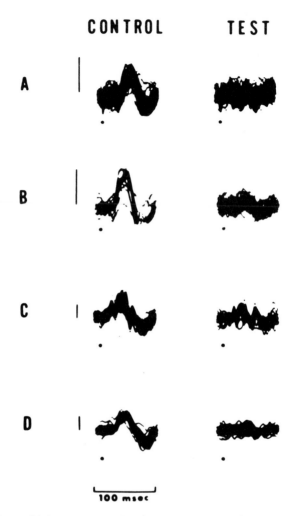

100 msec

Fig. 1. *Effects of behavioral arousal and attention on evoked cortical association responses.* A: suppression of association response following increase in bodily activity (control = sitting quietly, eyes open, test = standing quietly, eyes open); response evoked by ipsilateral forepaw shock stimulus. B: suppression of association response by "novel" visual stimulus (control = sitting quietly, eyes open, test = same posture during sight of food); response evoked by click stimulus. C: suppression of association response by "novel" auditory stimulus (control = sitting quietly, eyes open, test = same posture during growling sound); response evoked by light flash stimulus. D: suppression of association response by sight of experimenter (control = sitting quietly, eyes open, test = same posture during sight of experimenter); response evoked by click stimulus. In each case the test response was recorded from the same electrode in the same animal within 4 min following recording of control response. Each pair of responses recorded from different animal; all records from area PMSA. Amplitude calibration 100 μV.

gross and single cell responses in association cortex using a chronic micro-manipulator system of the same general type described by Hubel (1959) and Evarts (1960). A permanent receptacle chamber was affixed to the skull; during a recording session glass-coated tungsten microelectrodes of 1- to 3-μ tip diameters with impedances ranging from 2 to 20 MΩ were inserted. Recording was monopolar against a distant indifferent. On-line averages of gross evoked responses and single and multiple unit poststimulus histograms were obtained using a Fabri-Tek Model 1062 and a Nuclear-Chicago Model 7100 computers. All unit data were also recorded on tape for subsequent computer analysis. Unless otherwise noted, all data were obtained when the cats were awake but "inattentive," i.e., sitting quietly or lying down head on forepaws with eyes open.

Individual examples of unit activity in area PMSA evoked by various peripheral stimuli are shown in Fig. 2. These data are illustrative of the multiunit data used for computation of poststimulus histograms. The majority of units tended to fire at relatively slow and variable spontaneous rates in the absence of stimulation. Note that the largest unit in Fig. 2 tends to fire within a given restricted latency range for each type of stimulus. However, the smaller units appear to have much broader latency ranges. In fact, in many cases it is not possible to distinguish between spontaneous unit activity and unit responses evoked by the stimulus on the basis of this type of individual response data.

Comparisons of averaged gross evoked potentials and unit poststimulus histograms in association area PMSA to peripheral stimuli are shown in Fig. 3. Each of these were direct, simultaneous no-line averages of 1024 successive gross responses and the corresponding unit discharges recorded from a depth of approximately 1 mm below the surface of the cortex. Only the two or three largest unit responses were passed by the discriminator for this analysis. Note that the periods of maximum probability of unit discharge (peaks of poststimulus histograms) tend to occur just after the peaks of the negative components of the evoked responses.

Effect of stimulus repetition rate is illustrated in Fig. 3A (2-sec inter-stimulus interval) and 3B (.5-sec interstimulus interval) for light flash. Note that the faster repetition rate results in a marked depression of the amplitude of the gross response and the amplitude of the poststimulus unit histogram. Response to click stimulation is illustrated in Fig. 3C and response to a simultaneous light-flash–click stimulus is shown in Fig. 3D. Note that the poststimulus histogram shows a later peak corresponding to a later negativity in the averaged gross response to the combined visual–auditory stimulus. In all cases there is a close and consistent relationship between the gross evoked response waveforms and the periods of maximum unit activity following the stimulus, the histogram peaks occurring at (Fig. 3B) or more

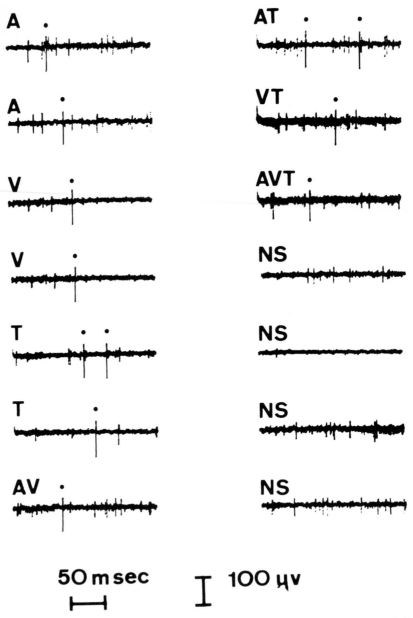

50 m sec ⊢——⊣   **I 100 μv**

Fig. 2. *Examples of unit responses in area PMSA in waking cat.* Responses to click (A), light flash (V), ipsilateral forepaw shock (T) and simultaneous combinations of these (AV = click–flash, AT = click–shock, VT = flash–shock, AVT = click–flash–shock) are shown. Spontaneous activity is indicated in tracings with no stimuli (NS).

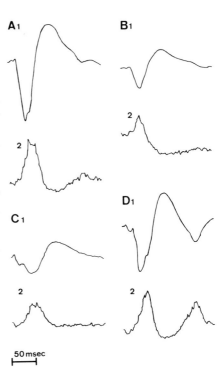

Fig. 3. *Comparisons of simultaneously recorded averaged gross evoked responses* (upper tracings of each pair) *and unit post-stimulus histograms* (lower tracings of each pair) *from area PMSA in normal waking cat*; microelectrode approximately 1 mm below surface of cortex. A1,2, response to light flash with an interstimulus interval of 2 sec. B1,2, response to light flash with an interstimulus interval of 0.5 sec. C1,2, response to click (2-sec intervals). D1,2, response to simultaneous click–flash (2-sec intervals). Only the largest spikes were included in the unit analysis. Each tracing is the average of 1024 successive responses.

commonly just beyond (Figs. 3A, C, D) the negative peaks of the gross responses when only the largest amplitude spikes are included in the analysis. The averaged gross evoked responses illustrated in Fig. 3 are essentially identical in latency and waveform to gross responses recorded from the same depth in area PMSA in the chloralosed cat (Thompson, Johnson, & Hoopes, 1963).

As Dr. Verzeano indicated in his presentation, there is at present considerable interest, and some controversy, concerning the form of the relationship between the gross evoked cortical potential and the probability of unit discharge to a peripheral stimulus (see Verzeano, page 27). Thus Fox and O'Brien (1965) reported a close correspondence between the peak of the unit histogram and the positive peak of the evoked potential in visual cortex. More recently, Verzeano and associates have presented evidence indicating that in lateral geniculate body and visual cortex, if only the largest amplitude spikes are included in the analysis, the unit histogram peaks occur a few milliseconds after the negative peak of the gross potential, sometimes on the negative peak of the gross response, but most frequently on its positive slope; however, if both larger and smaller amplitude spikes are included in the unit analysis, the histogram peaks correspond closely to the negative peaks of the first derivative of the gross potential (Dill, Vallecalle, & Verzeano, 1968; Verzeano, Dill, Vallecalle, Groves, & Thomas, 1968). We completed a comparable analysis for unit activity in association area PMSA to light flash stimulation. Data were obtained under identical conditions to those for the data of Fig. 3, except that the discriminator level was lowered to include both smaller and larger spikes. Figure 4 illustrates: A, the gross evoked response;

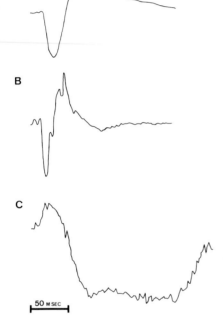

Fig. 4. Comparison of: A, gross evoked association response; B, first derivative of gross response; and C, poststimulus unit histogram to light flash. Both larger and smaller spikes included in unit analysis. Each tracing is the average of 1024 successive responses.

50 M SEC

B, the first derivative; and C, the poststimulus histogram obtained. Note that the region of maximum unit response probability corresponds to the region of maximum negative peak of the first derivative of the evoked potential. Note also that there is a more pronounced and longer duration decrease in unit activity following the period of maximum response under these conditions. Our findings for association cortex thus agree with Dr. Verzeano's studies of visual thalamus and cortex.

So far we have demonstrated that there appears to be a relatively invariant relationship between pattern of the gross evoked potential and probability of cell discharge following a peripheral stimulus in association cortex. A basic question concerns the effects of behavioral attention on gross and unit activity. Figure 5 illustrates a comparison of gross evoked reponses and multiple unit poststimulus histograms recorded from area PMSA in the normal waking cat in the inattentive and attentive states. In this experiment the

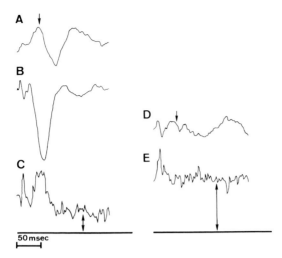

Fig. 5. *Effect of attention on averaged earspeaker click evoked gross responses and unit poststimulus histograms in association cortex* (*area PMSA*) *in normal waking cat.* A: surface gross response; B: gross response 1 mm below surface of cortex; C: multiple unit post-stimulus histogram corresponding to B; A, B, C: control condition, animal sitting quietly with eyes open. D: gross response; and E: poststimulus histogram under same conditions as B, C except that animal given series of novel visual stimuli. Note marked increase in level of ongoing "spontaneous" unit activity during attention (arrow from baseline to tracing in E) in contrast to control state (arrow from baseline to tracing in C). Each tracing average of 256 successive responses.

peripheral stimulus was a repeated earspeaker click. Figure 5A is the surface gross association response to click (indicated by arrow) in the normal in-attentive cat. Figures 5B and C are the depth gross response and correspond-ing unit poststimulus histogram under the same conditions. Figures 5D and E illustrate the marked reduction in both the gross evoked response and the unit poststimulus histogram during attention to novel visual stimuli. Note the marked increase in baseline activity in cells during attention [arrows from baseline to spontaneous level of unit activity in C (inattentive) and E (atten-tive) states]. The gross evoked and unit activity to the repeated probe stimulus are reduced in proportion as the ongoing level of discharge of cells increases during attention to novel stimulation.

REFERENCES

Dill, R. C., Vallecalle, E., & Verzeano, M. Evoked potentials, neuronal activity and stimulus intensity in the visual system. *Physiology and Behavior*, 1968, **3**, 797–801.

Evarts, E. V. Effects of sleep and waking on spontaneous and evoked discharge of single units in visual cortex. *Federation Proceedings*, 1960, **19**, 828–837.

Fox, S. S., & O'Brien, J. H. Duplication of evoked potential waveform by curve of probability of firing of a single cell. *Science*, 1965, **147**, 888.

Goldring, S., Sheptak, P., & Karahashi, Y. Averaged responses from association areas in waking cat. *Electroencephalography and Clinical Neurophysiology*, 1967, **23**, 241–247.

Hubel, D. H. Single unit activity in striate cortex of unrestrained cats. *Journal of Physiology*, 1959, **147**, 226–238.

Thompson, R. F., Johnson, R. H., & Hoopes, J. J. Organization of auditory somatic sensory, and visual projection to association fields of cerebral cortex in the cat. *Journal of Neurophysiology*, 1963, **26**, 343–364.

Verzeano, M., Dill, R. C., Vallecalle, E., Groves, P., & Thomas, J. Evoked responses and neuronal activity in the lateral geniculate. *Experientia*, 1968, **24**, 696–698.

DISCUSSION

NORMAN M. WEINBERGER

WEINBERGER: I'll be very brief because we are not studying the relationships between units and evoked potentials. I will present an incidental
finding which is consistent with Dr. Verzeano's elegant results, that is, that
the greatest probability of unit firing occurs during the steepest part of
the negative slope of the evoked potential.

While recording click evoked potentials in the inferior colliculus of the
anesthetized rat we were also able to discriminate the activity of many units
using appropriate high-pass filtering. This slide (shown below) illustrates
results obtained using an electrode having a tip of about 30 μ in diameter,
neural activity being referenced to a frontal sinus screw. Negativity is up and
the entire sweep is 50 msec.

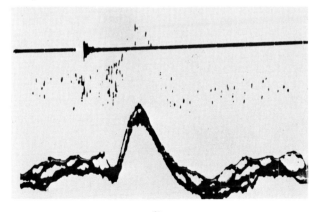

The lowest trace depicts 10 superimposed click evoked potentials. The "spotty" trace above this was achieved by intensifying the beam each time a spike occurred, so that the same evoked potentials are traced out by the unit firing occurring simultaneously. The region of highest spike density (not including during the stimulus artifact) occurs during the negative slope of the evoked potential. This finding is quite in line with those of Drs. Verzeano and Thompson. Thank you.

Discussion

JOHN: I'd just like to add a few points if I might. Steve Fox has been working with a very nice procedure. He computes the probability that a cell will fire and the probability that the EEG or the evoked potential amplitude will reach a given value. Then he produces the correlation between those two probabilities. And he shows that many cells have the characteristic of a firing probability that co-varies with the amplitude of either the resting EEG, or the evoked potential. He then differentiates the EEG as you do, or the evoked potential, and repeats the calculation, and he finds that there are essentially a variety of types of cell. One type of cell has the characteristic that its spike discharge probability correlates much better with the slope of the slow wave than with the amplitude of the slow wave. Another kind of cell has the characteristic that its discharge probability correlates better with the amplitude than with the slope. Then he finds cells which show a change in a relationship when they're driven by a stimulus, and cells which do not show a change in relationship when they're driven. And finally, he has a number of cells which show a relationship between the firing probability and the evoked potential, or the EEG, and also a relationship to the slope of the slow wave, but on driving, only one of these two relationships changes, and in some cells it will be the relationship between the probability of firing and slope, and in others it will be the relationship between amplitude of slow waves and probability of firing. So he believes that these methods begin to permit a fractionation of populations in terms of the different kinds of synaptic drive, which impress on the cell, and he suggests that as a crude first approximation with respect to cortical cells axosomatic inputs influence the amplitude firing probability relationship, and axodendritic inputs influence the slope firing probability relationship. I think that's a very interesting idea, which if it were correct, would provide a very nice analytical tool that could be used very simply. One really needs the same kind of electrode you were working with and a little bit of filtering and differentiation and correlation to be able to parcel out different influences in the system.

Now, I'd like to make two points on the basis of our own work. One is that the relationship between probability of firing and let's say sign of slow wave or sign of evoked potential, and I suspect also slope, varies from region to region. It seems quite clear to us that there are regions in which the relationships are quite the way you describe them. And yet one can find regions not very far away, where the relationship seems to be rather different. Particularly, if you look very carefully at the lead–lag relationships between whether the peak is reached first in the slow wave or first in the unit population. You find unit populations which sometimes lead the slow wave activity and unit populations a little way distant, which sometimes lag the slow wave.

The last point I'd like to make relates to the statistical proposition that you made, with which I concur heartily. I'd like to mention the findings. Suppose you take a multiple unit recording of the sort that you've been talking about and you look at the detailed shape of the post-stimulus histogram in an animal, who let's say is performing twenty correct responses to twenty trials of a given stimulus, and that post-stimulus histogram let's say is characterized by the fact that there are four peaks which occur with different latencies. Let's call them peaks one, two, three, and four. Now you move your microelectrode so that you find one cell, and you can set a comparator or discriminator so that your histogram is composed absolutely from a single unit, which you are following for a period of time. And you take a small sample, by which I mean several hundred responses, and you'll find that that histogram will have only one peak. It may be a line with peak one or two or three or four of the multiple unit histogram. So you say, "Well, okay." The multiple unit histogram is a composite of the different types of cells and their states in the population, and when you look at a group of cells you see what these different specialized fellows are doing, but when you pursue that matter further, it doesn't seem to stand up. Namely, keep the same cell on which you found that the post-stimulus histogram had one peak and spend a whole day with it and every time the animal looks as though he's willing to perform a behavioral response, challenge him, and record the pattern of discharge in that cell. When you get up into the thousands, like 4000, or 5000 responses, then you'll find that from that one cell, you'll get a histogram which will still have peak one in it, but it now has peaks two, three, and four at a lower amplitude. What I'm saying is that we begin to believe that a cell has a preferred state and a preferred mode of response to a particular stimulus. And that mode of response can be seen in the group activity. But if you give the cell a very long time to display the different states which it may enter, then you find that the cell is capable of displaying the kinds of behaviors viewed on a very long term basis that you can find in a population around that cell, viewed on a very short time basis. In other words, the cell can enter any one of these states with varying probability.

VERZEANO: With respect to relations between neuronal discharge and *spontaneous* gross waves: My collaborators and myself have demonstrated the existence of consistent relations between neuronal activity and gross waves way back in 1954, as well as in a whole series of investigations conducted between that time and the present, and yet, many people still maintain that there are no relations between the two phenomena, or that such relations can be found only very sporadically. For this reason, I am always happy to hear that other investigators have found such relations and that the general skepticism surrounding them is receding.

In investigating these phenomena, we found that the relations between neuronal discharge and spontaneous gross waves is based on the periodic circulation of activity through the neuronal networks discharge and the gross waves are recorded. Each gross wave in the recording corresponds to a passage of circulating activity through the network. As these periodic "sweeps" of activity pass through the network they activate a large number of neurons in their path. This pathway itself is not identical at every passage, but shifts continually through the network, and the composition of the group of neurons incorporated into it changes at every passage, so that some of the neurons previously involved are left out and some new ones are taken in. One cannot predict if a specific neuron is going to be involved or not in a specific passage of circulating activity. For this reason, when one looks at the activity of a *single* neuron one may either miss the association with the gross wave altogether, or one may find a variable association, changing from one wave to the next. This fits in with what you say about the possibility that a neuron may enter one of several states, with varying degrees of probability. In the case of the spontaneous waves it may either enter a state of excitation and participate in the "sweep" of activity that passes through the network at a given time, or it may be inhibited, at that time, and become a part of the inhibited territory that the "sweep" of activity creates around it and in its wake. And if you observe an isolated neuron over a long period and many "sweeps" of circulating activity, you find that this is, actually, the case.

With respect to the relations between neuronal discharge and the gross *evoked* response: When we separate the multineuronal discharge into several amplitude ranges, by means of the pulse height analyzer, we find that the highest probability of discharge of the neuronal spikes of *low amplitudes* corresponds to the *negative* slope of the gross evoked response and the highest probability of discharge of the neuronal spikes of *higher* amplitudes corresponds to later phases of the gross response; the higher the amplitude of the spikes, the later the phase to which they correspond. The only explanation I can offer for this is that when we separate the amplitudes of the spikes, we look at the activity of neural elements of different size, firing in succession, from the smaller to the larger, so that one is tempted to visualize a series of impulses, triggered by the stimulus, "traversing" a network of elements such as presynaptic terminals, dendritic processes, smaller somata of interneurons perhaps, and larger somata, such as those of pyramidal cells.

With respect to Steve Fox's findings, that is the "fluidity" of the relations between the activity of *single* neurons and the phase of the gross waves, according to the kind of cell and according to whether the cell is driven or not driven, the only think I can suggest is that it may have something to do with the different pathways along which spontaneous and evoked activities may circulate through the network, and according to whether the activity of the particular *one* neuron under observation, may or may not be incorporated in one kind or another kind of pathway, at a particular time, under a particular set of conditions. The distinction between the roles of axodendritic and axosomatic inputs, in this respect, is not unreasonable. If we assume that the spontaneous gross wave represents the statistical result of a "sweep" of circulating activity through a neuronal network, involving the activity of many neural elements of different kinds, it is not unreasonable to postulate that the discharge of a single neuron may correspond to one or another phase of a gross wave, depending on whether this particular phase of this particular gross wave, results from the summation of the activities of one kind or another kind of neural element.

Now with respect to your own work, you say that the lead–lag relationship between gross response and neuronal discharge may vary from one region to another. We find that, when we look at a large population, the relations between probability of neuronal discharge and gross response are very consistent. When we move to another region, the waveform of the gross response may change. If it does, the probability of neuronal discharge changes accordingly, so that the highest probability still corresponds to the negative slope of the gross response. It is only when we look at very small populations or at single neurons that the lead–lag relation may change from one region to another.

To come back to your finding that a single cell may enter one of several states of activity with varying probabilities: We, too, find that, when we look at single cells, we see, in the time histogram, one very prominent peak, representing the highest probability of discharge of that cell, as well as one or several much smaller peaks, representing much smaller probabilities of discharge. In fact, we often find these several peaks with only a few hundred responses. And, when we look at the population around that cell, we find that the small peak of the single cell histogram, corresponds, precisely, to one of the population peaks (Fig. 8 of my chapter). And I believe, the way you do, that a cell has a preferred mode of response for a particular stimulus, expressed by its "probability profile" in its time histogram. Some of the probabilities in the time histogram of a single cell may be so small that it takes a very large number of responses to bring them out.

HORN: What proportion of your cells show correlation with the slopes? And do you find some in the rising phase, some in the peaks, and some in the troughs?

VERZEANO: We do, indeed, find that the discharge of different cells may correspond to different phases of the gross response. By far the largest majority of the discharging elements, represented by spikes of low amplitude, correlate with the negative slope. The high amplitude spikes, by far the fewer, correlate occasionally with negative slopes, but more frequently with positive slopes. In general, there is a "shift to the right," according to amplitude: The higher the amplitude of the spike, the greater the shift toward a correlation with a positive slope.

HORN: But is it not true that, sometimes, the correlation breaks down?

VERZEANO: When I look at large populations of cells, I find that the correlation is very consistent. When I look at single cells, I find, most of the time, the different kind of correlations that I just mentioned.

BUREŠ: I think that one of the things that must be taken into account is the depth at which the recording is taken, because in the cortex for instance, you would find a different relation in depth from what you would find close to the surface. Another question is what is the causal relation between the slow waves and the spikes?

VERZEANO: With respect to the depth of recording, I expected, as you did, to find different relations at different depths. To my great surprise, I found that, when you record from large neuronal populations, the fundamental relation remains the same at any depth: The greatest probability of discharge *in the population* corresponds to the steepest negative slope of the gross response. When you record from single cells, the discharge of one cell near the surface may correlate with the negative slope, the discharge of another cell 1.5 mm below the cortical surface may correlate with the positive slope of the gross response (Figs. 12 and 13 of my chapter). The explanation for this is that by far the largest majority of the spikes in the population, *at any depth*, are the low amplitude spikes, which seem to always correlate with the steepest negative slope of the gross response. This difference in the behavior of the low and high amplitude spikes leads me to speculate that they may be generated by different kinds of neural elements: It may be that the very low amplitude spikes are generated by presynaptic or dendritic elements; their enormous number and their very short duration would favor this view; it may be that the high amplitude spikes are action potentials of neuron somata. And it is possible that presynaptic and dendritic activity may correspond to the negative slopes of the gross response and somatic activity may correspond to either negative or positive slopes.

This brings me to the second part of your question, about the causal relation. I believe, as many people do, that summations of post-synaptic potentials have something to do with the generation of slow waves, spontaneous or evoked; but I also believe that this explains only a small part of the enormously complex phenomena involved in the generation of slow waves. I believe that many other factors are involved, such as axonal activities, presynaptic, dendritic and somatic activities. Another very important factor is the dynamics of the neuronal network. There is no development of gross waves anywhere without circulation of activity through the network and coordination of the activities of the various groups of neurons through feedback systems. But, on the basis of the data available at present, it is not possible to say, precisely, which activity of which element, is related to which aspect of the gross waves.

BUREŠ: There is also the possibility—suggested by Kuffler—that these slow phenomena might be extraneuronal. Accumulation of potassium around a fiber tract might generate a field which, because of the syncytial character of the glia, may have the character of a dipole which may, then, account for a rather uniform field around the tract.

VERZEANO: It is possible that the glial system may be involved in the generation of these slow phenomena. But regardless whether glial elements are involved or not, it is evident that slow phenomena can be recorded from fiber tracts. Quite some years ago we have shown that spontaneous as well as evoked gross waves, may be recorded with a very fine microelectrode, from pure fiber regions, such as the internal capsule, the pyramidal tract, the optic nerve, and the optic tract, at such distances from any somatic or synaptic structures that no field effect from any of these structures was possible. Furthermore, as we, repeatedly, moved the microelectrode away from the cortex (or the retina), there was no decrement in the amplitude of the recorded slow waves, a decrement which one would expect if the slow waves were electrotonically transmitted from gray matter. Now, since there are many fiber tracts within the cortex and within the thalamic nuclei, the possibility that axonal activity may contribute to the generation of gross waves within these structures, has to be considered.

OLDS: I want to argue against your statistical dynamics idea, not because I think it is "wrong" but only insofar as it would suggest any shift from unitary studies (accompanied by EEG studies) to studies based solely on the more gross techniques. Let us ask ourselves what is the consensus so far as EEG and evoked potentials are concerned. Certainly changes in polarization are influential in modifying certain electrogenic responses. Undoubtedly also both electrogenic responses and chemogenic responses are accompanied by large and detectable electrical changes. So what you are seeing when you observe an electrical wave of EEG or evoked-potential or slow-wave variety is both causal and consequential, and some people would like to analyze the set of processes involved. Recording the totality, I contend, would tell us something but would leave out a great deal more if our probe were planted in an information rich field. Let us suppose we had a small probe (say 50 μ in diameter) in such a field. An information-rich field of neuronal activity would be one where neighboring neurons were doing different things. The question then arises what could be gained in such a field by deriving a single measure of the melange. This melange would include incoming excitatory and inhibitory drive summed with a mix of the EPSP, IPSP, and propagated response activity. The answer is that with such a gross method we could (and have) detected brain areas greatly and rapidly affected by a stimulus as opposed to other areas minimally and slowly affected. Could we have detected the same thing by recording and counting separately the responses of the 25 largest spikes recordable by the same probe and then averaging these? No interpretation suggested here today would hold this to be improbable. Could we have gained more knowledge about the way the information rich field responded by the latter than the former method (presuming we could also separate the different spikes and count them separately)? Most of us would answer yes. In a more general vein I would argue against too rapid jumps to "lighter levels of analysis." If there is some "molecular" level of analysis which supervenes the "unitary," the chances are it will not be established by fiat but instead it will be discovered. Some giant-fiber-like entities perhaps will be discovered in the mammallian brain or other analytic units, larger than neurons but still reasonably small, will be found. These have not been discovered yet. If they are discovered, I believe it will probably derive from more careful neuronal recording, not from a return to less refined techniques. I call your attention to the way our interest is more captured by Dr. John's unitary data than by his "wave" data. Let me make an analogy with chemistry, apologizing in advance to those who abhor analogies between sciences. Modern chemistry is based on the table of atomic weights, not vice versa whatever people may say against reductionism. While the theory of oxidation may have superseded the theory of phlogiston prior to the advent of Mendeleev's table, it should be remembered that the tools for the advance were precisely the same as those for the discovery of the periodic table. In other words the progress toward an understanding of relations between atoms and molecules is precisely what systematized our science of molecules. For reasons such as this, I cannot imagine any significant advance at present in our understanding of EEG-like waves which would not be guided and interpreted by single unit techniques. If one had to choose between wave and unitary analysis he should according to my mind choose the latter. Better still do both.

JOHN: I am not saying that one should not study single cells. What I am saying is that populations are important. It may be that what the single cell does is informationally significant to the brain. Personally I am dubious about that proposition. I think that what the ensemble does, in a nonrandom way, may be informationally significant to the brain. The important thing is to be informed about both.

SEGUNDO: The question raised here is whether it is better to explore a pool of neurons by way of separate individually well-identified records from several nerve cells or by way of "multiunit" records. Though the latter method is relatively simple and does provide some information, I am not aware that there is anything that can be illustrated by it and cannot be illustrated at least as precisely, and often far more so, using individually resolved action potentials. There are, therefore, certain doubts in my mind as to the usefulness of multiunit recording, especially now that single cell recording in freely moving unanesthetized animals has become more feasible and approaches the other technique in terms of simplicity.

My argument can be summarized as follows: At the technical level, there is no conclusive evidence that multiunit records resolve the activity of a population of cells that escapes the other method. In fact, in a multiunit record there is no clear-cut boundary between the larger action potentials and a background with multiple components like smaller action potentials, filtered EEG, and so on. The control level often has to be identified *a posteriori*, when the animal has been sacrificed, for example. Furthermore, there is no guarantee that summation between different components and even between separate action potentials is linear. This possibility of nonlinear action potential summation, as well as the normal variability of single cell spikes, opens doubts as to the consistent reliability of the "window-circuit" criterion.

At the conceptual level, many conclusions from multiunit work imply changes in overall rate, accelerations for example. Such conclusions usually are imprecise in several respects. Firstly, because the degree of acceleration in impulses per second squared can be estimated only in a very coarse manner. Secondly, because the proportion of cells that accelerate can be estimated no better than coarsely. In fact, it often is not possible to differentiate between acceleration of active cells and recruitment of silent cells. Thirdly, because when using multiunit records one has little idea as to the finer discharge features of the individual spike trains and of their correlation. Contrastingly, a reasonable number of individually identifiable records of few neurons enable the investigator to indicate accurately the observed rate changes, to estimate precisely (at any desired confidence level) the proportion of accelerating cells, and to describe the important statistical features of each spike train (e.g., interspike interval mean, standard deviation, histogram, etc.) and of their correlations (e.g., cross correlation histograms, etc.).

In short, it appears to me that we are confronted with the alternative of choosing between two procedures, neither of which implies overwhelming technical difficulties, and of which one, individual cell recording, provides us with more abundant and more precise information.

JOHN: The questions that Dr. Segundo raised are answered very nicely by the fact that the discriminators can be set at different levels. You find that the activity of the population you are fractionating is time locked to the stimulus in the same way in several levels. Noise would not be time locked to a stimulus in a coherent fashion. As you drop your discriminator low enough, you do get into noise and, then, this time-locked pattern disappears.

The critical thing is not whether it is better to look at single units or at multiple units. One should look at both when one has the opportunity. The critical thing is that with these new techniques, such as Verzeano's multiple microelectrodes, you can see relationships between cells, which are extremely difficult to see when you look at one cell. You can't see circulation from electrode one to two to three, with only one electrode.

VERZEANO: Evidently, the controversy about the technique is clouding and confusing other important problems. Actually, the controversy revolves around three distinct points: (1) The validity of the results; (2) The merit of the technique; (3) The statistical aspects of nervous system function.

(1) Regardless of any other points, the validity of the results is unimpeachable. First, facts remain facts, whether they are discovered by multineuronal or single neuronal analysis. The relation between the slope of the evoked response and the probability of neuronal discharge was first demonstrated by our multineuronal analysis. This does not make it less real in any way. Second, further analysis, by *single* neuronal recording confirmed the original findings. Third, further multineuronal as well as single neuronal analysis conducted in other laboratories, in different regions of the brain, confirmed, again, the original findings (see R. F. Thompson and N. Weinberger, pages 55 and 63, respectively). All this provides sufficient evidence to conclude that, indeed, there are clear relations between the slope of the gross response and the probability of neuronal discharge.

(2) With respect to the technique, I think it should be clear to everybody that multineuronal as well as single neuronal recordings are indispensable. There are certain kinds of information which can be obtained only by multineuronal recording, other kinds only by single neuronal recording, and certain kinds of information which can be obtained by either technique but can be enormously refined and clarified by the use of both techniques, separately or simultaneously. For instance, it would have been difficult, if not impossible, to demonstrate the spontaneous circulation of activity in thalamic and cortical networks, and to study its characteristics and its relations to gross waves, if we had not used arrays of multiple microelectrodes, each of which provided

separate but overlapping multineuronal recordings, and if we had not followed up with single neuronal recording.

(3) When I speak about the statistical aspects of nervous system function, considerations of technique cloud the issue again. Single neuronal or multineuronal recordings have nothing to do with it. What I mean to say is that the very nature of nervous system function is based on the activity of large numbers of neurons, that there is no single, isolated neuron, which can be held responsible for the accomplishment of a specific function or the maintenance of a specific state. When, for instance, the EEG becomes synchronized, it is not because a single, privileged neuron, somewhere in the thalamus, tells the EEG to behave itself and become nice, regular, and periodic; it is because very large numbers of neurons in several thalamic and cortical systems change their activities in a specific way which leads to synchronization. One can detect this change in activity either by looking at several neurons simultaneously or by isolating them and looking at them one by one, sequentially, or even better, by doing both of these things. But the way one looks at them is not important. What is important is that, no matter how one looks at them, the statement one makes about their behavior is a statement of probability: Out of a total of so many neurons that one has observed, a certain number have behaved in a way which is related to the synchronization of the EEG; furthermore, if one keeps looking at a single one of these neurons, in isolation, it is impossible to predict what this *one* neuron is going to do, when the next gross wave comes along; it is only on the basis of the previous observation of large numbers of neurons that one may be able to state that the probability is so much, that this neuron will or will not participate in such or such activity related to synchronization. Thus, one of the important aspects of the statistical nature of nervous function, is that the networks and systems of neurons whose activity underlies a specific brain function, operate in a probabilistic way. Meaning that, if and when it should be possible to make a quantitative statement relating the activity of the neuronal systems to that brain function, the statement will be one of probability.

PERCEPTUAL MECHANISMS

THE ROLE OF PHOTOPIGMENTS IN VISION

FREDERICK CRESCITELLI

DEPARTMENT OF ZOOLOGY, UNIVERSITY OF CALIFORNIA, LOS ANGELES, CALIFORNIA

The initial event in vision is the absorption of light by a pigment, the visual pigment, which is located in the outer segments of rods and cones. These photosensitive pigments are highly oriented components located within the membranous discs which are characteristic structural elements of the normal outer segment. Visual pigments have been investigated by direct visual observation, by extraction and spectrophotometric analyses of the extracts, by microspectrophotometric measurements of regions of the retina, and by examination of the pigment *in situ* within the outer segment.

Chemically, the visual pigments belong to one class of biochemical compounds, the chromoproteins, in which the protein, called opsin, about which little is known, is considered to be covalently bonded, via a Schiff base linkage, to vitamin A aldehyde. The ε-NH_2 group of lysine has been implicated in the formation of the Schiff base (Bownds, 1967). Accordingly, there are two main groups of visual pigments: (a) one based on retinal (formerly retinal$_1$), (b) a second based on 3-dehydroretinal (formerly retinal$_2$). Functionally, these two groups of photopigments behave in the same manner but there are certain physicochemical differences which may have biological significance. The 3-dehydroretinal pigments as a group absorb light at longer wavelengths than do the retinal pigments as a group. This is because of the

Aided by a grant from the division of Research Grants and Fellowships, National Institutes of Health, U.S. Public Health Service.

added conjugation due to the second double bond in the ring. The spectral absorbance curves of the 3-dehydroretinal pigments are broader so that a different nomogram for this system has been devised, distinct from that for the retinal system of pigments (Dartnall, 1953; Munz & Schwanzara, 1967). The 3-dehydroretinal pigments have a photosensitivity some 70% of the value for the retinal group (Dartnall, 1967). This is due, not to a lower quantum efficiency, but to a lower molar extinction for the 3-dehydroretinal pigments. These and other differences for the two groups of pigments have been pointed out by Bridges (1967), and by Williams and Milby (1967).

The retinal photopigments have been found in the retinas of mammals, birds, reptiles, some amphibia, many teleost fishes, elasmobranchs, and all invertebrates which have been looked at. The 3-dehydroretinal pigments have been detected in some teleosts. Some vertebrates have both groups of pigments in the retina at the same time (some teleosts) or at different developmental stages of a metamorphic life cycle (some amphibia, perhaps lampreys, perhaps the eel). Teleost fishes are known in which the retina contains both groups but in which the proportion changes according to the season, presumably a function of the day-length (Bridges, 1965; Dartnall, 1962; Dartnall, Lander & Munz, 1961).

The catching of light quanta is the specific role of the visual pigment but the prosthetic group by itself does not absorb appreciably at wavelengths in the visible region. It is the opsin, which when joined to the aldehyde, interacts in such a way as to lead to a large bathochromic shift which brings the system into the functional region of the spectrum. Thus, the spectral region over which the visual pigment absorbs is determined in two ways: (a) through the use of the same opsin but linked either to retinal or 3-dehydroretinal and (b) through the use of the same prosthetic group but employing opsins of various specific types. Examples of the first type are probably those pigments in which the nature of the aldehyde changes during a metamorphic life cycle (Crescitelli, 1958; Liebman & Entine, 1969) or as a function of the season (Bridges, 1965; Dartnall *et al.*, 1961). Examples of the second type are the rhodopsin and iodopsin of chicken and turkey (Crescitelli, Wilson, & Lilyblade, 1964; Wald, Brown, & Smith, 1955) both of which use retinal; and the three pigments of the frog tadpole (*Rana pipiens*), i.e., pigments 438 (green rods), 527 (red rods), and 620 (single cone and principal member of double cone) all three of which use 3-dehydroretinal (Liebman & Entine, 1969). It is a good possibility that the nature of the opsin is genetically determined and that this involves a specific sequence of amino acids in the primary structure of the protein (McFarland & Munz, 1965). There are definite indications that the visual pigments can interconvert during the life of certain species and under particular environmental conditions. Tadpoles of the tree frog (*Hyla regilla*) and of the bullfrog (*Rana catesbiana*) possess in their rods a 3-dehydroretinal system; this is gradually replaced, as metamorphosis proceeds, by a retinal pigment (Crescitelli, 1958). In this interconversion, which was not found in all amphibia (Crescitelli, 1958), the thyroid gland appears to be involved (Wilt, 1959), but the mechanism of its action is not yet known. We have recently found in our laboratory that the albino rat depleted of vitamin A, but sustained by means of retinoic acid, will form, following the administration of crystalline vitamin A_2, normal rat rhodopsin containing retinal.

I. Stereospecificity of the Visual Pigment System

A. STEREOSPECIFICITY OF THE PROSTHETIC GROUP

It is well known that a specific isomer, having the 11-*cis* configuration, combines with opsin to form the naturally occurring visual pigment (Hubbard & Wald, 1952). The 9-*cis* isomer will also combine with the same opsin but will form, not a naturally occurring pigment, but an isopigment absorbing at lower wavelengths than the natural compound. Thus cattle opsin from the rods will form, with 11-*cis* retinal, normal cattle rhodopsin with maximal absorption at 498 nm. With 9-*cis* retinal this opsin will form isorhodopsin with maximum at 487 nm. No pigment is formed with all-*trans* retinal (Hubbard & Wald, 1952). These well-defined facts strongly suggest that stereospecific features of the prosthetic group in relation to the opsin are involved in forming a visual pigment and in endowing it with characteristic properties. These steric factors are assumed to apply to both retinal and 3-dehydroretinal photopigments.

(2)

B. Stereospecificity of the Opsin

Visual pigments are colored, i.e., absorb selectively in the visible region of the spectrum. This bathochromic shift of the chromophore is believed to be the result of an interaction of the chromophore with the opsin. At one time it was considered that the color might be explained on the basis of two prosthetic groups in conjugation in the visual pigment molecule. This view was abandoned for a number of reasons (Dartnall, 1957), particularly cogent being the finding that cattle rhodopsin contains only one such chromophore per molecule (Hubbard, 1954). Recent speculations have invoked the chromophore–opsin interaction to account for both the magnitude of the bathochromic shift and the multiplicity of spectral positions to which these chromoproteins are shifted. According to one idea (Kropf & Hubbard, 1958) the Schiff base in the visual pigment is protonated which by itself would lower the energy of excitation transition and carry the absorption maximum to about 440 nm. This is insufficient, however, and the remaining shift is assumed to be the result of the above-mentioned interaction and the stabilization of the positive charge on the chromophoric chain by means of negative groups on the protein so that the energy of transition from the ground state to the first excited state is lowered, thus shifting the spectrum further toward longer wavelengths. A second idea (Dartnall & Lythogoe, 1965) assumes that the Schiff base linkage is unprotonated and that dipole–dipole interaction between polyene chain and protein occurs and that because of the specific physicochemical structure of specific opsins, the dipoles of the polyene chain are "frozen" in different positions leading to variations in the absorption spectra such as are recorded in the various visual pigments. These are interesting speculations but they only highlight the need for specific knowledge about the visual pigment proteins. Whatever may be the true explanation for the bathochromic shift, it is clear that an intimate and specific relationship probably exists between the stereospecific prosthetic group and the complementary configuration of the opsin. We will next turn to direct evidence that stereospecific relations do indeed exist between protein and retinal in the visual pigment molecule.

C. Circular Dichroism

In the spectral region of optically active absorption bands circularly polarized light interacts with the dissymmetric molecular structure to generate two interrelated effects: anomalous rotatory dispersion (ORD) and circular dichroism (CD). These effects, collectively known as the Cotton effect after their discoverer, Aimé Cotton (1869–1951), have made available to the physical chemist, the organic chemist, and the biochemist a powerful and promising approach to the study of stereochemistry. In the region of an optically active absorption band left and right circularly polarized light will be unequally absorbed. A plot of the difference in absorbance ($\varepsilon_L - \varepsilon_R$) as a function of wavelength will give the Cotton effect (CD) for this optical transition. Figure 1 shows the circular dichroism for Cu-d-tartrate and for Cu-l-tartrate and the relation to the absorbance curve. For comparison the lack of dichroism of Du-dl-tartrate is shown. Related to circular dichroism is the optical

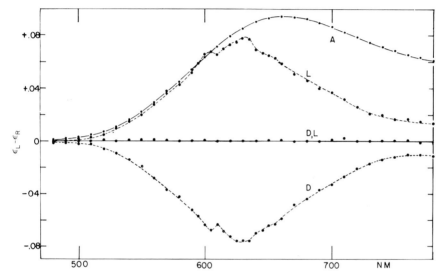

Fig. 1. Circular dichroism of Cu-l-tartrate (L), Cu-d-tartrate (D), and Cu-dl-tartrate (D, L) compared with absorbance curve (A). The circular dichroism was measured with a Beckman DU spectrophotometer provided with a circular polarizer placed between the Beckman exit slit and the solutions to be measured.

rotatory dispersion which results from the fact that in an optically active medium the refractive indices for left and right circularly polarized light will differ and the speed with which these two forms will travel through the medium will differ leading to a rotation (α) of the electric vector ε which is the resultant of the two equal rotating vectors ε_L and ε_R associated with left and right circularly polarized light. A plot of the rotation as a function of wavelength will then give the optical rotatory dispersion. The curve may be a plain dispersion curve, showing no maxima or minima within the spectral region under study, and indicating the absence of optically active absorption bands in this region, or the curve may be an anomalous one (indicating a Cotton effect) due to the presence of an optically active absorption band in the region under inspection. Figure 2 gives an example of a plain or normal dispersion and of an anomalous dispersion. Until recently, and because of instrumental

Frederick Crescitelli

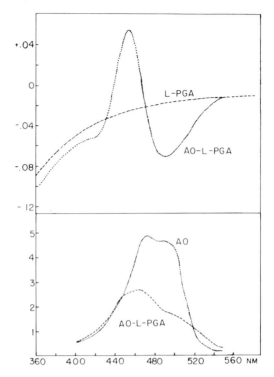

Fig. 2. Optical rotatory dispersion of L-polyglutamic acid (L-PGA) which illustrates a plain dispersion curve; acridine orange-L-polyglutamic acid complex (AO-L-PGA) which illustrates an anomalous dispersion. Below: the absorbance curves for acridine orange (AO) alone and the acridine orange-L-polyglutamic acid complex (AO-L-PGA). In all cases the L-polyglutamic acid was in the α-helical conformation. Adapted from Styrer & Blout, 1961.

limitations, the ORD has been the method of choice in preference to circular dichroism. The measurement of CD has certain important advantages over ORD because CD, unlike ORD, is not contaminated by activity at more distant spectral regions extending into the region of measurement of the Cotton effect. In the case of ORD such contamination often complicates and even masks the contribution by the optically active chromophore under observation. The remainder of this report will be concerned chiefly with circular dichroism, although it will be necessary, in places, to interrelate with past studies of ORD.

1. *Extrinsic Circular Dichroism*

Cotton effects have been recorded when a chromophore, itself optically inactive, interacts with an asymmetric local environment of a protein or polypeptide. Such effects are induced, so to speak, by the effect of the environment and are a result of the dissymmetry of attachment. These have been named extrinsic Cotton effects (Ulmer & Vallee, 1965). An example of such an extrinsic Cotton effect (Fig. 2) is provided for us in the binding of acridine orange to polyglutamic acid (Stryer & Blout, 1961). When bound to poly-D-glutamic acid in the α-helical conformation a positive Cotton effect (ORD) was recorded in the visible region of the spectrum in which the dye-PGA complex absorb. With poly-L-glutamic acid, the Cotton effect was reversed in sign. The authors also observed that acridine orange when apparently bound to polyglutamic acid in the random coil conformation resulted in no Cotton effect. There is some question about the latter result, however, since Myhr and Foss (1966) did obtain a Cotton effect with the acridine orange-PGA complex when the PGA was in the random coil form. To obtain this it was necessary to add the dye *after* the random coil form was generated, the suggestion being that the dye prevents or retards conformational changes and might account for the failure of Stryer and Blout to record extrinsic optical activity for the random coil form. Myhr and Foss' interesting observation focuses attention on the origin of dissymmetry in the random coil and suggests the possibility of small localized regions of ordered structure in a polypeptide which is otherwise a random coil. The possible existence of such loci of dissymmetry is also indicated by the work of Blake and Peacocke (1966) who recorded extrinsic Cotton effects in aminoacridine dyes bound to DNA and who noted that such effects were not abolished after denaturing the DNA by heat or acid.

Extrinsic Cotton effects have been reported to occur in a number of naturally occurring compound proteins. An example (Torchinskii, Livanova, & Pikhelgas, 1967) is phosphorylase b which has pyridoxal-5-phosphate as the prosthetic group. At neutral pH the enzyme shows an absorbance band with maximum at 333 nm, and associated with this is a positive circular dichroism. Neither the protein, nor the pyridoxal phosphate are optically active in this region of the spectrum. The ORD in this region showed no obvious Cotton effect but only a plain dispersion, illustrating the advantage of CD over ORD in this case. Another example of an extrinsic Cotton effect is illustrated by aspartate transaminase (Brevso, Ivanov, Karpeisky, & Morozov, 1964) having pyridoxal phosphate as the coenzyme and for which the active holoenzyme exists in two forms: the pyridoxylidene and the pyridoxamine. Both forms gave positive circular dichroisms in the region of the absorption bands but the CD of the latter was lower in magnitude than that of the former. The authors interpreted this decrease as being the result of fewer binding sites between coenzyme and protein. It seems, therefore, that a good case has been made for the origin of extrinsic Cotton effects in the binding of optically inactive molecules to specific sites in polypeptides and proteins and that the magnitude of the Cotton effect may be determined by the "tightness" of fit or orientation of the prosthetic group at the dissymmetric locus. Let us next examine how this idea applies to visual pigments.

2. *The Extrinsic Circular Dichroism of Visual Pigments*

In the visible region of the spectrum, rhodopsin is known to display two characteristic absorption bands: the A-band and a second, and much lower absorption (B-band), at lower wavelengths. For the rhodopsin of the frog (*Rana pipiens*) these bands are at 502 and 347 nm, respectively (Fig. 3). Both these absorptions represent optically active transitions, for a measurement of the circular dichroism reveals two definite Cotton effects, one at about 490 nm and a second at about 335 nm, both indicating greater absorption for left circularly polarized light (Crescitelli, Mommaerts, & Shaw, 1966). The B-band, though having a lower extinction, has as high, or perhaps a little higher, circular dichroism than the A-band; in other words the B-band has much greater optical activity. It will be observed, additionally, that the dichroism does not reduce to zero in the region between the two peaks (Fig. 3).

Here then is another example from biology of an extrinsic Cotton effect. A chromophore, retinal$_1$, itself optically inactive, combines with opsin to form a colored compound with optical activity in both regions of absorption. This, it appears, is direct evidence of a firm and stereospecific binding of 11-*cis* retinal$_1$ to the opsin. In the formation of this dissymmetric attachment it is possible that the bent 11-*cis* retinal$_1$ is itself involved in "cocking" the protein to some specific conformation. Such an induction has already been mentioned for certain enzyme systems. For the case of aspartic amino transferase (Fasella & Hammes, 1964) it has been suggested that the coenzyme (pyridoxal phosphate) might have an ordering effect on the apoenzyme. Another case is that of D-amino acid oxidase (Aki, Takagi, Isemura, & Yamano, 1966) which has flavin adenine dinucleotide (FAD) as the prosthetic group. In this enzyme the stability of the apoenzyme is less than the holoenzyme, suggesting that the FAD somehow stabilizes the protein. This resembles opsin which is known to be stabilized by attachment to the retinal$_1$ (Dowling & Wald, 1958). The apoenzyme of the D-amino acid oxidase showed, in the 300- to 500-nm region, a plain ORD. In contrast, the holoenzyme gave anomalous ORD, indicating optical activity in this region and dissymmetric attachment at the FAD-protein site. The authors of this interesting paper suggested that the coenzyme induces conformational changes in the protein leading to greater stability of the holoenzyme. It was also found that the holoenzyme is more stable with the coenzyme in the reduced form (FADH$_2$) and that, in fact, the CD of reduced and oxidized forms of the holoenzyme can be distinguished from each other. Within the framework of present knowledge opsin appears to be like some apoenzymes which are

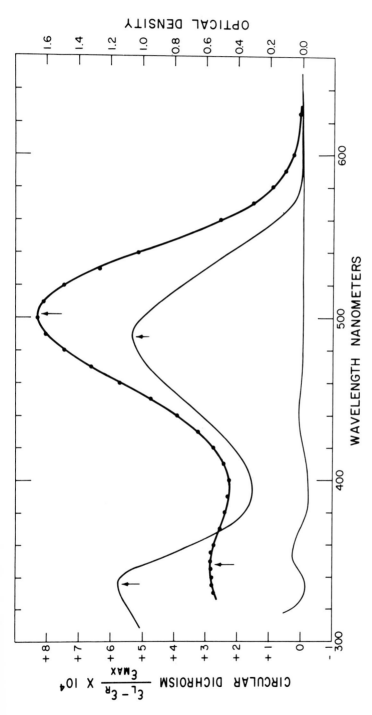

Fig. 3. *Circular dichroism of frog (Rana pipiens) rhodopsin.* (●): absorbance curve of rhodopsin dissolved in 2% digitonin, pH = 6.7, arrows indicate peaks of A- and B-bands. Heavy line with arrows: CD spectrum of same solution before bleaching, traced with a Jasco recording dichograph, arrows indicate peaks of Cotton effects. Thin line: CD spectrum of same solution after exposure to white light until all the color had faded to yellow.

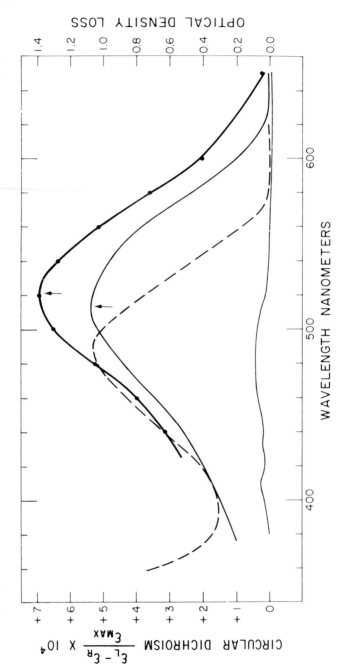

Fig. 4. *Circular dichroism of carp porphyropsin.* (●): difference spectrum (loss of density after bleaching) which indicates typical carp porphyropsin spectrum with density maximum at 522 nm. Solid line: circular dichroism of same solution before bleaching. Note absence of any indication of a second Cotton effect in region of B-band. Dashed line: circular dichroism curve for frog rhodopsin to show the spectral displacement of rhodopsin and porphyropsin comparable to displacement of absorbance curves. Solid line at bottom: circular dichroism of carp porphyropsin after bleaching.

stabilized by attachment to their prosthetic groups. The stabilization may well be the result of a conformational alteration induced by the prosthetic group. The extrinsic Cotton effect is not limited to frog rhodopsin. We have found it in Conger eel chrysopsin and in carp (*Cyprinus carpio*) porphyropsin (Crescitelli *et al.*, 1966; Crescitelli, Mommaerts, & Shaw, 1967; Crescitelli & Shaw, 1964) as well as in the rhodopsins of *Rana pipiens*, *Rana catesbiana*, and of cattle. The circular dichroism of carp porphyropsin is particularly interesting because it did not reveal any optical activity in the region of the B-absorption band (Fig. 4). This porphyropsin has an A-absorption band with maximum at 523 nm (Crescitelli & Dartnall, 1954) and contains 3-dehydroretinal as its name suggests. The CD band associated with the A-band, is, as expected, shifted to longer wavelengths compared to the Cotton effect of rhodopsin (Fig. 4). For carp porphyropsin the CD peak is at 517 nm but there is no indication of a second Cotton effect at lower wavelengths, although from the position of the B-band in the absorbance spectrum of the porphyropsin of yellow perch (Wald, 1959) this second Cotton effect should peak at about 365 nm and should begin to rise at about 422 nm. No evidence of this kind is seen in the CD spectrum of carp prophyropsin (Fig. 4). If this absence is confirmed it will make yet another difference, added to those previously mentioned, in the properties of retinal and 3-dehydroretinal pigments.

It is important to point out that the nature of the solvent is not apparently involved in causing these Cotton effects. We have observed similar CD spectra with rhodopsin solubilized in digitonin, cetyl trimethyl ammonium bromide, and Triton-X-100. It was also possible to measure the same dichroism in the presence of hydroxylamine which is a point of some significance in the results to be described later. Because of certain technical difficulties, we have not yet attempted to measure Cotton effects in visual cell suspensions or with the isolated retina. We expect, however, that these results obtained with visual pigment solutions are applicable to the visual pigment within the cell.

3. The Results of Other Investigators

The optical rotatory dispersion of cattle rhodopsin has been examined (Hubbard, Bownds, & Yoshizawa, 1965; Kito & Takezaki, 1966) but no definite Cotton effect in the visible spectrum was noted, although Kito and Takezaki (1966) mentioned that the ORD, obtained before bleaching the rhodopsin, was somewhat complex and that, after bleaching a plain curve was obtained. By measuring the differences in rotation between unbleached and bleached rhodopsin, Williams (1966) obtained a curve reminiscent of an ORD Cotton effect which he interpreted to be an example of an induced asymmetry. Williams also found that photoreversed rhodopsin was as active as extracted rhodopsin. Recently, Takezaki and Kito (1967) confirmed our results on the circular dichroism of cattle rhodopsin. They also reported the presence of two peaks of dichroism associated with the two absorption bands in the visible spectrum. The peak at lower wavelengths was shown to be of somewhat greater amplitude as we have found (Fig. 3). Takezaki and Kito (1967) also added an important new finding, viz., that isorhodopsin is similarly dichroic in the visible spectrum. Now rhodopsin has the 11-*cis* retinal which is not only bent, but is twisted in order to overcome the steric hindrance between the adjacent H and CH_3 groups of the bent molecule [formula (2)]. When joined to opsin the 11-*cis* retinal might be twisted only in one direction, either right-handed or left-handed, and this asymmetry might account for the Cotton effect. But isorhodopsin has the 9-*cis* retinal which is bent but lacks the steric interference of the 11-*cis* form and need not be twisted. Yet the isopigment also possesses the two Cotton effects associated with the A- and B-absorptions though the dichroism of iso-rhodopsin was found to be somewhat less than for rhodopsin, as if the 9-*cis* isomer is held less rigidly than the 11-*cis* form. The feature of twist in the chromophore as a relevant factor in the dissymmetry may be thus eliminated as a result of this finding by Takezaki and Kito.

4. The Effect of Bleaching

Current views of the action of light on visual pigments is that the absorbed quanta isomerize the 11-*cis* isomer to the all-*trans* form which as a result of the configurational change lessens the interaction between chromophore and opsin (Hubbard *et al.*, 1965; Wald, 1959). One might therefore expect to find, after exposure of the visual pigment to light, a change in the extrinsic Cotton effect. At present we cannot state what the detailed changes are; all we can say is that at room temperature, exposure to a bleaching light abolishes the dichroism (Figs. 3 and 4). There is no evidence that the products thus formed are optically active since the recordings made after a total bleach are not significantly different from those made with the solvent alone (Fig. 5, top recordings). Moreover, the same result was achieved after bleaching with or without hydroxylamine. This compound reacts with retinal to form the corresponding oxime so that the products and their corresponding spectra are different in the presence of hydroxylamine than without this compound. In spite of this there were no Cotton effects in either case. In addition, heating a rhodopsin solution at 60°C in the dark for about 30 min led to a bleaching and the thermally bleached product was not optically active. This is a condition in which a conformational change occurred without isomerization, for Hubbard (1958) has shown that heat can bleach rhodopsin without isomerization. These effects of light and heat on the circular dichroism of rhodopsin have been confirmed by Takezaki and Kito (1967).

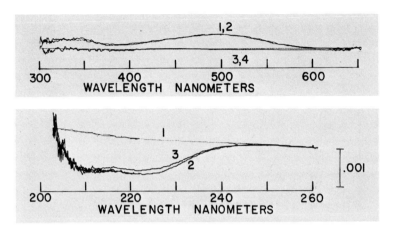

Fig. 5. *Unretouched photographs of recordings made with Jasco dichrograph.* Upper traces: bullfrog rhodopsin dissolved in 1% Triton-X-100 at pH 6.4. This solution had an absorbance of 0.732 at 502 nm. Numbers 1,2 indicate a double recording of same solution. Curve 3: recording of Triton-X-100 alone. Curve 4 (noisier trace): recording of bullfrog rhodopsin after total bleaching. Lower traces: Cattle rhodopsin dissolved in 2% digitonin ($\varepsilon = 0.84$ at 598 nm) and diluted 1:75 in 0.01 M phosphate buffer pH 6.7. Curve 1: digitonin alone. Curve 2: rhodopsin before bleaching. Curve 3: same solution after total bleach.

5. *Intrinsic Circular Dichroism*

Studies of polypeptides and proteins have revealed that variations in the peptide bond configuration lead to a number of polypeptide chain conformations some of which are characterized by specific Cotton effects in the far ultraviolet region of the spectrum (Harrington, Josephs, & Segal, 1966; Holzwarth & Doty, 1965; Sarkar & Doty, 1965; Simmons, Cohen, Szent-Györgyi, Wetlaufer, & Blout, 1961; Timasheff & Gorbunoff, 1967). Such structurally based Cotton effects have been designated as intrinsic Cotton effects (Ulmer & Vallee, 1965). Understanding in this subject is far from complete and one must be cautious, but it is becoming apparent that Cotton effects in the region of absorption of the peptide bond (180–240 nm) may be related to conformational features of the polypeptide. Holzwarth and Doty (1965), for example, reported that the circular dichroism of poly-L-glutamic acid in this spectral region differs according to whether one has the α-helical or the random coil form of this synthetic polypeptide. The right-handed α-helical form gave a CD spectrum with two negative peaks: at 222 and 209 nm, with a trough between them centered at 215 nm. In addition, there occurred a positive peak at 191 nm. In contrast, the random coil conformation revealed a weak positive dichroism in the region 235–210 nm along with a strong negative peak at 202 nm. Similar results were obtained with sperm whale metmyoglobin (Holzwarth & Doty, 1965) and myosin (Mommaerts, 1966) insofar as the α-helical form is concerned.

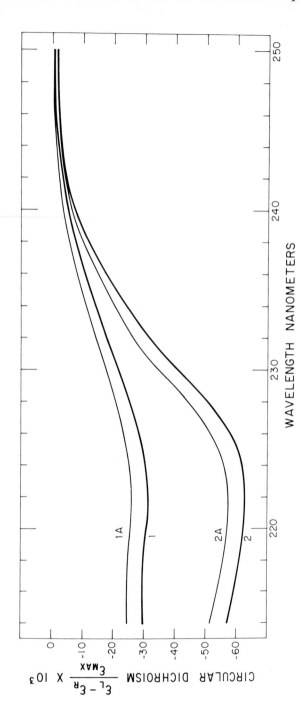

Fig. 6. Intrinsic circular dichroism of frog rhodopsin (curve 1) and carp porphyropsin (curve 2). Curves 1A and 2A: the comparable curves for the same two solutions after bleaching.

These findings, as well as others, encouraged us to look for intrinsic circular dichroism in solutions of visual pigments and to examine the effects of bleaching. With our instrument we were unable to penetrate the region below 203 nm but as far as we were able to make recordings it was possible to demonstrate an apparently compound CD spectrum with a negative peak at about 223 nm, a second negative peak at about 210 nm, and a trough between them at about 217 nm (Fig. 5, lower records). As far as it goes, this suggests a CD spectrum characteristic of the right-handed α-helical conformation. On exposing the solution to light the CD did not disappear, as did the extrinsic CD, but it was diminished (Fig. 5). A similar circular dichroism was found for solutions of carp porphyropsin and frog rhodopsin and the effect of light was quantitatively the same (Fig. 6) even though the total magnitude of the negative circular dichroism was greater for the carp pigment (Fig. 6). It will be noted by comparing the ordinate scale values of Fig. 6 with those of Figs. 1 and 2 that the magnitude of the change with light is about 10 times greater for the intrinsic Cotton effect than for the comparable effect with the chromophore. We cannot tell from our recordings what the specific nature of the conformational change is which followed exposure to light; all that we can say at present is that there occurred an apparent loss of α-helical structure. The loss of negative CD, following illumination, is only a small fraction (10–15%) of the total CD. We do not know how pure, with respect to other proteins, were these visual pigment solutions. If the total CD is assumed to be largely photopigment CD, then the small change implies, perhaps, that only a relatively small and localized region of protein is involved in the photoconformational effect.

6. *The Results of Other Investigators*

The view that a visual pigment apoprotein suffers conformational alterations as a consequence of illumination arises from a number of experimental findings. Until recently the basis for this view was in the spectroscopic, kinetic, and thermodynamic behavior of rhodopsin solutions following illumination and the study of these properties in the several intermediates which result from the action of light (Abrahamson & Ostroy, 1967). In the last few years more direct evidence in favor of this view has been appearing. One line of evidence is based on ultraviolet absorption curves of polypeptides and proteins. It has been suggested that these curves change in characteristic manner as a polypeptide chain undergoes a helix to coil transition (Glazer & Rosenheck, 1962; Glazer & Smith, 1961; Imahori & Tanaka, 1959; Rosenheck & Doty, 1961). The appearance of a peak at about 230 nm in the difference spectra of certain proteins following denaturation (Glazer & Smith, 1961) is specially relevant to this discussion. Glazer and Smith concluded that this peak, though probably complex in origin, is related to polypeptide backbone conformational changes. Relating this now to visual pigments, it has been reported (Takagi, 1963; Takagi & Sekoguti, 1961) that the difference spectrum of cattle rhodopsin, resulting from bleaching, shows a loss of absorbance in the far ultraviolet, maximal at about 234–235 nm. This was interpreted by Takagi (1963) to be associated with a conformational change, possibly of a helix to coil type. An important point made by Takagi (1963) is that rod outer segments behave as do rhodopsin solutions in this matter. A similar absorbance loss in bleaching was reported by Hubbard *et al.* (1965). Correlated with these findings are the reports (Hubbard *et al.*, 1965; Kito & Takezaki, 1966), based on measurements of ORD, of a negative Cotton effect at about 235 nm, and the fact that the magnitude of this effect decreases slightly as a result of bleaching. Again, this result was interpreted as being associated with a decrease in helix content of the opsin. Recently, Takezaki and Kito (1967) have confirmed our findings with circular dichroism and have concluded from the CD spectra between 200 to 250 nm that rhodopsin has a large content of α-helix and that illumination gives rise to a decrease in CD, indicative of an opsin conformational change. All these recent findings confirm more directly that a change in structure of the opsin is a consequence of the action of light. It is interesting that long ago, in terms of the technical progress made since, it was observed that the isoelectric point of visual purple changes after bleaching, suggesting an alteration in protein structure (Broda, Goodeve, Lythgoe, & Victor, 1939; Broda & Victor, 1940). This, too, has recently been confirmed (Fukami, 1960).

7. *The Relation of Extrinsic and Intrinsic Cotton Effects*

It is tempting to believe that these two effects are causally related, that, for example, the isomerization of the retinal and the change in its shape loosens the weak interaction between opsin and chromophore and this results in a local change in conformation of the helix. No irreversible change is involved because the addition of 11-*cis* retinal$_1$ to cattle opsin, for example, regenerates rhodopsin (Hubbard & Wald, 1952). It has been demonstrated also that restoring rhodopsin by means of a second flash, in a solution which has been bleached by a first flash, leads to a photoreversed rhodospin with as great an extrinsic Cotton effect (ORD) as the original rhodospin (Williams, 1966). There are some reports which suggest that the extrinsic and intrinsic Cotton effects of certain enzymes may be related in their alterations. Wellner (1966), for example, worked with L-amino acid oxidase from snake venom and found changes, when the enzyme was inactivated, in both the extrinsic and intrinsic Cotton effects. Wellner interpreted his results as indicating that inactivation (which is reversible) altered the conformation of the protein at the active site, where the two molecules of FAD coenzyme are asymmetrically attached, altering the distance between these two, or their orientation, and thus inactivating the system without actually releasing the coenzyme from the apoenzyme. In this case extrinsic and intrinsic Cotton effects are intimately related. On the other hand, there are examples where the two Cotton effects seem to be less closely related and perhaps independent entities. In the case of D-amino acid oxidase, for example, it was found that removal of the coenzyme (FAD) abolished the extrinsic Cotton effect in the visible spectrum but led to no significant change in this effect (ORD and CD) in the far ultraviolet spectrum, which indicated an α-helix form. The authors interpreted this to mean that FAD or $FADH_2$ induces an ordering of the protein apoenzyme but in a nonhelical portion of the polypeptide chain (Aki *et al.*, 1966). We cannot be certain, of course, but the visual pigment Cotton effects appear to be more like those of L-amino acid oxidase.

A potentially useful way to study this question is to examine the kinetics of change of these two Cotton effects following illumination. Which optical activity decreases first? This is the same as asking: what are the Cotton effects of the various intermediates of photoisomerization and bleaching? Nothing yet is known on these questions. Takagi (1963) considered that the change in ultraviolet absorbance, after illumination, may occur rather late, perhaps after metarhodopsin I. Yoshizawa and Wald (1963) suggested that the change in structure of the opsin may occur in the transition from lumi-rhodopsin to metarhodopsin and Hubbard *et al.* (1965) wrote of a preliminary finding showing a decrease in absorbance at 280 nm associated with the rhodopsin–metarhodopsin conversion. Another approach is that of Bownds and Wald (1965) who reported that borohydride is able to reduce meta-rhodopsin II but not rhodopsin or metarhodopsin I. Their explanation for this is that the protein protects the Schiff base from attack by the borohy-dride until at the stage of metarhodopsin II when the opsin structure has been opened up enough for reduction to occur. Kinetic studies on the decay of the various intermediates of the rhodopsin cycle have not always been in agreement (Abrahamson & Ostroy, 1967) but one point seems to emerge and that is that up to the appearance of lumirhodopsin there appears to be little evidence for a conformational change in the opsin. Thus the trend of ideas has been to consider photoisomerization as a primary process and protein conformational effects to follow. In any case the evidence so far has not eliminated the possibility that a structural change in the opsin of the outer segment discs may be the event which triggers off excitation and which may be involved in the amplification process. It should be pointed out here that there are some who consider that the process of excitation (including ampli-fication) is explainable in terms of the change in shape and properties of retinal as a result of the isomerization (Jahn, 1963).

There is one final point in relation to the α-helical conformation of visual pigments and the fact that this conformation suffers a change after absorption of light quanta (Fig. 5). Unless stabilized in some way the α-helix is unstable in aqueous solutions. One way to stabilize this conformation is to provide a hydrophobic environment. Lotan, Yaron, and Berger (1966) have demonstrated how such stabilization may be achieved, i.e., by increasing the length of the aliphatic portion of the side-chain in a helical polypeptide. This stabilization occurred in an aqueous environment but not in organic solvents, whether helix-promoting or helix-breaking. It will be recalled that rhodopsin has lipid tightly bound to it and that bleaching appears to release phospholipid (Krinsky, 1958). Bounds (1967) also called attention to the hydrophobic environment at the region of attachment of retinaldehyde to opsin. Since visual pigment is the crucial constituent of the membranes of the discs in the outer segments, these features of the photopigment are important. This importance is stressed by recent reports concerning the nature of the proteins in cell membranes. Lenard and Singer (1966) used purified membrane preparations from red blood cells and *Bacillus subtilis* and determined the ORD and CD spectra of these. They obtained a Cotton effect, believed to be due to the protein, characteristic of an α-helical conformation. These investigators proposed a model of the cell membrane which differed from the classical Davson–Danielli model in that the polar heads of the phospholipids are assumed to be held together to charged groups of the proteins and this complex forms the inner and outer aqueous surfaces of the membrane. The α-helical portions of the proteins are imagined to be imbedded within the interior of the membrane and stabilized by the hydrophobic environment of phospholipid tails and other lipids. Recently (Lenard & Singer, 1968), evidence was adduced for this model in the action of phospholipase C which was found to hydrolyze the membrane phospholipids without apparently affecting membrane structure, as revealed by phase microscopy, and without altering the membrane protein Cotton effect, either qualitatively or quantitatively. It was suggested that hydrophobic interactions at the interior of the membrane are largely responsible for maintaining the integrity of the membrane and the proper conformational features. Our results relate directly to this model. Since the visual pigment is a constituent of the membranes of the discs, and no one questions this conclusion, and since this protein carries a specific and identifiable label in its color and photolability, it can be definitely stated that the protein portion of this cell membrane does indeed possess an α-helical form, at least in part. Moreover, a portion of the conformation is altered by the very stimulus which in the cell leads to excitation. This suggests that visual excitation, whatever else it may involve, is intimately associated with a membrane configurational alteration. Circular dichroism may be the technique of choice in studying the membrane change.

In 1936, Mirsky (1936) gave his opinion, based on analogy with the behavior of hemoglobin and certain enzyme systems, that the action of light and darkness on visual purple could be described in terms of a protein denaturation and a reversal of this. He even speculated that denaturation might be involved in excitation. Though we define denaturation differently these days, and though we have made many measurements and written many papers since 1936, it cannot be said that we have departed very far from Mirsky's general view of the matter. All that we have done is to describe and define denaturation a little more precisely.

REFERENCES

Abrahamson, E. W., & Ostroy, S. E. The photochemical and macromolecular aspects of vision. *Progress in Biophysics and Molecular Biology*, 1967, **17**, 181.

Aki, K., Takagi, T., Isemura, T., & Yamano, T. Optical rotatory dispersion and circular dichroism of D-amino acid oxidase. *Biochimica et Biophysica Acta*, 1966, **122**, 193.

Blake, A., & Peacocke, A. R. Extrinsic Cotton effects of aminoacridines bound to DNA. *Biopolymers*, 1966, **4**, 1091.

Bownds, D. Site of attachment of retinal in rhodopsin. *Nature*, 1967, **216**, 1178.

Bownds, D., & Wald, G. Reaction of the rhodopsin chromophore with sodium borohydride. *Nature*, 1965, **205**, 254.

Brevso, Y. N., Ivanov, V. I., Karpeisky, M. Y., & Morozov, Y. V. Circular dichroism of aspartate transaminase. *Biochimica et Biophysica Acta*, 1964, **92**, 388.

Bridges, C. D. B. Absorption properties, interconversions, and environmental adaptation of pigments from fish photoreceptors. *Cold Spring Harbor Symposia on Quantitative Biology*, 1965, **30**, 317.

Bridges, C. D. B. Spectroscopic properties of porphyropsins. *Vision Research*, 1967, **7**, 349.

Broda, E. E., Goodeve, C. F., Lythgoe, R. J., & Victor, E. Cataphoretic measurements on solutions of visual purple and indicator yellow. *Nature*, 1939, **144**, 709.

Broda, E. E., & Victor, E. The cataphoretic mobility of visual purple. *Biochemical Journal*, 1940, **34**, 1501.

Crescitelli, F. The natural history of visual pigments. Photobiology, Proceedings of the 19th Annual Biology Colloquium, Oregon State University, Corvallis, Oregon, 1958.

Crescitelli, F., & Dartnall, H. J. A. A photosensitive pigment of the carp retina. *Journal of Physiology*, 1954, **125**, 607.

Crescitelli, F., Mommaerts, W. F. H. M., & Shaw, T. I. Circular dichroism of visual pigments in the visible and ultraviolet spectral regions. *Proceedings of the National Academy of Sciences, U. S.*, 1966, **56**, 1729.

Crescitelli, F., Mommaerts, W. F. H. M., & Shaw, T. I. The circular dichroism of visual pigments, particularly in the ultra-violet. *Journal of Physiology*, 1967, **189**, 74P.

Crescitelli, F., & Shaw, T. I. The circular dichroism of some visual pigments. *Journal of Physiology*, 1964, **175**, 43P.

Crescitelli, F., Wilson, B. W., & Lilyblade, A. L. The visual pigments of birds, I. The turkey. *Vision Research*, 1964, **4**, 275.

Dartnall, H. J. A. The interpretation of spectral sensitivity curves. *British Medical Bulletin*, 1953, **9**, 24.

Dartnall, H. J. A. *The visual pigments*. London: Methuen, 1957.

Dartnall, H. J. A. The photobiology of visual processes. In H. Davson (Ed.), *The eye.* Vol. 2. *The visual process.* New York: Academic Press, 1962. Pp. 323.

Dartnall, H. J. A. The photosensitivities of visual pigments in the presence of hydroxylamine. *Vision Research,* 1967, **8,** 339.

Dartnall, H. J. A., Lander, M. R., & Munz, F. W. Periodic variation in the visual pigments of a fish. In B. C. Christensen & B. Buchmann (Eds.), *Progress in photobiology.* Amsterdam: Elsevier, 1961.

Dartnall, H. J. A., & Lythogoe, J. N. The clustering of fish visual pigments around discrete spectral positions, and its bearing on chemical structure. In A. V. S. de Reuck & J. Knight (Eds.), *Colour vision, physiology and experimental psychology.* Ciba Foundation Symposium. Boston: Little, Brown, 1965.

Dowling, J. E., & Wald, G. Nutritional night blindness. *Annals of the New York Academy of Sciences,* 1958, **74,** 256.

Fasella, P., & Hammes, G. G. An optical rotatory dispersion study of aspartic amino transferase. *Biochemistry,* 1964, **3,** 530.

Fukami, I. On the electrophoresis of cattle rhodopsin. *Japanese Journal of Physiology,* 1960, **10,** 666.

Glazer, A. N., & Rosenheck, K. Solvent and conformational effects on the ultraviolet spectra of polypeptides and substituted amides. *Journal of Biological Chemistry,* 1962, **237,** 3674.

Glazer, A. N., & Smith, E. L. Studies on the ultraviolet difference spectra of proteins and polypeptides. *Journal of Biological Chemistry,* 1961, **236,** 2942.

Harrington, W. F., Josephs, R., & Segal, D. M. Physical chemical studies on proteins and polypeptides. *Annual Review of Biochemistry,* 1966, **35,** 626.

Holzwarth, G., & Doty, P. The ultraviolet circular dichroism of polypeptides. *Journal of the American Chemical Society,* 1965, **87,** 218.

Hubbard, R. The molecular weight of rhodopsin and the nature of the rhodopsin-digitonin complex. *Journal of General Physiology,* 1954, **37,** 381.

Hubbard, R. Bleaching of rhodopsin by light and by heat. *Nature,* 1958, **181,** 1126.

Hubbard, R., Bownds, D., & Yoshizawa, T. The chemistry of visual photoreception. *Cold Spring Harbor Symposium on Quantitative Biology,* 1965, **30,** 301.

Hubbard, R., & Wald, G. *Cis-trans* isomers of vitamin A and retinene in the rhodopsin system. *Journal of General Physiology,* 1952, **36,** 269.

Imahori, K., & Tanaka, J. Ultraviolet absorption spectra of poly-L-glutamic acid. *Journal of Molecular Biology,* 1, 1959, 359.

Jahn, T. L. A possible mechanism for the amplifier effect in the retina. *Vision Research,* 1963, 3, 25.

Kito, Y., & Takezaki, M. Optical rotation of irradiated rhodopsin solution. *Nature,* 1966, **211,** 196.

Krinsky, N. I. The lipoprotein nature of rhodopsin. *A.M.A. Archives of Ophthalmology,* **60,** 1958, 688.

Kropf, A., & Hubbard, R. The mechanism of bleaching rhodopsin. *Annals of the New York Academy of Sciences,* 1958, **74,** 266.

Lenard, J., & Singer, S. J. Protein conformation in cell membrane preparations as studied by optical rotatory dispersion and circular dichroism. *Proceedings of the National Academy of Sciences, U. S.,* 1966, **56,** 1828.

Lenard, J., & Singer, S. V., Structure of membranes: reaction of red blood cell membranes with phospholipase C. *Science,* 1968, **159,** 738.

Liebman, P., & Entine, G. Visual pigments of frog and tadpole (*R. pipiens*). *Vision Research,* 1968, **8,** 761.

Lotan, N., Yaron, A., & Berger, A. The stabilization of the α-helix in aqueous solution by hydrophobic side-chain interaction. *Biopolymers*, 1966, **4**, 365.

McFarland, W. N., & Munz, F. W. Codominance of visual pigments in hybrid fishes. *Science*, 1965, **150**, 1055.

Mirsky, A. E. The visual cycle and protein denaturation. *Proceedings of the National Academy of Sciences, U. S.*, 1936, **22**, 147.

Mommaerts, W. F. H. M. Ultraviolet circular dichroism of myosin. *Journal of Molecular Biology*, 1966, **15**, 377.

Munz, F. W., & Schwanzara, S. A. Anomogram for retinene₂-based visual pigments. *Vision Research*, 1967, **7**, 111.

Myhr, B. C., & Foss, J. G. Polyglutamic acid-acridine orange complexes. Cotton effects in the random coil region. *Biopolymers*, 1966, **4**, 949.

Rosenheck, K., & Doty, P. The far ultraviolet absorption spectra of polypeptide and protein solutions and their dependence on conformation. *Proceedings of the National Academy of Sciences, U. S.*, 1961, **47**, 1775.

Sarkar, P. K., & Doty, P. The optical rotatory properties of the β-configuration in poly-peptides and proteins. *Proceedings of the National Academy of Sciences, U. S.*, 1965, **55**, 981.

Simmons, N. S., Cohen, C., Szent-Györgyi, A. G., Wetlaufer, D. B., & Blout, E. R. A conformation-dependent Cotton effect in α-helical polypeptides and proteins. *Journal of the Chemical Society*, 1961, **83**, 4766.

Stryer, L., & Blout, E. R. Optical rotatory dispersion of dyes bound to macromolecules. Cationic dyes: polyglutamic acid complexes. *Journal of the American Chemical Society*, 1961, **83**, 1411.

Takagi, M. Studies on the ultraviolet spectral displacements of cattle rhodopsin. *Biochimica et Biophysica Acta*, 1963, **66**, 328.

Takagi, M., & Sekoguti, Y. Effect of illumination on the ultraviolet absorption spectrum of rhodopsin. *Biochimica et Biophysica Acta*, 1961, **49**, 589.

Takezaki, M., & Kito, Y. Circular dichroism of rhodopsin and isorhodopsin. *Nature*, 1967, **215**, 1197.

Timasheff, S. N., & Gorbunoff, M. J. Conformation of proteins. *Annual Review of Bio-chemistry*, 1967, **36**, 635.

Torchinskii, Y. M., Livanova, N. B., & Pikhelgas, V. Y. Circular dichroism and optical rotatory dispersion of muscle phosphorylase b. *Molekulyarnaya Biologiya*, 1967, **1**, 23.

Ulmer, D. D., & Vallee, B. L. Extrinsic Cotton effects and the mechanism of enzyme action. *Advances in Enzymology*, 1965, **27**, 37.

Wald, G. The photoreceptor process in vision. In H. W. Magoun (Ed.), *Handbook of physiology*, Vol. 1. *Neurophysiology*, Baltimore: Williams and Wilkins,1959. Pp. 671.

Wald, G., Brown, P. K., & Smith, P. H. Iodopsin. *Journal of General Physiology*, 1955, **38**, 623.

Wellner, D. Evidence for conformational changes in L-amino acid oxidase associated with reversible inactivation. *Biochemistry*, 1966, **5**, 1585.

Williams, T. P. Induced asymmetry in the prosthetic group of rhodopsin. *Vision Research*, 1966, **6**, 293.

Williams, T. P., & Milby, S. E. The thermal decomposition of some visual pigments. *Vision Research*, 1967, **8**, 359.

Wilt, F. H. The differentiation of visual pigments in metamorphosing larvae of *Rana catesbiana*. *Developmental Biology*, 1959, **1**, 199.

Yoshizawa, T., & Wald, G. Pre-lumirhodopsin and the bleaching of visual pigments. *Nature*, 1963, **197**, 1279.

Addendum to the Text

Enough time has elapsed between the completion of this manuscript and
its submission to the publishers so that several papers have been added to
the literature which are relevant to the subject matter of this report and which
are included in this addendum.

Some results have appeared dealing with the properties of rhodopsin
extracts made according to procedures intended to purify the visual pigment
(Heller, 1968a; Shichi, Lewis, Irreverre, & Stone, 1969; Shields, Dinno,
Henriksen, Kimbel, & Millar, 1967). These studies are in general agreement
with regard to the amino acid composition and the molecular weight of
cattle rhodopsin. The molecular weight was reported to be in the range of
27,700 to 28,600; values lower than the figure of 40,000 given by Hubbard
(1954) in her analysis of the digitonin–rhodopsin complex. The presence of
carbohydrates in the molecule has been noted and Heller (1968a) reported
the carbohydrates to be glucosamine, mannose, and galactose. Unlike some
previous analyses, Heller (1968a) reported little or no phospholipid in the
molecule but Shields *et al.* (1967) considered rhodopsin to be a lipoprotein
from which phospholipid may be removed under certain conditions. The
properties of rhodopsin extracts appear to show some differences according
to the method of preparation. No B-peak was seen (Heller, 1968a) in spectral
absorbance curves of cattle rhodopsin extracted with cetyl trimethylam-
monium bromide (CTAB). In contrast, extracts of comparable purity, as
judged by the $A_{278}:A_{498}$ value, made with the nonionic detergent Emul-
phogene BC-720, showed the well-defined B-peak at 350 nm (Shichi *et al.*,
1969). The property of regeneration is known to occur in solutions with
digitonin but appears to be absent in extracts made with CTAB or Triton-X-
100 (Snodderly, 1967; Johnson & Williams, 1969).

Further ideas have appeared with regard to the nature of the chemical
bond holding the chromophore to the opsin. Heller (1968b) compared the
amino acid composition of cattle rhodopsin before and after a light exposure-
borohydride reduction treatment. The results suggested that only one residue
of lysine per rhodopsin molecule was lost, indicating the presence of only
one chromophoric group per rhodopsin molecule, in agreement with the
previously published conclusion of Hubbard (1954). The appearance of one
sulfhydryl group per molecule after illumination led Heller (1968b) to
postulate a two-point attachment of retinal to opsin, one bond being a C–N
link to lysine, the second being a C–S bond to cysteine. Heller was not concerned about the reduction in length of the conjugated system caused by such
bonding, rather he considered that the charge interaction between the lone
pair electrons of the C–S–C bond and the orbital system of the polyene chain

of retinal could lead to charge delocalization and thus account for the batho-chromic shift of rhodopsin. Recently, another view has been published relative to the nature of the retinal–opsin bond (Poincelot, Millar, Kimbel, & Abrahamson, 1969). This idea conceived the bond in native rhodopsin to be a Schiff base, not to lysine, but to phosphatidylethanolamine. This conclusion was derived from analytical results with acid methanol extracts made under conditions presumed to involve no hydrolysis or imine exchange of the chromophore. Under such conditions evidence was obtained for the presence of N-retinylidene phosphatidylethananolamine. The presence of such a bond was considered for native rhodopsin and for the metarhodopsin I (absorbing at 478 nm). For metarhodopsin II (absorbing at 380 nm) N-retinyl lysine was found. The authors interpreted these data to indicate that retinal in rhodopsin is bound to a phospholipid moiety of the opsin and that after bleaching, in the transition metarhodopsin I to metarhodopsin II, there is a migration of the chromophore to lysine. The possible binding of retinal in this manner and the explanation thereby of the bathochromic shift of rhodopsin is suggested in a model experiment by Daemen and Bonting (1969). In this model all *trans* retinal was allowed to combine with 1,2-dioleoyl-3-phosphatidylethanol-amine and under anhydrous conditions a protonated Schiff base was formed with an absorbance peak at 450 nm. The source of the proton was considered to be the phosphoric acid group of the lipid, an internal protonation, as the authors described it. The remaining shift to about 500 nm, as required for rhodopsin, was ascribed to conformational twisting of the chromophore.

The conformational properties mentioned in the text have been further examined with solutions of visual pigments. Using well-purified extracts of cattle rhodopsin, Shichi *et al.* (1969) confirmed the characteristic Cotton effects in the far ultraviolet region and concluded that rhodopsin in solution has 62% helical structure and 21% of this is lost after bleaching. Using data from gel filtration chromatography, Heller (1968b) concluded that a con-formational change from a compact to a more expanded structure occurred in the opsin following the absorption of light energy. Rhodopsin and iso-rhodopsin from the squid (*Loligo bleekeri*) were examined by Kito, Azuma, and Maeda (1968) and found to have optical activity (circular dichroism) associated with the A- and B-absorbance bands. This activity in the visible spectrum was lost on illuminating the digitonin solutions. A Cotton effect in the far ultraviolet region was also obtained for squid rhodopsin but no change in dichroism was observed as the result of illumination, even though a specific decrease in absorbance was measured at 233 nm, which was taken to indicate a conformational change in the protein. These studies on rhodopsin solutions made with several kinds of solubilizers and utilizing rhodopsins from several species all indicate the same thing: An optical activity in the visible region indicating the effect of the dissymmetric environment of the protein in inducing the extrinsic Cotton effect on the chromophore, and the loss of this optical activity with bleaching. It would be desirable to extend these studies to the visual pigment *in situ* within the outer segment and some studies have already appeared on this which are in disagreement. A paper by Crescitelli, Foster, and Shaw (1969) suggested that changes in circular dichroism of frog outer segment suspensions occur which are similar to those already observed in solution of frog rhodopsin. In contrast, Shichi *et al.* (1969) were unable to find any change in circular dichroism in the far ultraviolet for cattle outer segments as the result of bleaching. They concluded that the change in helical content observed for solutions may be of no physiological significance.

REFERENCES

Crescitelli, F., Foster, R. F., & Shaw, T. I. The circular dichroism of suspensions of frog rod outer segments. *Journal of Physiology*, 1969, **202**, 189–195.

Daemen, F. J. M., & Bonting, S. L. Internal protonation in retinylidene phosphatidylethanolamine and the red-shift in rhodopsin. *Nature*, 1969, **222**, 789–881.

Heller, J. Structure of visual pigments. I. Purification, molecular weight, and composition of bovine visual pigment$_{500}$. *Biochemistry*, 1968, **7**, 2906–2913. (a)

Heller, J. Structure of visual pigments. II. Binding of retinal and conformational changes on light exposure in bovine visual pigment$_{500}$. *Biochemistry*, 1968, **7**, 2914–2920. (b)

Hubbard, R. The molecular weight of rhodopsin and the nature of the rhodopsin-digitonin complex. *Journal of General Physiology*, 1954, **37**, 381–399.

Johnson, R. H., & Williams, T. P. Thermal stability of rhodopsin extracted with Triton-X-100 surfactant. *Vision Research*, 1970, **10**, 85–93.

Kito, Y., Azuma, M., & Maeda, Y. Circular dichroism of squid rhodopsin. *Biochimica et Biophysica Acta*, 1968, **154**, 352–359.

Poincelot, B. P., Millar, P. G., Kimbel, R. L., Jr., & Abrahamson, E. W., Lipid to protein chromophore transfer in the photolysis of visual pigments. *Nature*, 1969, **221**, 256–257.

Shichi, H., Lewis, M. S., Irreverre, F., & Stone, A. L. Biochemistry of visual pigments. I. Purification and properties of bovine rhodopsin. *Journal of Biological Chemistry*, 1969, **244**, 529–536.

Shields, J. E., Dinno, E. C., Henriksen, R. A., Kimbel, R. L., Jr., & Millar, P. G. The purification and amino acid composition of bovine rhodopsin. *Biochimica et Biophysica Acta*, 1967, **17**, 238–251.

Snodderly, D. M., Jr. Reversible and irreversible bleaching of rhodopsin in detergent solutions. *Proceedings of the National Academy of Sciences, U. S.*, 1967, **57**, 1356–1362.

Question and Answer

QUESTION: (DEVALOIS): Since most of the surface of rhodopsin is internal, inside of rods, and the combinational change in order to alter a permeability change of the membrane has to be transmitted laterally to the membrane, why do you insist on a permeability change?

ANSWER: (CRESCITELLI): Oh, I don't insist. I gave it as an alternative that there might be an electronic conduction. At this stage I'd rather not speculate on what the excitatory mechanism specifically is because I don't think we are quite ready for it. It could be a permeability change, that's one possibility, but that would have an objection in terms of what we know about these discs or sacs. They seem to be isolated from the rest of the membrane, and so your point is well taken. But, I think the fact that they seem to be well isolated does not mean to say that no permeability change could take place. An active substance is released and somehow gets transmitted down to the inner segments, so one can't be too specific or one cannot worry too much about the specific nature of the excitatory processes. But I think what this offers is a basis for saying that the excitation is related to protein change and will apply. But I believe that you're perfectly right, that the possible transmission to isolated sacs is a problem.

BEHAVIORAL AND CELLULAR RESPONSES TO NOVEL AND REPEATED STIMULI

GABRIEL HORN

UNIVERSITY OF CAMBRIDGE, DEPARTMENT OF ANATOMY, CAMBRIDGE

The great majority of cells in the afferent pathways, leading from the sense receptors to specific sensory cortex, show a remarkable stability in their response to adequate sensory stimulation. Thus the receptive field properties of cells in the ventrobasal nuclear complex of the thalamus are similar in the anesthetized and unanesthetized animals (Poggio & Mountcastle, 1963). In conscious human beings cells in this complex show little variation in response whether the subject attends to or is distracted from the applied somatic stimulus (Jasper, 1966; Jasper & Bertrand, 1967). The receptive fields of cells in the striate cortex of unrestrained cats (Hubel, 1959) are similar to those of lightly anesthetized cats (Hubel & Wiesel, 1962), and the depth of anesthesia and the type of anesthetic used have no obvious influence on the size and shape of receptive fields of cells in the lateral geniculate body of these animals. This stability is not surprising when viewed teleogically, for it confers the great advantage that the stimulus analyzing apparatus of the brain continues to function over a wide range of conditions, so long as the receptor surfaces are adequately excited.

When considered from the anatomical point of view, however, this stability is very surprising indeed. One might expect, in the light of the functional stability, that the nuclear groups in the afferent cortical pathways would contain only axons from the particular sense organ in question and the neurons needed to pass the signal on to the next anatomical level. One would expect little else except, of course, certain architectural complexities of the nucleus to allow for some reorganization of the incoming signals. In the event, these expectations are rarely, if ever, fulfilled. Nuclear groups on the cortical transmission lines receive extensive connections from other regions of the brain. I will describe such connections as centrifugal. Precisely what these connections are depends in part on the transmission line, in part on the nuclear group, and in part on the kind of animal being considered. In so far as it is possible to generalize, it appears that the connections come from the cerebral cortex, the reticular formation and, probably, from certain other regions of the brain.

On the one hand, therefore, we can demonstrate a surprising constancy in the response properties of sensory neurons and, on the other hand, an extensive anatomical substrate capable, presumably, of modulating these properties. Of course the paradox would be resolved by demonstrating that these modulating influences *increase* the stability of the system, as indeed appears to be the case in the somatic sensory system. Here fibers arising in the sensorimotor cortex terminate on neurons in the gracile nuclei. These corticofugal fibers change the excitability of the cells in the same direction as a stimulus applied to the peripheral part of their cutaneous receptive fields (Gordon & Jukes, 1964). Such centrifugal influences may have the effect of improving sensory contrast (Dewson, 1967; Gordon & Jukes, 1962; Horn, 1960). But it certainly would be unjustifiable in the present state of knowledge to suppose that all of the fiber systems that could modulate the input, do so with this effect. Cells in the visual cortex respond to nonvisual stimuli (Horn, 1965; Lömo and Mollica, 1962; Morrell, 1967; Murata, Cramer, & Bach-y-Rita, 1965). The proportion which do so vary, in part at least, according to the number of stimuli which are given to elicit a significant change in the firing pattern of the cell relative to its background discharge. My own impression is that responses to nonvisual stimuli as brisk as responses elicited by visual stimuli are rarely encountered. Such heteromodal responses occur in some 10% of the cells studied in the visual cortex (Horn, 1965) yet the centrifugal innervation of the visual cortex almost certainly goes to more than 10% of the cells there.

One is left with the uncomfortable feeling that we have not yet asked the right questions as to the functions of these centrifugal fibers,[1] and their role in sleep and possible role in binocular rivalry, saccadic suppression, and in reafferentation are clearly worth investigating.

---

[1] But see, for example, the effects of bodily tilt on visual receptive fields of invertebrate (Wiersma, 1967) and vertebrate (Horn & Hill, 1969) visual interneurons.

For the time being then, we must accept this stability. However, the occurrence of an evoked discharge in the response-stable cells of the afferent cortical pathways does not imply a perceptual response. Thus Jasper and Bertrand (1967) have shown, in the few units studied, a maintained response to tactile stimulation of cells in the basal nuclear complex of man, although the subject was distracted from the stimulus and was not aware that it had been applied. Nor does the occurrence of an evoked discharge in these response-stable cells imply a behavioral response. Thus these cells continue to respond to a slowly repeated stimulus (Jasper, 1966) although the behavioral responses associated with the first few stimuli of the series might be expected to have disappeared. It seems, therefore, that such response-stable cells in the afferent channels leading to the primary sensory areas of the cerebral cortex do not exercise an imperative control over the putative groups of neurons commanding perceptual and behavioral responses.

Stripped of its jargon this conclusion is not very far from the one which might be drawn from common sense reasoning, for behavior is rarely under the immediate control of events in the external environment. If behavior were so controlled we would be a good deal further on in our understanding of its neural basis than we are now. It is not coincidence that our most thorough knowledge of neural mechanisms controlling a unit of behavior comes from studies of spinal reflexes (Eccles, 1957; Sherrington, 1906) where the stimulus–response relationship is relatively stable and predictable.

There is however, another situation where behavior is controlled by a stimulus in a fairly predictable way. This situation exists when a novel stimulus, one which has not been applied, or applied only rarely, in the past, is presented to an organism. The organism may respond, or ongoing behavior may be interrupted. The response is known as an orientation response but since it occurs widely in the animal kingdom and because the response has many components both somatic and autonomic, it is perhaps best referred to as a novelty response. If the stimulus is repeated a few times it gradually ceases to elicit a response. Thus novel stimuli appear to exercise a control over the command systems underlying perceptual and behavioral responses, not shown by otherwise identical stimuli which have lost their novelty by repetition. These command systems clearly cannot come under the direct control of the response stable cells in the sensory pathways. There are however cells in the central nervous system which discharge vigorously when a stimulus is first presented, but which cease to respond if the stimulus is repeated several times. Cells such as these are likely candidates for controlling the novelty response and in the past few years a number of workers have been looking at the response properties of these cells in some detail. In this presentation I shall describe some of the experiments I have been doing over the past few years in collaboration with Dr. Richard Hill and Dr. Hugh Rowell, working with the former on the rabbit and with the latter on the locust. These animals come from different phyla but this should not occasion too much concern in the present state of knowledge since the novelty response in one form or another appears to be a characteristic of the behavioral repertoire of multicellular organisms throughout the animal kingdom.

The novelty reponse contains certain quite reproducible features (Sokolov, 1963). The response can be elicited by a stimulus which has not been presented for some time in the past, but if that stimulus is repeatedly applied once every few seconds or so the response gradually wanes, or habituates. The response can be restored to a greater or lesser extent following the presentation of such a group of stimuli by withdrawing the stimulus for some time and then reapplying it once more. Very often the magnitude of recovery of the behavioral response is a function of the interval between the two groups of stimuli. The novelty response habituates when the stimulus is presented at regular or at random intervals of time and the rate of decline is influenced by the intervals between successive stimuli. The degree of recovery following a lapse of time is influenced by the number of stimuli that comprise the preceding set. Occasionally if a stimulus continues to be repeated after the response has disappeared, the response returns, apparently quite spontaneously. If a stimulus in a sequence is omitted the novelty response sometimes appears at the time when the expected stimulus would have occurred, i.e., there is a " response " when no stimulus is present. In addition to all of these properties, response decrement is closely tied to the parameters of the stimulus that have been presented. The specificity is not exact and there is some generalization to include stimuli that are closely similar to the repeated one. Another interesting feature of habituation is that once the response to the stimulus has declined it is possible, under certain circumstances to restore the response to that stimulus by injecting into the sequence of presentations some additional stimulus. Restoration of the response to a repeated stimulus brought about in this way is known as dishabituation.

The cells that we have studied in the midbrain of the anesthetized rabbit and in the tritocerebrum of the brain of the unanesthetized locust, show many of the properties described above for the behavioral response. Response decrement to a slowly repeated stimulus is a common feature of these cells. The responses plotted in Fig. 1A were obtained from a unit in the optic tectum of the rabbit. The unit fired spontaneously and this activity could be inhibited by a puff of air applied to the cutaneous receptive field. When the stimulus was repeatedly presented once every 3 sec the inhibitory effect increased to a maximum by the third presentation (solid line) and thereafter the influence of the stimulus on the spontaneous discharge (dashed line)

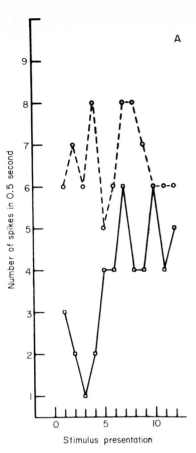

Fig. 1. *Effects of stimulus repetition on response.* The units whose responses are plotted in A (Horn & Hill, unpublished data) and B (Horn & Hill, 1966) were both recorded from the superior colliculus of the anesthetized rabbit. In each case the stimulus was a puff of air applied to the cutaneous receptive field of the cell once every 3 sec. The number of impulses present in the half second before (spontaneous activity) and after (response) each stimulus were counted. Spontaneous activity curves are drawn with dashed lines and response curves with solid lines.

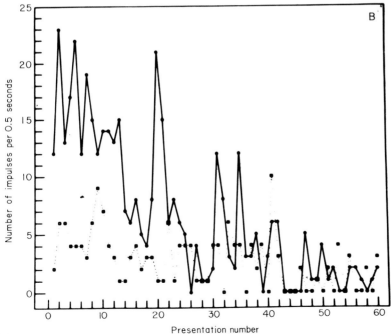

gradually waned. The buildup of the effect was unusual, whereas the waning of the effect was common.

Often the response declined irregularly and more slowly (e.g., Fig. 1B) than that shown in Fig. 1A. The unit whose responses to a tactile stimulus are plotted in Fig. 1B was also recorded from the rabbit tectum. The responses (solid line) are quite irregular to start with but gradually decline, until by the 25th presentation they oscillate around the spontaneous background level. There is very little change in the spontaneous discharge (dotted line) throughout the whole period of stimulation.

Response decrement occurs, with very rare exceptions (Horn & Rowell, 1968), whether the stimulus is presented at regular or irregular intervals of time. Figure 2 illustrates a typical result. The responses plotted in this figure

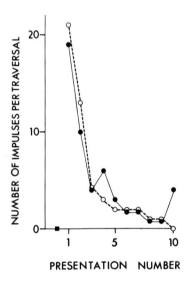

PRESENTATION NUMBER

Fig. 2. *Tritocerebral unit of locust.* Responses to disk moved across the visual field at regular intervals of 10 sec (●) and at intervals varying randomly about a mean value of 10 sec (○). The filled square (■) in this and in all figures in which it is present represents the number of impulses which would be expected in the time taken for the disk to traverse the visual field, calculated from the background firing rate of the cell (Horn & Rowell, 1968).

are from a unit in the tritocerebrum of the locust. The stimulus in this and in all other experiments with the locust was a small black disk which was moved across the visual field at a rate of approximately 60°/sec. Each point on the curves represents the number of impulses evoked by a single movement of the disk. When the disk was moved at regular intervals of 10 sec the responses (solid line) declined rapidly. A closely similar response curve was generated when the interstimulus intervals were *on average* 10 sec, but each interval was selected at random from a range of values of between 5 and 15 sec.

The rate at which responses decline depends upon the rate at which the stimuli are presented. This effect is illustrated in Fig. 3A. The responses

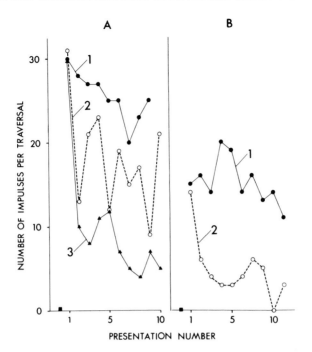

Fig. 3. *Tritocerebral cell.* Effects of varying the interstimulus interval on response to movement of the disk. A: curve 1 interstimulus interval (isi) 120 sec; curve 2 isi 40 sec; curve 3 isi 5 sec. B: another unit, curve 1 isi 10 min; curve 2 isi 10 sec (Horn & Rowell, 1968).

plotted in this figure were obtained from a tritocerebral cell when the disk was moved along an axis in the visual field. In the first sequence of movements (curve 1), the interval between successive stimuli was 120 sec. Several minutes after this sequence had been completed the disk was moved along the axis at intervals of 40 sec (curve 2). At the end of this experiment the disk was withdrawn for some minutes and then presented again, but this time the intervals between successive movements was 5 sec (curve 3). In each of these three experiments the response to the initial movement was 30 or 31 impulses, but the rates at which the responses waned are clearly different—reducing the interstimulus interval led to a more rapid attentuation of the responses. A similar effect, obtained from a different cell, is illustrated in Fig. 3B where the disk was moved across the visual field once every 10 min (curve 1) and once every 10 sec (curve 2).

The degree of recovery of response to sensory stimulation depends on the intervals between the groups of stimuli. The records shown in Fig. 4A are those of a unit in the rabbit optic tectum. The unit responded to a spot of light moved in its receptive field. Four sequences of movement were presented,

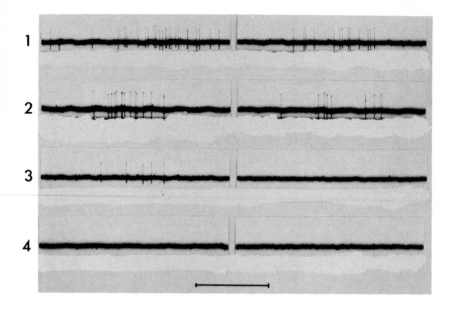

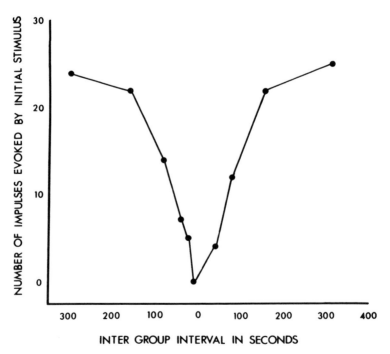

each sequence consisted of 10 movements. The interval between each movement was 4 sec. Following the initial exploratory procedures, during which the receptive field was plotted, the stimulus was withdrawn for 320 sec. Record 1 of Fig. 4A shows the response to the first and second movements following this interval. Both evoked a vigorous discharge, the second slightly less than the first. The response disappeared by the eighth presentation. At the end of this first sequence of 10 movements the stimulus was withdrawn for 80 sec and the responses to the first and second movements following this interval are shown in record 2. Both responses contain fewer spikes than the corresponding responses (record 1) following the 320-sec pause. At the end of the second sequence there followed a pause of 20 sec. The first stimulus following this interval evoked only a very weak discharge and the second and subsequent stimuli no response at all (record 3). A 10-sec pause preceded the last sequence during which all stimuli failed to evoke a discharge.

The curve plotted in Fig. 4B was obtained from an experiment with a different cell in the rabbit tectum from that illustrated in Fig. 4A, though the stimulus and the method of delivering it were similar. Each point on the curve of Fig. 4B represents the number of impulses evoked by the first stimulus (movement) of the sequence. This response is plotted against the interval of time preceding that stimulus. It can be seen that the number of impulses evoked by the first stimulus of a group declines as the interval between groups is reduced and increases again as the interval is increased.

There are occasional departures from this relationship and one exception may be seen in Fig. 5. The responses plotted in this figure are from a tectal unit which responded to a moving spot of light. The response which followed a 45-sec-intergroup interval is greater than that following a 60-sec interval. As a general rule, however, there is a relatively simple relationship between the duration of the intergroup interval and the magnitude of recovery of response to the first and subsequent stimuli. Another example illustrating this relationship is shown in Fig. 6. The unit from which the responses plotted in this figure were obtained was recorded in the tritocerebrum of the locust. The cell responded to a disk moved across the visual field once every 10 sec. The response to the first of a group of stimuli, presented after a 960-sec pause

Fig. 4. *Units from the rabbit optic tectum.* The units responded to a spot of light moved across the receptive field. Top: responses to the first and second (reading from left to right) stimuli of four sequences of movements. Record 1 responses following 320-sec interval during which no stimuli were delivered; record 2 following 80-sec interval; record 3 following 20-sec interval; record 4 following a 10-sec interval. Time scale: 0.5 sec. Bottom: Each point on the curve represents the response to the first movement of a group of 10 movements presented at 4-sec intervals. At the end of a group of movements the stimulus was withdrawn. The number of impulses evoked by the first movement of a group is plotted against the duration of the preceding intergroup interval in seconds (Horn & Hill, unpublished data).

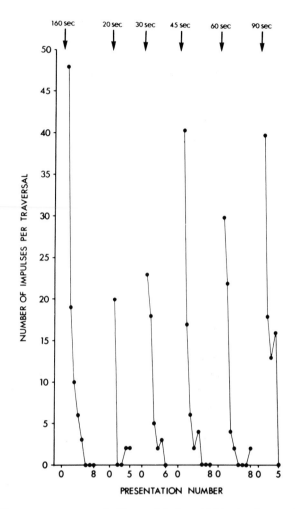

Fig. 5. The responses were evoked in a unit in the rabbit tectum by a spot of light moved across the receptive field at intervals of 4 sec. The number of impulses evoked by each movement are plotted against the presentation number. In this and in Figs. 6–10 and 14 the numbers above the arrows indicate the length of time, in the unit stated. The stimulus was withdrawn before the next group of stimuli were presented (Horn & Hill, unpublished data).

consisted of 23 impulses. Following an intergroup interval of 120 sec the response to the initial movement contained 22 impulses. However, the responses waned more quickly than they did after the 960-sec interval. The response to the initial stimulus presented after a 60-sec interval contained only 14 spikes. Responses to subsequent stimuli quickly waned and the unit failed to show any significant recovery following a 15-sec intergroup interval.

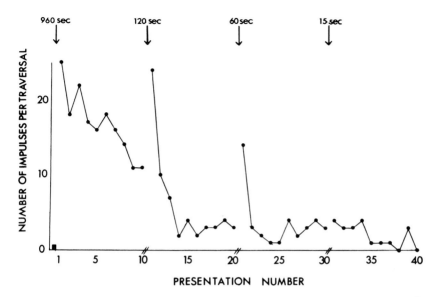

Fig. 6. The effect of varying the intergroup interval on the response to a black disk moved in visual field once every 10 sec (locust, tritocerebral unit) (after Horn & Rowell, 1968).

A large majority of units in both rabbit and locust, recover their responsiveness to a stimulus more or less completely if 2 or 3 min of rest are allowed to follow a short sequence of stimulation. Occasionally, however, recovery is not complete when much longer intervals elapse between the presentation of groups of stimuli. Such units are found more commonly in the locust than in the rabbit. It is not clear whether this difference is a biological or a methodological one, for it is relatively easy to record from units in the locust, but not from the acute rabbit, for 24 hr or more. The responses plotted in curve 1 (Fig. 7) were elicited from a tritocerebral interneuron by a disk moving upward along an axis in the visual field once every 10 sec. This group of 10 movements followed a period of 23 min during which the stimulus had been withdrawn. The first movement elicited 71 impulses and the tenth elicited 16. An interval of 5 hr elapsed before the next group of upward movements were made along the original axis. The first of these movements evoked only 25 spikes. The response declined to 4 impulses by the fifth presentation of the disk (curve 2). These results might merely express the deteriorating state of the animal. If the preparation were deteriorating the response to movement in all planes would be expected to fail. This did not happen. Control movements were made in the forward direction, one movement before the above experiment and one immediately after. The response to the first control movement (▲) in Fig. 7 consisted of 66 impulses; the

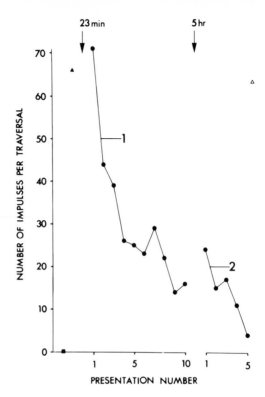

Fig. 7. Each filled circle (●) represents the response of a tritocerebral unit to an upward movement of the disk presented once every 10 sec. An interval of 5 hr elapsed between the first sequence of movements (responses plotted in curve 1) and the second (responses plotted in curve 2). Movement in a forward direction, immediately after the second group of upward movements evoked almost as many spikes (△) as were evoked by the forward movement before the first set of upward movements was presented (▲) (after Rowell & Horn, 1968).

response to the second control movement, (△), consisted of 63 impulses. Thus the low level of responsiveness to the second group of upward movements (curve 2) was not accompanied by any significant change in responsiveness to movement in the forward plane, and to this extent, therefore, was stimulus specific. It appears, therefore, that very long aftereffects may follow repeated stimulation.

These aftereffects may take on some quite interesting forms, one of which is illustrated by the response curves plotted in Fig. 8. The responses to the first group of nine movements of the disk, presented soon after the general receptive field properties of the cell had been established, are plotted in curve 1. The responses, though variable, show no persistent downward trend, and the responses to the second and also to the third (curve 2) groups

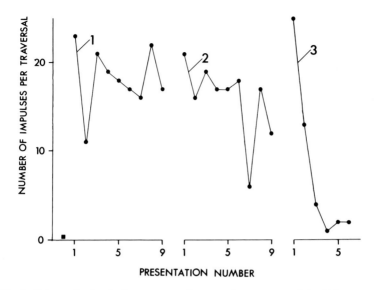

Fig. 8. *Tritocerebral unit.* Responses to downward movement of the disk presented at intervals of 5 sec. In curves 1 and 2 are plotted the responses to the first and third sets of movements of the experiment. An intergroup interval of 30 min preceded the third group of movements. Responses plotted in curve 3 followed an intergroup interval of 90 min (Horn & Rowell, 1968).

of stimuli waned only slightly. Subsequently however, although the response to the *first* movement within a group could always be restored, provided the intergroup interval was 5 min or more, the responses to subsequent movements within that group rapidly declined. The best approximation to the responses plotted in curves 1 and 2, was elicited from this unit later in the day, and is plotted in curve 3. This is a response curve to a group of stimuli delivered after a rest of 90 min. The number of spikes (25) evoked by the first stimulus of this group was numerically greater than the corresponding responses in curves 1 and 2 (23 and 21 impulses, respectively); but the number of spikes elicited by subsequent stimuli declined rapidly. Apparently a long term change in the responsiveness of the cell is brought about by the repetition of the originally novel stimulus, such that the response becomes subject to habituation.

Another factor that influences the responsiveness of cells is the amount of stimulation which they have received prior to the test sequence. This effect was demonstrated in an experiment which gave the results plotted in Fig. 9. In this experiment the cell was stimulated six times by moving the disk across the visual field at intervals of 10 sec. The stimulus was then withdrawn for 300 sec and the group of six movements (short series) applied again. This was done several times. Several groups each containing 60 stimuli (long series), were

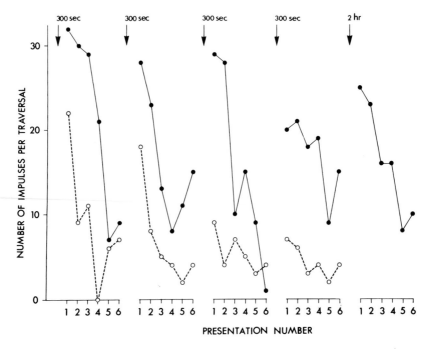

Fig. 9. *Tritocerebral unit.* The influence of prior stimulus exposure on responsiveness. The short series (●) are responses to six movements of the black disk. An interval of 300 sec intervened between successive groups of movements. The open circle curves (○) are severally the responses to the first six of a group of sixty movements (long series). The intergroup interval was 300 sec. The long series of presentations followed the short series. After the last of the long series of movements had been made the stimulus was withdrawn for 2 hr and presented again, when the responses plotted in the extreme right-hand curve were generated. In all cases the interstimulus interval was 10 sec (Horn & Rowell, 1968).

then presented, the interstimulus and intergroup intervals being the same as for the short series. If prolonged stimulation affected the ability of the cell to respond to a succeeding group of stimuli we would expect the responses to the first six stimuli following a long series to be weaker than those following a short series. In the experiment on which Fig. 9 is based, five groups each containing six stimuli, and five groups each containing 60 stimuli, were delivered. Responses to the first six stimuli of each of the last four groups in each series are plotted. It may be seen that for each group, the first six responses of the long series (○) are much weaker than the six responses of the short series (●), there being only one point of overlap (third pair of curves). There was significant ($P < 0.001$) difference between the mean evoked discharge of the pooled long series (6.4 ± 1.0 impulses) and the mean of the pooled short series (17.6 ± 1.6 impulses). Furthermore, as groups of sixty stimuli were successively applied, the responsiveness of the cell to the first six stimuli of each group gradually declined, a fact which is reflected in the falling response to the initial stimulus (○). This effect was not clearly present in the responses to the short series of stimuli. Two hours after the long series had been given the cell had recovered to the level of responsiveness observed at the beginning of the experiment.

As in behavior, so in the responses of cells, there are occasions when, after the discharge to a repeated stimulus has waned to a low level, the response, for no obvious reason, suddenly becomes vigorous again. The results of an experiment in which this behavior occurred are shown in Fig. 10. The unit was recorded from the superior colliculus of the rabbit, and responded to a 1000-Hz tone. Once the response characteristic had been established, the stimulus was withdrawn for 5 min, and then presented once every 2 sec. After the evoked discharge had declined the stimulus was withdrawn for 40 sec. After this interval the unit responded vigorously to the tone, but once again (middle curve) the responses rapidly waned. After this group of stimuli had been presented there followed an intergroup interval of 20 sec after which the initial response was greater than on previous occasions and remained sustained at a high level for many presentations of the tone, before finally dropping to zero. Such "spontaneous" changes in responsiveness though not common, occur not only in the rabbit but also in the locust.

Neither in the rabbit midbrain nor in the tritocerebrum of the locust (Horn & Rowell, 1968) have we observed units which, following habituation, gave a "response" when one stimulus out of a sequence of regularly presented stimuli was omitted (cf. Sokolov, 1963). It seems probable that cells showing this sort of behavior occur in restricted regions of the central nervous system.

The results presented so far have been concerned chiefly with the temporal properties of habituation; but there is another aspect to this behavior of cells—its specificity to the iterated stimulus. The records shown in Fig. 11 demonstrate that this specificity exists for heteromodal stimulation. This unit, which was recorded from the rabbit tectum, responded to both acoustic and tactile stimuli. The tactile stimulus was a puff of air applied to the cutaneous receptive field of the cell and the sound was produced by a klaxon horn. The upper trace of record 1 shows the response to the horn (artifact on lower trace of record 1) presented before any attempt was made to attenuate the response to a stimulus. Subsequently the puff of air was repeatedly applied and the response to it, initially brisk (record 2) gradually (record 3) waned to zero (record 4 upper trace above lower left-hand bar). The horn was then sounded (record 4 large artifact on lower trace) and a brisk response evoked which was not less vigorous than the response to the horn on the first occasion on which it was presented (record 1). When, after the acoustic stimulus had been delivered, the tactile stimulus was applied, no response was evoked

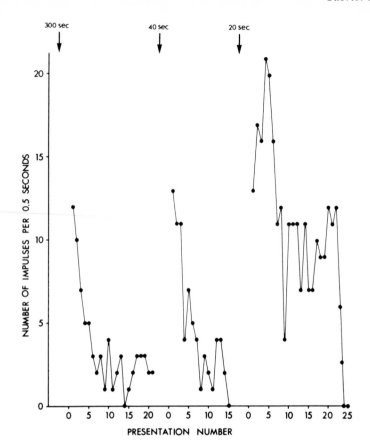

Fig. 10. *Unit from superior colliculus of rabbit.* Stimulus: 1000-Hz tone, 60 dB (~ 0.0002 dyn/cm²) .5-sec duration, presented .5 sec. The first set of stimuli presented after a pause of 300 sec evoked responses which are plotted in the first curve (reading from left to right). Brisk responses (middle curve) were elicited by the first few stimuli of the next series, presented after a pause of 40 sec, but again the response rapidly declined with successive presentations. Following a 20-sec-intergroup interval the unit repeatedly responded vigorously to 20 stimuli before the response declined (third curve) (Horn & Hill, unpublished data).

(record 4 upper trace above lower right-hand bar). Thus, habituation of the response to the tactile stimulus was without influence on the ability of the cell to respond to the auditory stimulus; and a brisk response to the latter failed to reestablish the response to the tactile stimulus.

Specificity within a modality also exists. One example was shown in Fig. 7 which was derived from an experiment in which the responses of a tritocerebral unit to upward movements of the disk were depressed for 5 hr after an habituating sequence of upward movements, though the response to a

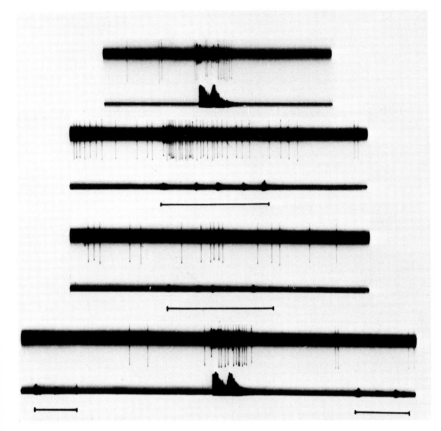

Fig. 11. *Selective attenuation of the response to a tactile stimulus* (air blown on tight shoulder). Tactile stimulus present throughout period indicated by bars. Records 2 and 3 show activity during the fifth and seventeenth presentations, respectively, of the tactile stimulus. Between the forty-sixth (record 4 above left hand bar) and forty-seventh (above the right-hand bar) presentation of this stimulus a horn was sounded (middle artifact on lower trace of record 4). The unit responded as vigorously to this stimulus as it had done when this stimulus was first applied (record 1) before delivering the sequence of air puffs. A brisk response to the horn was without effect on the response to the tactile stimulus. Scale, lower right-hand bar .5 sec. The discharge was recorded from a unit in the superior colliculus of the rabbit (Horn & Hill, 1966).

forward movement was effectively unchanged. This is an example of spatial specificity. It is also possible to evoke a response in some cells that have ceased to respond to a stimulus, by changing the intensity of the stimulus. The responses of a unit behaving in this way are illustrated in Fig. 12. This collicular unit responded to a spot of light moved across its receptive field at an angular velocity of 20° of arc per second. The luminance of the spot was controlled by

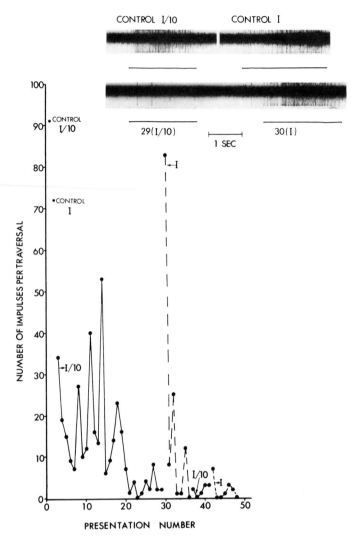

Fig. 12. Response to a spot of light drawn repeatedly across the receptive field, showing the effect on the response of a change in stimulus intensity. The spot was moved in one direction only, from posterior to anterior, along a horizontal meridian. Maximum intensity of spot was 21 cd/m², diameter 2°, background intensity 6 cd/m². Scale: 1 sec. Unit recorded in rabbit optic tectum (after Horn & Hill, 1966).

neutral density filters placed in front of the light source. The interstimulus interval was sufficiently long to permit the filters to be changed without interrupting the rhythm of stimulus presentation. Control responses to movement of the spot at full intensity ($I = 21$ cd/m^2) and reduced intensity ($I/10$) were obtained before the habituating sequences were presented. The control responses are plotted in Fig. 12 and the actual records shown in the inset. The interval between the control presentations was 20 sec. Twenty seconds after the control records had been taken the spot (intensity $= I/10$) was repeatedly presented at intervals of approximately 2 sec until the response was consistently weak (first solid line reading from left to right). The response to the last stimulus of this set (29 presentations) consisted of two spikes only and is shown in the inset. The neutral density filter was then removed. The spot at full intensity was moved across the receptive field, and a brisk response was evoked which is plotted as the first point (83 spikes) on the first dashed line. This discharge is shown in the inset. The response to the more intense spot, (I) on this, the 30th stimulus presentation, was more vigorous than the control response (72 spikes) to this stimulus. There was thus no reduction of the responsiveness of the cell to the more intense spot as a consequence of the diminished responsiveness to the less intense spot. The response to the more intense spot rapidly attentuated on repeatedly presenting it. There was no recovery of response to the less intense spot when this was substituted for the more intense one (second solid curve); and only a marginal recovery when the more intense spot was presented again (Fig. 12 second dashed line).

Another example of intramodality specificity is shown in Fig. 13. This unit, also recorded from the superior colliculus of the rabbit, responded to acoustic stimulation. The response to a 1000-Hz tone (record 1) was attenuated by repeated presentation at intervals of approximately 1.5 sec. When the response to this tone had waned (record 2) a 900-Hz tone was presented in place of the repeated stimulus. The novel tone evoked a response (record 2), but the 1000-Hz tone, resubstituted 1.5 sec later, failed to evoke a discharge. This procedure was repeated with similar results (record 4). A 1050-Hz tone evoked an " off " discharge (record 5). Thus failure of response to the 1000-Hz tone was not accompanied by a failure to respond to tones 100 Hz lower or 50 Hz higher in frequency. Several minutes after this sequence of presentations, the unit responded at control level (record 6) to the 1000-Hz tone. Before the habitutation sequence was begun it was established that the unit responded to both 1000-Hz and 950-Hz tones. Following habituation to the 1000-Hz tone, however, the 950-Hz tone also failed to evoke a response (record 3). This broadening of the region of response decrement to include frequencies other than that of the repeated stimulus appears, operationally, to be similar to stimulus generalization as seen in behavior.

On no occasion in our studies of cells in the rabbit midbrain were we able

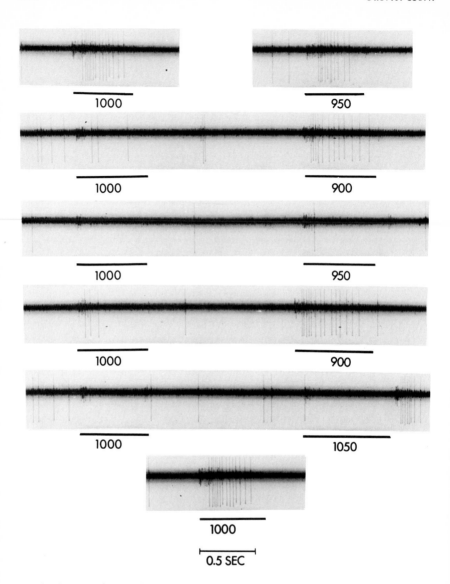

Fig. 13. *Specificity and generalization.* Rabbit tectal unit. The unit initially responded briskly to a tone of 1000 Hz and 950 Hz (record 1). When the response to the 1000-Hz tone had waned, the unit responded to a 950-Hz tone (records 2 and 4) and to a 1050-Hz tone (record 5), but failed to respond to the 950-Hz tone. Several minutes after this experiment had been completed, the unit responded again to the 1000-Hz tone (record 6). Records 2 to 5 form a continuous sequence in which the interval between stimuli was about 1.5 sec. Scale: 0.5 sec (Horn & Hill, unpublished data).

to induce recovery of response to a repeated stimulus by interpolating into the sequence of presentations some other additional stimulus. This failure could be a consequence of the use of urethane as a general anesthetic for the rabbits, or to an inadequate additional stimulus. However, Segundo and his collaborators (Bell, Sierra, Buendia, & Segundo, 1964) have induced recovery in this way in the curarized cat, and Rowell and I have been consistently successful in the locust (Rowell & Horn, 1968), once we had found the right stimulus for bringing about the effect. We were not successful in inducing recovery of response to the moving disk by using auditory, tactile, or visual stimuli as the additional stimulus, but we were successful when we stimulated the neck connective contralateral to the lobe containing the cell that was being recorded. Dishabituation brought about in this way is illustrated in the specimen response curves plotted in Fig. 14. In the experiments illustrated in this figure the animal saw a black disk move forward across its visual field at 10-sec intervals. Each traversal took 1.4 sec. The number of spikes elicited by each traversal of the disk declined (curve 1). A pause of 120 sec followed this group of stimuli during which counts of background activity were made for successive periods of 1.4 sec. The response (curve 2) which followed this interval was back to the initial level of curve 1. After a second pause of 120 sec (curve 3) recovery was not complete. In the interval between the responses plotted in curves 3 and 4 a total of 40 sec elapsed. During the first 10 sec of this interval the contralateral connective was stimulated with shocks of 0.5-sec duration delivered at a frequency of 36/sec. The sequence of disk presentations continued without a break. The unit now (curve 4) responded to the disk more vigorously than on any previous occasion. A high level of response (greater than 19 impulses/traversal) was maintained for 10 presentations, i.e., for 100 sec, before falling to lower levels. When the response had declined, the contralateral connective was again stimulated, without interrupting the sequence of presentations of the disk. This procedure was repeated twice and the response curves (5, 6, and 7) were plotted. It may be seen that the dishabituating potency of the connective stimulus gradually waned and that the period of augmented response to visual stimulation was sometimes preceded by a brief period (curves 5 and 6) when the response was low. Four hours elapsed between the sequences of stimuli which generated response curves 7 and 8, and during this time the results described above were repeated and confirmed. Curve 8 is the response curve to the disk following a pause of 15 min showing the usual recovery following a lapse of time. After 60 presentations the ipsilateral connective was stimulated, and stimulated again after the 75th presentation. This procedure was not followed by recovery (curves 9 and 10). In the 10-sec intervening between the 90th and 91st presentations the contralateral connective was stimulated and the unit gave a vigorous and well-maintained response to the disk (curve 11). When the responses plotted

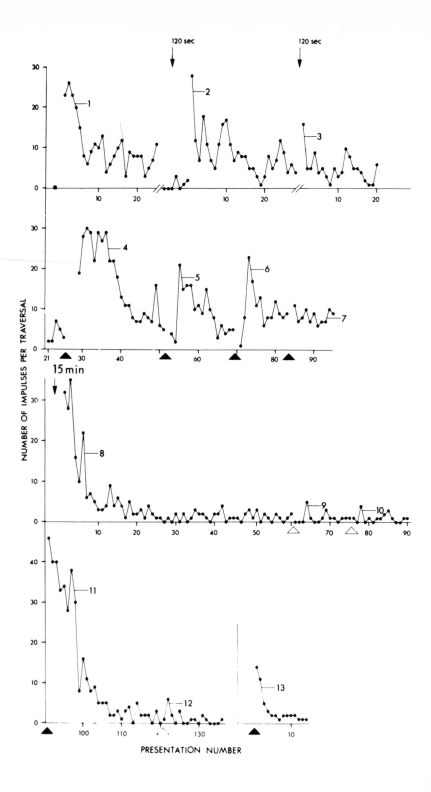

in curve 11 had declined the ipsilateral connective was stimulated between presentations 120 and 121. Once again there was no dishabituation (curve 12). Stimulation of the contralateral neck connective led to prolonged elevation of the background firing rate of cells recorded from the tritocerebrum; so it is possible that the increased responsiveness illustrated in Fig. 14 reflects this effect alone. However, the number of spikes in the 1.4-sec period that would be expected on the basis of this elevation of spontaneous activity is plotted in curve 13. It may be seen that the counts are much smaller than the values obtained when the moving disk was present in the period following stimulation of the contralateral connective (e.g., curves 4 and 11).

The neural mechanisms that underlie habituation are still only poorly understood and although there has been no dearth of speculation, experimental evidence is badly needed. We also need to know at what loci in the transmission link from receptor to muscle, habituation can first be detected (cf. Wall, 1967) and whether or not all synapses can be made to habituate if challenged appropriately. In many ways, close parallels can be drawn between the response characteristics of the cell described above and the somatic and autonomic behavior of intact organisms to novel and repeated stimuli (Horn & Hill, 1964, 1966; Horn, 1965, 1967; Thompson & Spencer, 1966). But there has been no direct experimental test of the hypothesis that the output of such cells controls this behavior.[2]

[2] See, however, a number of contributions in the volume edited by Horn and Hinde (1970).

ACKNOWLEDGMENTS

The author's experimental work was supported by grants from the Medical and Science Research Councils, the International Brain Research Organisation (UNESCO), the United States Public Health Service (Grant NB-04787), and the Wellcome Trust.

Fig. 14. *Habituation to a repeated stimulus and dishabituation following stimulation of the contralateral neck connective, but not following stimulation of the ipsilateral neck connective.* The visual stimulus was a disk moved through an angle of 40° in 1.4 sec. The interval between successive movements was 10 sec. The large filled (▲) and open (△) triangles indicate the time at which a train of shocks was applied to the contralateral and ipsilateral connectives, respectively. The curve between curves 1 and 2 is a control, giving dummy counts in the absence of stimulation. The values plotted in curve 13 were obtained from an earlier experiment with the unit in which the effect on background firing rate was studied following stimulation of the contralateral connective. From this experiment was calculated the number of impulses present in 1.4 - sec periods measured in successive 10-sec intervals after stimulating the contralateral connective, and in the absence of visual stimulation. The data obtained in this way are used as controls for the results plotted in curves 4–7, and 11 (Rowell & Horn, 1968).

REFERENCES

Bell, C., Sierra, G., Buendia, N., & Segundo, J. P. Sensory properties of neurones in the mesencephalic reticular formation. *Journal of Neurophysiology*, 1964, **27**, 961–987.
Dewson, J. H., III. Efferent olivocochlear bundle. Some relationships to noise masking and to stimulus alternation. *Journal of Neurophysiology*, 1967, **30**, 817–832.
Eccles, J. C. *The physiology of nerve cells.* London: Oxford University Press, 1957.
Gordon, G., & Jukes, M. G. M. Correlation of different excitatory and inhibitory influences on cells in the nucleus gracilis of the cat. *Nature*, 1962, **196**, 1183–1185.
Gordon, G., & Jukes, M. G. M. Descending influences on the exteroceptive organisations of the cat's gracile nucleus. *Journal of Physiology*, 1964, **173**, 291–319.
Horn, G. Electrical activity of the cerebral cortex of the unanaesthetised cat during attentive behavior. *Brain*, 1960, **83**, 57–56.
Horn, G. The effect of somaesthetic and photic stimuli on the activity of units in the striate cortex of unanaesthetised, unrestrained cats. *Journal of Physiology*, 1965, **179**, 263–277.
Horn, G. Neuronal mechanisms of habituation. *Nature*, 1967, **215**, 707–711.
Horn, B., & Hill, R. M. Habituation of the response to sensory stimuli of neurons in the brainstem of rabbits. *Nature*, 1964, **202**, 296–298.
Horn, G., & Hill, R. M. Responsiveness to sensory stimulation of units in the superior colliculus and subjacent tectotegmental regions of the rabbit. *Experimental Neurology*, 1966, **14**, 199–223.
Horn, G., & Hill, R. M. Modifications of receptive fields of cells in the visual cortex occurring spontaneously and associated with bodily tilt. *Nature*, 1969, **221**, 186–188.
Horn, G., & Hinde, R. A. *Short-term changes in neural activity and behavior.* Cambridge, 1970.
Horn, G., & Rowell, C. H. F. Medium and long-term changes in the behavior of visual neurones in the tritocerebrum of locusts. *Journal of Experimental Biology*, 1968, **49**, 143–170.
Hubel, D. H. Single unit activity in striate cortex of unrestrained cats. *Journal of Physiology*, 1959, **147**, 226–238.
Hubel, D. H., & Wiesel, T. N. Receptive fields, binocular interaction and functional architecture in the cat's visual cortex. *Journal of Physiology*, 1962, **160**, 106–154.
Jasper, H. H. Pathophysiological studies of brain mechanisms in different states of consciousness. In J. C. Eccles (Ed.), *Brain and conscious experience.* Berlin: Springer, 1966.
Jasper, H. H., & Bertrand, G. Exploration of the human thalamus with microelectrodes. *Physiologist*, 1967, **7**, 167.
Lömo, T., & Mollica, A. Activity of single units in the primary optic cortex in the unanaesthetised rabbit during visual, acoustic, olfactory and painful stimulation. *Archives Italiennes de Biologie*, 1962, **100**, 86–120.
Morrell, F. Electrical signs of sensory coding. In G. C. Quarton, T. Melnechuk, & F. O. Schmitt (Eds.), *The neurosciences.* New York: Rockefeller University Press, 1967.
Murata, K., Cramer, H., & Bach-y-Rita, P. Neuronal convergence of noxious, acoustic and visual stimuli in the visual cortex of the cat. *Journal of Neurophysiology*, 1965, **28**, 1223–1239.
Poggio, G. F., & Mountcastle, V. B. The functional properties of ventro-basal thalamic neurons studied in unanaesthetized animals. *Journal of Neurophysiology*, 1965, **26**, 775–806.

Rowell, C. H. F., & Horn, G. Dishabituation and arousal in the response of single nerve cells in an insect brain. *Journal of Experimental Biology*, 1968, **49**, 171–184.
Sherrington, C. S. *The integrative action of the nervous system*. London: Constable, 1966.
Sokolov, Y. N. *Perception and the conditioned reflex*. New York: Macmillan (Pergamon), New York, 1963.
Thompson, R. F., & Spencer, N. A. Habituation: A model phenomenon for the study of neuronal substitute of behaviour. *Psychological Review*, 1966, **173**, 16–43.
Wall, P. D. The laminar organisation of dorsal horn and effects of descending impulses. *Journal of Physiology*, 1967, **188**, 403–423.
Wiersma, C. A. G. Visual central processing in crustaceans. In C. A. G. Wiersma (Ed.), *Invertebrate nervous systems*. Chicago: The University of Chicago Press, 1967.

REFERENCES FOR QUESTIONS AND ANSWERS

Holmgren, B., & Frenk, S. Inhibitory phenomena and "Habituation" at the neuronal level. *Nature*, 1961, **192**, 1294–1295.
Horn, G., & Wright, M. J. Characteristics of transmission failure in the squid stellate ganglion: A study of a simple habituating system. *Journal of Experimental Biology*, 1970, **52**, 217–231.
Hubbard, J. I., & Willis, W. D. Hyperpolarisation of mammalian motor nerve terminals. *Journal of Physiology*, 1962, **163**, 115–137.
Rowell, C. H. F., & Horn, G. Dishabituation and arousal in the response of single cells in an insect brain. *Journal of Experimental Biology*, 1968, **49**, 171–184.

Questions and Answers

Question: (VERZEANO) Did you ever find any neurons that did not habituate?

Answer: (HORN) Yes. There are neurons in the rabbits' tectum that do not habituate, but none that we studied in the locust tritocerebrum.

Question: (VERZEANO) The reason I ask you that is because some years ago, for other purposes, we studied the responses of lateral geniculate neurons in the cat to large numbers of repeated stimuli. We found quite a number of neurons which appeared to respond for long periods without changing their pattern of response, and others which did. Might several different systems exist within the same anatomical region?

Answer: (HORN) Without a doubt. I am certain of it in the rabbit.

Comment: (BUREŠ) I think that in interpreting these results one must take into account the fact that it is a neuron which displays habituation, but that a neuron is not necessarily really responsible for the decrement. I think a very simple interpretation is that these are units which are responding to arousal or to a process of attention, and are part of an habituating system, a system which starts reacting less and less to the same stimulus. I think, for example, the first presentation of the stimulus produces arousal and that there are many neurons throughout the brain which will respond in some way to the first presentation. With repeated stimulus presentation, as was shown for habituation of EEG arousal, this arousing effect of the stimulus diminishes. So, in my opinion, the most important thing in the further analysis of this phenomenon is to find a way in which it would be possible to discriminate between the cells which are just part of a system where the habituation occurred many synapses away from the actual cell being studied, and from the cell which really displays the necessary plastic change which has something happening to the input to this particular cell.

128

With reference to Dr. Verzeano's previous question, we have seen quite a large number of neurons in inferior colliculus which don't habituate during as many as several thousand presentations of a stimulus.

Question: (THOMPSON) First let me compliment you on a beautiful job. I'm very pleased that your ideas agree so well with ours. I think in the case of Wall's study one has to be careful because as I recall he reported that when he obtained "novelty" cells he was using decerebrate cats. When he later sectioned the cord he did not find this habituation. It was not necessarily the same phenomenon one would find in the acute spinal preparation. Perhaps it is the result of decending influences.

Answer: (HORN) That is true. Much of your own research was, of course, done on the spinal animal. Did you look for and did you find, changes in responsiveness as abrupt as some of those which I have described here?

Question: (THOMPSON) No, not so abrupt. It depends upon the stimulus of course, but it is not immediate.

Answer: (HORN) One of the major problems, implicitly referred to in your first question, concerns that nature of the neural processes underlying habituation. Can habituation occur at monosynaptic junctions or are complex neural networks necessary? My guess is that one could generate response curves, similar to those derived from interneuronal responses, using a very simple synaptic system (see Horn & Wright 1970).

Question: (McGAUGH) Have you encountered any circadian effects on the rate of habituation?

Answer: (HORN) Yes, we have in the locust.

Question: (McGAUGH) The reason I ask that is that it seems to be possible that what you see or describe as long term effects might really be not that but just the rehabituation at a different time with respect to the animal's circadian rhythm, that is, particularly when you are looking 10 hr later, that is almost the other side of the circadian rhythm. Is that a possibility?

Answer: (HORN) Well, that's a possibility of course, but that 10-hr lapse brought us, as it were, full circle around to approximately the same time as the very beginning of the experiment the day before.

Question: (McGAUGH) But there is a difference in background firing rates depending upon the time of day?

Answer: (HORN) These cells have a very low rate of spontaneous activity and there was little obvious change, if any, with time of day. However, the responsiveness of some of the cells did appear to be different at night time compared with daytime (Rowell & Horn 1968).

Question: (JOHN) Regarding the question of long term persistence of habituation, it might be worthwhile to recall some of the earlier work, for example, by Sharpless and Jasper on evoked potentials and electrographic studies of habituation. You may remember that they distinguished between a phasic and tonic mechanism, one involving the mesencephalic reticular formation and the other the medial thalamic nuclei. They pointed out that the time rate of these two processes was sharply different. In the work that Killam and I did on habituation about 10 yr ago, we found that short term habituation could be established to a train of flashes in a naive animal in a matter of a few minutes, but this dishabituated rather readily on the introduction of an extraneous stimulus or simply allowing some time to pass. We found that it took 21 days to achieve lasting habituation in the lateral geniculate body. It took only about 4 days to accomplish it in the hippocampus.

Question: (HORN)   This was in terms of the EEG change?

Answer: (JOHN)   EEG and evoked potential. The point that I'm making is that both the phasic and the tonic changes in habituation proceed at different rates at different anatomical regions in the first place, and secondly, with respect to any one of these regions where habituation has proceeded to a given point, whether or not dishabituation will take place depends on whether the long, the tonic habituation, has been accomplished. So, I think that you might want to reexamine some of your conclusions about what may or may not be possible, perhaps in terms of some of the previous data.

Answer: (HORN)   To which conclusions are you referring?

Question: (JOHN)   Well, as to whether, for example, geniculate habituation can occur. I suspect it can but it would take a very much longer exposure to the stimulus than you're able to present in this kind of experiment.

Answer: (HORN)   Yes. I am aware of the work on habituation and changes in evoked potentials in the lateral geniculate body and the visual cortex. It's a very controversial field. I am not aware of any unequivocal evidence that there are response decrements of a reproducible kind in the lateral geniculate body with evoked potentials, provided one takes, you know, the usual precautions and employs appropriate controls. There is no doubt, however, that very long term habituation is a real phenomenon. Perhaps there are two different neural mechanisms, one responsible for habituation of short duration and another for habituation of long duration. I do not have any direct experimental evidence bearing on this question.

Question: (SEGUNDO)   The intracellular observations by Spencer and Thompson in the spinal cord and our own observations in the reticular nuclei on cells which exhibit response decrement to repeated stimulation indicate that together with this decrease in response there's no change in the resting level of the cell, there is no change in its ability to fire spikes, and the only thing that happens is that the PSP's, be they excitatory, inhibitory, or mixed postsynaptic potentials, decrease in size. Now Spencer and Thompson have shown very nicely that the decrease in excitatory post synaptic potentials in the spinal interneurons is not due to superimposed IPSP's. All this evidence is negative, certainly. One does not explore every possible cell and the cells that are impaled are a sample, probably the largest ones; one does not explore every region. But the fact is that I think there is no evidence for inhibitory feedback loops determining this event and I would concur with you that the most likely interpretation is that there is a weak link somewhere.

Answer: (HORN)   There is one piece of evidence. Holmgren and Frenk (1961) recorded from interneurons in the snail central nervous system and found waves of hyperpolarization that gradually built up as the response of the neuron to afferent stimulation declined. These observations are consistent with an inhibitory build-up theory of habituation. I know of no other direct experimental evidence for this theory.

Question: (WEINBERGER)   It seems that these novelty cells in the rabbit and locust are particularly interesting because they behave in a manner similar to the behavior of the whole animal. So, in a sense, you might say that if you looked at the orienting response of the whole animal the whole animal might be considered a novelty detector. An example would be head movement to a novel stimulus. Moving one step back, if you're going to look at the motor neuron which caused the head movement, you could say that the motor neuron is a novelty detector. Insofar as the tectum is a region which has many motor outputs, have you a reason to believe that you're not recording from output or motor neurons at the level of the mesencephalon, such as a cell contributing to the tectotegmental or tectospinal tract?

Answer: (HORN)   No. However, units which behave as novelty detectors have been recorded in many places in vertebrate and invertebrate nervous systems, including the sensory pathways. It is extremely doubtful if all of those cells are motor neurons, though it is, of course, possible that they control the output of the motor neurons.

Comment: (WEINBERGER)   The only reason I bring up the question is it seems to me that the mere fact that we're recording something which is occurring inside of the brain, in this case from a neuron, doesn't necessarily make that data terribly more illuminating in understanding behavioral plasticity which presumably is the end point of all these kinds of investigations.

Question: (GROVES)   You often see in the acute spinal cat when recording the flexion reflex, an initial potentiation, particularly at higher frequencies and this seems to increase with increasing frequency of stimulation. Do you ever see a potentiation in the rabbit tectal neurons?

Answer: (HORN)   With high frequency stimulation?

Question: (GROVES)   With smaller interstimulus intervals than you've reported, 1 sec, 2 sec, 500 msec.

Answer: (HORN)   I do not have the answers to all of that question. The shortest interval we have used is 1/sec. However, we have observed an initial potentiation followed by a decrement of the response (see for example Fig. 1A).

Question: (KITZES)   In regard to the mechanism of decrement, in one of your slides, I believe, and of course, in the work of Thompson and Spencer, the initial response following the dishabituated stimulus was greater than the initial response of the train. Could you speculate about this mechanism.

Answer: (HORN)   This is a very interesting question. Hubbard & Willis (1962) have shown that the amplitude of EPP's at the neuromuscular junction may be potentiated by hyperpolarizing currents applied to the axon terminals. The potentiation is not immediate. It takes about 40 sec from the start of polarization for the potentiation to reach its maximum level. This build-up, therefore, shares some of the temporal properties of dishabituation and raises the possibility that, in the central nervous system, response recovery brought about by an interpolated stimulus is effective because the latter results in a hyperpolarization of the depressed terminals in the neuronal chain which is excited by the repeated stimulus.

Question: (GOODMAN)   When you speak of a response decrement you're speaking of slope, in other words a higher response first, followed by a lower response subsequently. However, there are clearly two slopes in your data. If you take the first five trials and separate them from the subsequent trials you've got obviously a very steep slope in the first and the second or the first five trials and then a very narrow slope, if any at all. Second of all, if you look at the first five trials again you have many cases that you showed where the response climbs up to a maximum, then falls. And thirdly, there is an expectation in a model such as this that there's an incremental buildup of something and that there is a nice straight line decrease, whereas in truth most of your declines are rhythmic, that is, the response is at a high level, it drops, it returns back up to a high level, it drops again, and it's almost a sinusoidal drop down to your base line.

Answer: (HORN)   There is a great deal of variability, from cell to cell, in the way a response declines. Sometimes the response is stable for several trials and then wanes. The waning may be highly irregular or, as you say, almost sinusoidal (see, for example Fig. 1B); in other cases the decline may be almost monotonic (see, for example Fig. 2). And, as you imply, the decrement is commonly, though not invariably, well fitted by an exponential function.

MOTIVATIONAL SYSTEMS

NEURAL MECHANISMS INVOLVED IN A CAT'S ATTACK ON A RAT

J. P. FLYNN, H. VANEGAS, W. FOOTE, AND S. EDWARDS

DEPARTMENTS OF PSYCHIATRY AND ANATOMY, YALE UNIVERSITY SCHOOL OF MEDICINE
NEW HAVEN, CONNECTICUT

I. Introduction

The term "emotion" has at least three meanings. First, it is regarded as a purely subjective feeling, recognized only through our own introspections or at second hand through those of other human beings—if they choose to tell us about them. The basic mechanisms within the central nervous system that mediate emotion in this sense can be investigated only in conscious human beings, and there is a relative paucity of such information. Second, emotion may refer to an expression or display, which may or may not be accompanied by a subjective feeling, such as the sham rage of a decorticate dog, or the facial expression of an actor. The parts of the neural axis that suffice for one such display, namely sham rage, were determined by Bard in 1928. Finally, certain complex forms of the organism's interaction with the environment are commonly regarded as emotional. Fighting, flight, and sexual behavior fall into this category. Both the second and the third types of emotion can be studied in animals, and most of our knowledge of the physiological basis of emotions is derived from work with them.

The present work was supported by USPHS grants 2RO1 MH 08936 and K2-MH-25466 to John P. Flynn.

135

We have studied attack as one component of fighting, a form of emotional behavior. Our general objective has been to determine the anatomical and physiological basis of attack behavior. The basic technique used in this analysis involves stimulation of the cat's brain and the elicitation of attack by the cat on an anesthetized rat. The cats used in our experiments do not attack rats spontaneously. (The majority of laboratory cats, contrary to general opinion, fall into this category.) A summary of our earlier experiments, dealing with the senses involved in attack, and the influence of the limbic system and mid-brain upon attack was presented in *Neurophysiology and Emotion* (Flynn, 1967). The present chapter deals with more recent work.

A. VALUE OF STIMULATION TECHNIQUE

Stimulation of the brain is employed since it elicits patterns of behavior reproducibly and under close experimental control. Ferocity of attack is a function of the parameters of stimulation regulated by the experimenter. The behavior elicited may be stable for long periods of time, and while it is more varied in form than a classical reflex, it is just as regular. In comparison to spontaneously occurring behavior, elicited attack is less variable. The form of the behavior can be selected within limits by the experimenter's choosing proper sites for the electrodes. For example, a tendency either toward biting or toward striking with the paw can be selected by the experimenter. Stimulation further tends to exaggerate particular aspects of a behavior pattern; often it gives rise to an effect associated primarily with one side of the body. Thus, during stimulation opening of the mouth may be triggered by touching the area of the lip contralateral to the side of the brain stimulated, but not by touching the ipsilateral lip. Similarly, the cat's use of either the right or the left forelimb in striking can be determined by the experimenter. The consistency and laterality of the responses elicited by stimulation provide the experimenter with an opportunity to study particular aspects of attack behavior in detail.

B. SETTING FOR STUDY OF ELICITED BEHAVIORS

The conditions under which we observe the effects of stimulating the brain approximate those likely to be found in nature. This differs from the approach of some physiologists on the one hand, and some psychologists on the other. Hess (1928), the physiologist who first described affective defense as well as many other reactions elicited by electrical stimulation, observed the cat in a situation in which there were virtually no objects other than the experimenter on which the cat might act. On the other hand, there is a tendency among psychologists interested primarily in the concept of motivation to investigate the effects of brain stimulation by observing the animal's behavior in a Skinner box. In the case of aggressive behavior, neither of these two experimental arrangements is really adequate to reveal the behavior induced by stimulation.

Stimulation of the brain elicits two types of responses. One class of responses is virtually independent of the environment. These are postural changes, facial displays, vocalization, and autonomic effects. These can be observed in the impoverished environment of the physiologist. The second class of responses depends upon the environment, for instance, the approach to the rat, the act of striking or biting at the rat, positioning of the rat with the paws, the biting of the neck or head, and other elements of the cat's attack on a rat. This second category of responses would be seen neither under barren physiological conditions as employed by Hess, nor so apparent if the cat were in a Skinner box.

For the second category of responses to appear elements of an environment are needed which are similar to that which an animal species may have encountered in its evolutionary history. Fighting has undoubtedly proved useful over the centuries, and one aspect of it, namely attack, can be studied by providing an object for the cat to maim or kill. It is our belief that when one elicits a well-integrated behavior such as attack upon stimulation of the brain, the nervous system is facilitated to act in certain specific ways. Mechanisms for striking and for biting are physiologically activated so that this form of behavior will appear, if the proper environment is provided.

The events in this second category of responses are sometimes regarded as the results of motivation brought about by stimulation, and motivation is considered to be free of the involvement of specific motor systems. In fact, evidence for motivation is secured by the animal's performing an arbitrary act inserted into a sequence of events. Even though the attacking animal may perform arbitrary acts (as in fact it will), it does not follow that attack elicited by electrical stimulation is free of specific motor involvement. On the contrary it is our belief, and a part of this chapter is devoted to buttressing this point, that the behavior is a result of facilitation of specific motor and sensory systems, which reach the level of overt behavior when an adequate environment is provided.

II. Behavioral Aspects of Attack

Two qualitatively different patterns of attack behavior can be elicited by hypothalamic stimulation. These individual patterns of behavior are not simply a function of the cat's past history, since both patterns can be seen within a single animal upon stimulation of the brain at different sites.

A. AFFECTIVE ATTACK

This form of attack is very similar to the affective defense that Hess and Brugger (1943) described. However, their observations were directed primarily to the cat's display, which they interpreted, as did Ranson (1934), as defense.

In our studies, the rat's behavior can scarcely be termed menacing. The rat is most often anesthetized; and even when it is unanesthetized, it often stands motionless or runs away when the cat moves or hisses. The basic character of the cat's response toward the rat is aggressive. Affective attack is more than the display that an observer may interpret as rage. A display similar to that of affective attack can be elicited without attack itself ever occurring. This is in accord with the findings of Masserman (1941), who regarded the display of rage elicited by stimulation of the hypothalamus as a pure motor phenomenon. [His interpretation was rightly contested by Hess and Akert (1955), who pointed out that the experimenter was sometimes attacked by the stimulated cats.] Sites from which a display of rage without attack can be elicited are found occasionally upon stimulating the hypothalamus, and regularly upon stimulating the central gray around the aqueduct of Sylvius.

Affective attack is characterized by a pattern of pronounced sympathetic arousal commonly regarded as indicative of feline rage. The response invariably begins with behavioral alerting and dilation of the pupils. At lower stimulus intensities, alerting constitutes the extent of the response, even if one stimulates for as long as 2 min.

As one increases the stimulus intensity up to attack threshold, in addition to the initial alerting, piloerection becomes prominent, especially along the midline of the back. The tail becomes bushy and fluffed out. Occasionally the ears go back. Hissing occurs alternately with low growls. Urination often occurs on the first trial of a session. If sitting, the animal leaps to its feet and begins to move with head low to the ground, back arched, claws unsheathed, hissing and/or snarling, sometimes salivating profusely, and breathing deeply. The cat either comes up to the rat directly or circles to the rear of the cage and then approaches the rat. The cat stands poised, appearing to watch the rat intensely, while the affective aspect of the reaction becomes still more pronounced. After a second or two, the cat raises a paw with claws unsheathed and then strikes with its paws in a series of swift, accurate blows. Any sudden movement of the rat serves to trigger the attack, but attack will occur even if the rat remains motionless. In some instances, the cat, instead of delivering discrete blows with a single paw, springs at the rat with a high-pitched scream and pounces, tearing at the rat with its claws. If the stimulus is continued, the cat will savagely bite the rat, although the initial part of the attack is clearly with its claws.

B. QUIET BITING ATTACK

The second form of attack pattern reminds obervers of an animal stalking a prey. At lower intensities, the alerting response, accompanied by mydriasis, is quite sudden and discrete. The cat often leaps to its feet almost with the onset of the stimulus and attentively looks about from side to side. If the stimulus is continued, it will walk about the cage but will ignore the rat. At higher stimulus intensities, above attack threshold, the cat moves swiftly with its nose low to the ground and hair slightly on end.

Sometimes the cat's nose twitches slightly, as if it were sniffing. The cat usually goes directly to the rat and bites viciously at its head and neck. The cat uses its paws primarily to knock the rat on its back in order to get at its throat. The paws are used neither to deliver discrete blows nor to rake the rat with the claws. Although the cat will sometimes bite the rat's stomach or back first, biting is ultimately aimed at the head and neck. On some trials, the cat circles around the observation box a few times, ignoring the rat or sniffing at it in passing. In the course of circling, the cat will suddenly pounce on the rat and savagely tear at it with its mouth. This circling behavior does not constitute a stereotyped motor response, in that it does not occur regularly nor is it always in the same direction for a given animal, although there is a tendency for it to be the side contralateral to the one stimulated.

The stalking attack is characterized, especially at low stimulus intensities, by only minimal signs presumed indicative of feline rage. Piloerection is present down the midline. The animals never growl, emit high-pitched screams, nor salivate profusely. The cat's movement around the cage, however, is quicker and more persistent. Although this prowling or stalking behavior is never as dramatic as the presumably "enraged" attack, it is, in reality, more effective and deadly, as far as the rat is concerned.

C. OTHER FORMS OF ATTACK

While these two forms of attack can be regularly distinguished, other mixed forms occur. Some cats show affective arousal and a biting mode of attack. Others show a stalking attack but occasionally hiss or snarl. As was indicated earlier, an affective display can be elicited without attack, and also without evidence of flight. Moreover, forms of biting, in which the cat gnaws and chews inedible objects, are also seen, in accordance with the observation of Hess (1956, p. 28).

D. THE OBJECTS ATTACKED

The question of how great a range of objects will be attacked by a stimulated cat has not been answered, but data have been gathered showing that objects are selected. In an experiment to be described later, most of the cats faced with a choice between horsemeat and an anesthetized rat regularly chose the rat. In addition, Levison and Flynn (1965) found that seven of the nine cats given a choice of an anesthetized rat, a stuffed rat, and as a third object either a hairy toy dog, a foam rubber block, or a styrofoam block never bit the foam rubber or the styrofoam blocks. Eight of the nine animals regularly chose either the stuffed or the anesthetized rat.

III. Attack in Relation to Flight and Eating

A. Flight and Attack

Attack behavior is frequently associated with flight. Delgado (1964, pp. 396–400) lists experimenters, beginning with Hess (1928), who have worked with rage and flight and many of them report rage as culminating in flight. Such behavior also occurs in our experience, but it has been our usual practice to avoid sites from which one gets both effects. However, the idea persists that attack, particularly affective attack, may be simply a response to noxious stimulation. It is clear that noxious stimulation by itself can bring about a display of rage not only in decorticate (Bard & Rioch, 1937) but also in decerebrate cats (Woodworth & Sherrington, 1904). Intact cats shocked through the paws attack rats (Ulrich, Wolff, & Azrin, 1964). Adams and Flynn (1966) showed that some forms of affective attack, namely those accompanied by several types of vocalization, were associated with noxious stimulation. On the other side of the coin, we found other forms of affective attack that were not associated with noxious stimulation. The data of Nakao (1958), who investigated flight reactions and aggressive reactions, also dissociate noxious stimulation and attack. Although both flight and aggressive reactions were accompanied by a marked display, they differed in that cats manifesting flight reactions made obvious attempts to escape and did not attack the experimenter or a stick thrust in front of the cat, whereas the aggressive cats attacked the experimenter or stick. Nakao (1958) trained both kinds of cats in a number of learning situations. The cats showing the flight reactions learned the expected responses, while the aggressive cats showed less evidence of learning. Four aggressive cats did not learn to press a paddle to terminate hypothalamic stimulation; another that had been pretrained to turn off shock to the feet did not terminate hypothalamic stimulation. Still another pretrained cat turned off hypothalamic stimulation, but its latencies to do so increased, so that it failed on the third session. Another aggressive animal did not avoid the compartment in which it was regularly stimulated. Two aggressive cats crouched, retracted their ears, trembled, ran, and jumped at the sound of a buzzer preceding hypothalamic stimulation. One gains the impression that while elements of both flight and aggressive reactions may be intermixed, they are nevertheless distinct behaviors.

This same conclusion is borne out by the work of Fonberg (1967). She distinguishes fear, defense, and rage reactions. The behavior of dogs showing the fear reaction is characterized by screaming, whining, attempts to escape, a crouched posture, and the dog's tail being curled under. In defense, attack was mixed with attempts to flee. The dogs bit the thongs restraining them, but rarely barked or growled. The biting was directed toward objects preventing flight. In the rage reaction, the dog bared its teeth, rolled its eyes, snarled with increasing violence, growled or barked, and attacked objects in the vicinity, including sticks and the experimenter's hand, if nearby. Fonberg (1967) attempted to train the dogs to avoid stimulation of the brain sites by flexing a leg. Stimulation of the brain was regularly preceded by a tone. The dogs that showed the fear reaction readily learned to avoid stimulation. The dogs showing the defense reaction took longer to learn. Two of the five did not learn. Of the four that showed rage behavior, three showed little or no sign of avoiding stimulation, while one animal with an electrode in the vicinity of the spinothalamic tract in the midbrain did so readily. In contrast to the results of Nakao (1958) she found no signs of classical conditioning of the rage symptoms to the conditioned stimulus. In summary, Fonberg's (1967) data indicate a separation of both rage and attack from aversive stimulation.

We have some data relevant to the same question. The experiment is still incomplete, but the present data show that flight and attack can be dissociated and that attack persists after flight drops out. The dissociation was accomplished by making bilateral lesions aimed at the region of centrum medianum and nucleus parafascicularis of the thalamus. Recent evidence (Mitchell & Kaelber, 1967; Urabe & Tsubokawa, 1965), indicates that a lesion in this region of the thalamus can abolish intractable pain in human beings, and in cats it can similarly abolish both avoidance and escape from electrical stimulation of the tooth or paws. In the present experiment, flight and attack were elicited by stimulation of the hypothalamus. In most instances, flight was elicited by stimulation of one site, and attack by stimulation of another within the same cat. However, there were some sites from which attack was evoked if a rat were present and flight if it were not. Both affective attack and quiet attack were investigated although the data on affective attack are limited. Quiet attack was investigated because there is also quiet flight. The data are shown in Fig. 1. In five cats the lesions were effective in abolishing flight evoked by stimulation, but they left attack still present. In the sixth cat, the lesions were not particularly effective in abolishing flight. In the one instance in this cat in which either flight or attack could be elicited by stimulation of the same site, flight was abolished and attack remained, in conformity with the general result. Thus, flight is not an essential element of attack behavior.

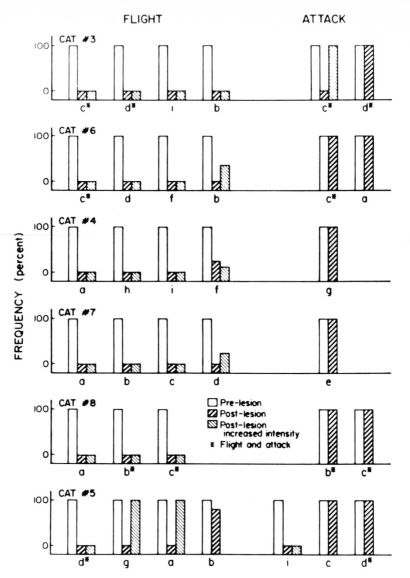

Fig. 1. In six cats (indicated by the number), both flight (jumping to the net at the top of the cage) and attack (biting or striking a rat) were elicited by electrical stimulation of the brain, through separate electrodes (indicated by a letter). From some electrodes (letter marked by an asterisk) flight could be elicited if a rat were not present, and attack if a rat were in the cage. In five cats after lesions were made in the region of the centrum medianum and nucleus parafascicularis of the thalamus, flight either was markedly reduced or could no longer be elicited, even when the stimulus intensity was increased, while attack could still be evoked. In the sixth cat, the lesion was only partially effective in bringing about a separation. In all six cases from which flight and attack could be obtained by stimulation of the identical electrode, attack was separable from flight.

B. EATING AND ATTACK

Another interpretation that has been presented is that the quiet attack elicited by stimulation of the hypothalamus is a learned instrumental response acquired during the period prior to the cats' being brought into the laboratory (Hutchinson & Renfrew, 1966). Contrary to the idea of the response having been learned, Roberts and Bergquist (1968) demonstrated that cats raised in isolation without the opportunity to learn this behavior displayed it immediately on being stimulated in the hypothalamus. According to Hutchinson and Renfrew (1966) attack is a form of food acquisition that is used when rats are the food. Their argument was based on the observation that eating could in all cases be elicited by stimulating the brain at the same site from which attack was evoked. When Wasman and Flynn (1962) first drew attention to this form of attack, we noted that if only a dish of food was in the cage the animals would sniff at the food, savagely bite it, and then continue prowling around the cage, with the food usually falling out of the cat's mouth. However, we did not test these same sites at lower intensities of stimulation as Hutchinson and Renfrew did. These authors report that the threshold for eating was lower than that for attack in 16 out of the 18 instances. There certainly are cases in which both eating and attack can be evoked from the same site within the brain. In conformity with Hutchinson and Renfrew, we find such sites. However, in marked contrast to them we also find sites from which eating is not evoked at any intensity, and from which quiet attack is readily elicitable.

This is shown by the following two experiments. In the first experiment, a single object was available on a given trial, either horsemeat or a rat. At each intensity of the stimulus to the brain, there was one trial with horsemeat, and one trial with the anesthetized rat. The lowest intensity used produced little or no reaction on the part of the cat. The intensity was raised in steps until the cat either ate the horsemeat or attacked the rat. If either event happened, a second trial at the same intensity was given. The same procedure was followed for five days, for a total of at least five trials with each object at each intensity. The results are shown in Fig. 2. These data indicate that quiet attack without eating is elicited from some sites in the hypothalamus, while both eating and attack are elicited from others. In addition to testing the cats with a single object on each trial, we investigated the cat's behavior when both food and rat were present. Since Hutchinson and Renfrew (1966) maintained that the choice of objects was a function of which object was closer, the experiment was arranged so that the horsemeat was always closer than the rat to the cat. The results of this second experiment are shown in Fig. 3. The data show that from some sites the rat was always chosen, while from others sometimes the food and sometimes the rat was chosen. Had all the cats behaved in

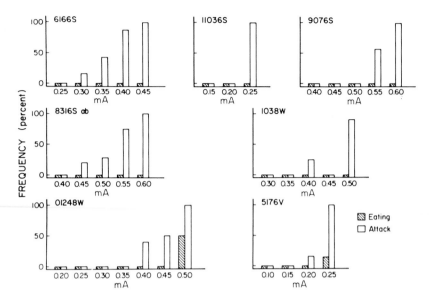

Fig. 2. The frequency with which a cat (indicated by a number followed by a capital letter) ate horsemeat (eating) or bit a rat (attack) when the cat was stimulated electrically is shown as a function of the intensity of the stimulus (mA) to the brain. The five cats in the upper part of this figure bit only the rat when a single object was available on a given trial. The two cats in the lower part of the figure both attacked and ate depending upon which object was present. There were at least five trials with each object at each intensity.

accordance with the observations of Hutchinson and Renfrew, the food would always have been chosen. The data indicate that quiet attack can be evoked from sites in the hypothalamus from which eating is not evoked.

IV. Neural Mechanisms Underlying Attack

Three general categories of neural mechanisms underlie attack elicited by stimulation of the brain. First of all, there are the brain sites, apart from known sensory systems, from which attack can be elicited. These may be called the patterning mechanisms. The afferent systems within the central nervous system that can be regarded as continuations of peripheral systems which are themselves effective peripherally in eliciting affective displays or attack ought to be separated from those parts of the brain which organize or integrate the behavior. It is the organizing or integrating mechanisms that we have called patterning mechanisms. Second, there are sites within the brain which modulate the activity of the patterning mechanism, but from which

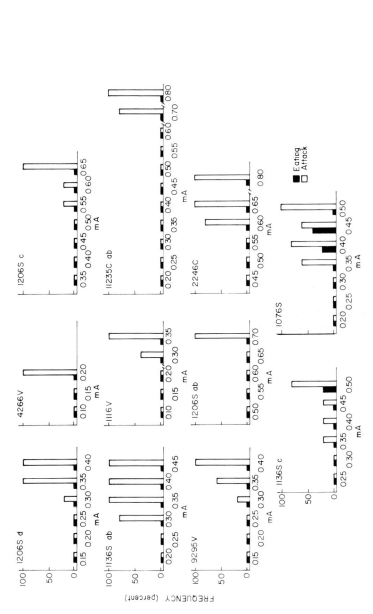

Fig. 3. In this experiment a choice of objects (horsemeat and a rat) was available to the cat being stimulated. The horsemeat was placed closer to the cat than was the rat. The seven cats (cat 1206 was stimulated at three different sites—indicated by small letters) whose data are in the upper part of the figure regularly bit only the rat, even though a bowl of horsemeat was available on each trial, and in fact closer to them. The two cats whose data are at the bottom of the figure sometimes ate horsemeat and on other trials bit the rat.

attack is not normally elicited. Data on these modulating structures were presented in the summary referred to earlier (Flynn, 1967). The third category consists of the sensory and motor mechanisms by which attack is carried out.

A. PATTERNING MECHANISMS

The sites from which various forms of rage or attack can be elicited are known from investigations carried out by Hess and Brugger (1943), Ranson and colleagues (Kabat, Anson, Magoun, & Ranson, 1935), Hunsperger (1965), Nakao (1958), and by others, including the authors.

Attack can be elicited from areas of the hypothalamus, the thalamus, the midbrain, and from the stria terminalis. Figure 4 shows sites from which affective attack and quiet attack have been elicited by monopolar stimulation in our laboratory. While both affective attack and quiet biting attack can be elicited from different sites within both the hypothalamus and the midbrain, only affective attack has been elicited from the stria terminalis, and only quiet attack from the thalamus.

What is the relationship between the various structures of the brain from which attack is elicited? Fernandez de Molina and Hunsperger (1962) proposed that the growling and growling–hissing patterns they obtained by electrical stimulation of the amygdala develop through the activity of the hissing zone of the hypothalamus, and the activity of the hypothalamus is maintained in turn by the presence of the central gray matter of the midbrain. This hypothesis was based on the findings that the growling–hissing pattern obtained on stimulation of the amygdala was suppressed by an ipsilateral lesion placed at midbrain or hypothalamic levels. The hissing pattern obtained from the hypothalamus was blocked by bilateral coagulation of the central gray of the midbrain. Their hypothesis is in accord with both their findings and the early findings of Woodworth and Sherrington (1904) who elicited partial patterns of rage in decerebrate cats and with Bard's (1928) findings of sham rage in hypothalamic animals.

Our own findings are in general agreement with this hypothesis and they further emphasize the importance of the midbrain structures. Fernandez de Molina and Hunsperger (1962) had found that relatively small lesions in the hypothalamus, while abolishing growling elicited by stimulation of the amygdala, did not abolish similar reactions elicited by stimulation of the central gray. These lesions, however, appear to be small in comparison to the field in the hypothalamus from which attack can be elicited.

With the idea that the display which Hunsperger elicited from the central gray was different from attack, in which a coordination of sensory and motor elements is required, Ellison and Flynn (1968) attempted to isolate the

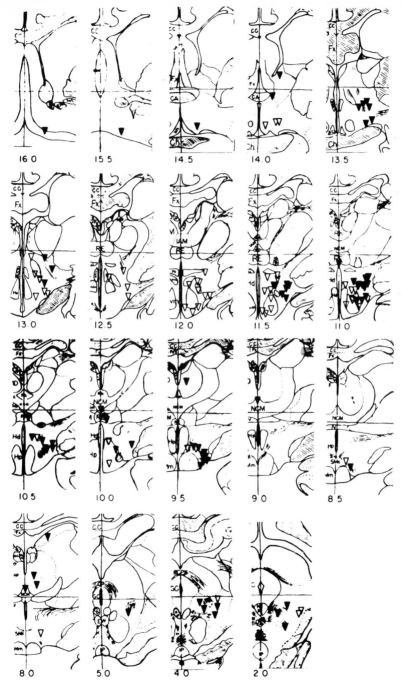

Fig. 4. The sites at which monopolar stimulation leads to attack are presented in frontal sections of the cat's brain (atlas of Jasper and Ajmone-Marsan). (▼) quiet biting attack. (▽) attack with display.

hypothalamus from the rest of the brain, and to determine whether rage and directed attack were possible following isolation of the hypothalamus. The experiment was carried out in two stages. In the first stage, two small knives were positioned in the brain, and the animals were allowed to recover for at least 10 days. The isolation of the hypothalamus was accomplished by rotating the two knives in opposite directions through 360° several times. In some twenty animals, the knives cut into the blood vessels at the base of the brain, causing the death of the animals. In four additional animals that survived the second operation for some time, the isolation of the hypothalamus was incomplete. The main data are derived from four other cats in which there was relatively complete isolation of the hypothalamus. Two examples of the lesions are given in Fig. 5. These animals remained inactive following the lesion. However, they could be aroused to activity by the sight of a mouse or a pinch of the tail, at which time they could show rapid and well-directed movements. A pinch of the cat's tail would elicit lowering of the head, flattening of the ears, pupillary dilatation, piloerection, retraction of the nictitating membrane, and either attempts at escape or a well-directed attack on the offending object. A similar response was elicited in one cat by electrical stimulation of the central gray around the aqueduct.

Some elements of the quiet form of attack were also demonstrated in each of the four cats. In three cats, electrodes were implanted in the region of the mesencephalic reticular formation prior to the isolation of the hypothalamus. In two of them, the threshold for the elicitation of attack was increased after the lesion, but on stimulation each cat would alert, pupils dilate, and a bite would be directed by vision toward the neck of an anesthetized rat. If a stuffed toy of the same size and color were placed in the cage, it was approached and sniffed on stimulation but not bitten. (Two other animals killed mice after isolation of the hypothalamus.) The third cat that had electrodes implanted in the midbrain spontaneously attacked rats and mice, but after the lesion it no longer attacked rats spontaneously, although it would attack them when stimulated. Attack was achieved after the lesion in the fourth cat by placing a small clamp on its tail. Under these conditions the cat would attack a rat or a mouse, if it could not get at the clamp.

In summary, the hypothalamus is not necessary for the occurrence of attack, although it probably does function regularly in a normal cat. Although our method was such that any deficits could be attributed to trauma, the lack of spontaneous behavior following isolation of the hypothalamus was particularly striking, even in animals which survived for a number of weeks. This is consistent with a number of other observations. Even in the acute case, there is a marked difference in activity between a cat whose brain stem is sectioned from the rostral border of the superior colliculus to the optic chiasm, and a cat whose brain stem is cut from the superior colliculus to the caudal portion of the mammillary bodies (Hinsey & Ranson, 1928). The activity level is much greater in the hypothalamic cat than in the decerebrate animal. Bard (1940) noted a marked lethargy in five cats, that survived for two weeks or more, after large lesions of the hypothalamus. Ranson (1939) similarly found that monkeys with lesions in the lateral portion of the hypothalamus at the level of the mammillary bodies were not only somnolent but also showed a distinct loss of motor initiative. Richter (1965) reports the case of a rat in which a large tumor developed obliterating the entire hypothalamus and at least part of the thalamus. While the rat ate and drank, its spontaneous activity dropped to extremely low levels. The hypothalamus, in our opinion, adds spontaneity to the animal's behavior.

Other data have been gathered in our laboratory which similarly point to the importance of the midbrain in affective defense. These were obtained by Adams (1968), who recorded the activity of single nerve cells in cats defending themselves from other cats. Two cats were placed in a box divided into two compartments, one cat in each compartment. The partition between the cats could be removed. One cat could be stimulated through electrodes in the hypothalamus to attack the other cat. The activity of individual nerve cells could be recorded from the cat defending itself from the attacker. Defense was defined as hissing or striking back at the attacking cat. Recordings were made in two areas of the brain which previously had been shown to be involved in affective defense or attack, specific regions of the hypothalamus and mid-brain. Ninety-five uninjured cells were recorded in fifteen cats. To determine whether or not the changes that were observed during affective defense were primarily associated with this form of behavior, a number of control pro-cedures were carried out. The control procedures regularly included lifting and dropping the cat, pinching the cat's tail, pulling the forelimb to elicit leg retraction, presenting flashes and clicks, and optionally included turning the cat's head, tapping on the partition separating the cats, touching the cat, moving one's hand in front of the cat's eyes, scratching the screen and making other noises. The responses of the cells during affective defense (AD) were evaluated in terms of their activity during these other manipulations. Figure 6 is a summary of this comparison. The cells in the midbrain are presented separately from those in the hypothalamus. The cells in the mid-brain appear to be more closely associated with affective defense than do those in the hypothalamus. The four cells that changed only during affective defense were in the midbrain. Four of the six cells that changed at least 50% more dur-ing affective defense than during any other manipulation were in the midbrain. These data again suggest that the central gray and adjacent tegmentum are of primary importance in the neural mediation of aggressive behavior.

The strongest evidence for the importance of the central gray and adjacent tegmentum comes from studies initiated by Hunsperger (1956) who made

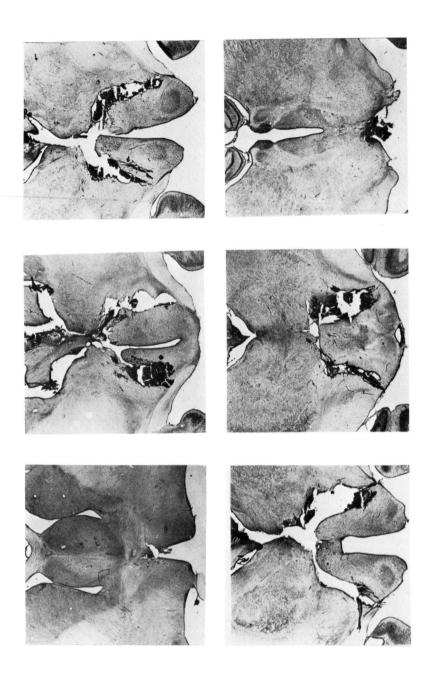

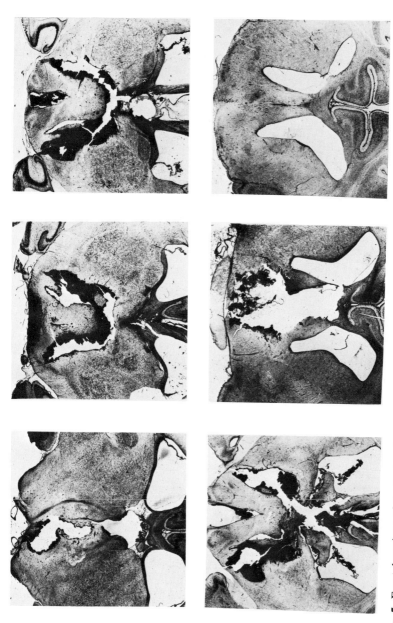

Fig. 5. Frontal sections of the brain of two cats in which the hypothalamus was isolated from the rest of the brain. Attack was still present following the lesion.

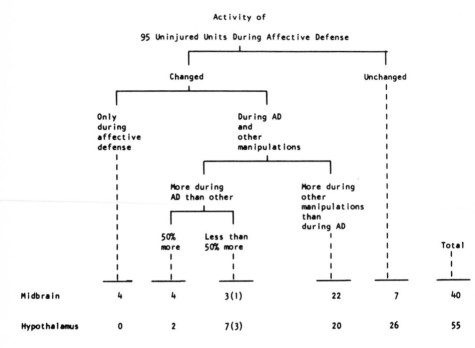

Fig. 6. A comparison of the activity of single cells in the midbrain and hypothalamus of unrestrained cats that were striking back or hissing at an attacking cat with the activity observed when the cats were subjected to a number of control manipulations. Manipulations, other than AD, regularly included: baseline activity, clicks, flashes, lifting and dropping cat, leg retraction following pull by experimenter, tail pinch; and optionally included: passive head turning, movement of hand in front of eyes, banging noise, tapping partition separating cats, scratching screen, touching cat.

lesions in the central gray and blocked the affective reaction elicited by stimulation of the hypothalamus, as well as the cat's response to a dog. The first reaction was blocked temporarily for 2 weeks. Skultety (1963) subsequenly obtained permanent blocking of attack elicited by stimulation of the hypothalamus in three of his cats with lesions involving more than 80% of the total cross-sectional area of the central gray. The lesion illustrated in his article extends out into the tegmentum.

These various lines of evidence suggest strongly that the midbrain has a crucial role in the mediation of affective display and attack itself.

In summary, the patterning mechanism consists of sites other than known sensory systems from which attack can be elicited. These sites include the stria terminalis, certain portions of the thalamus, and of the hypothalamus, as well as areas within the midbrain. On the basis of the display elicited in decerebrate cats by stimulation of the sciatic nerve (Woodworth & Sherrington,

1904), it is evident that there is a reflex mechanism for a display in the brain stem below the section of decerebration and this is probably in the midbrain. Moreover, the midbrain, even after the hypothalamus is isolated from the rest of the brain, is capable of integrating an attack response in an otherwise intact cat. The efficacy of the hypothalamus is dependent upon the midbrain. The thalamus, on the other hand, on the basis of preliminary experiments does not require the integrity of the hypothalamus for its ability to integrate attack behavior (MacDonnell & Flynn, 1968).

B. Effects of Stimulation on Motor and Sensory Systems

When one stimulates the hypothalamus or midbrain and elicits attack, changes are induced in both the motor and sensory systems. These changes are in large part responsible for the form that attack takes. In the case of attack marked by biting, certain specific mechanisms for positioning the head and for opening and closing the mouth are brought into play by the stimulation. In the case of attack marked by striking, that is induced by stimulation of the central gray, it is not striking with either paw that is elicited, but rather striking with the paw contralateral to the side of the central gray stimulated. In this section we will look more closely at some of the changes in the motor and sensory systems as a result of stimulation evoking attack behavior.

Stephen Edwards has been examining the neural mechanisms involved in attack marked by striking, and has elicited this form of attack by stimulating the central gray of the midbrain. It is customary in our laboratory to implant calibrated electrodes in unanesthetized cats so as to establish the sequence of behaviors that are obtained as the electrode is lowered through the brain. Edwards has done this for the superior colliculus and the central gray along a line approximately 1 mm lateral to the midline in a frontal plane approximately 2 mm anterior to the zero frontal plane. Figure 7 shows sections from the brains of cats in which this linear position was explored. The behaviors that were found are shown in Fig. 8. While some of the behaviors, such as the head position and the tendency to circle contralaterally, seem somewhat remote from the phenomenon of attack, they are nonetheless part of the elicited response. The cat's stance, with its limbs extended, and its tail erect, fits into the affective display more closely than the preceding behaviors. The vocalization, changing from hissing and ultimately to screaming is, together with the pupillary dilation, the piloerection, the flattening of the ears, part of the display that is commonly interpreted as rage. This affective display, which includes vocalization, can be obtained in the absence of either attack or defense. In fact, the region from which the display is obtained at these coordinates is much more extensive than the region from which attack is elicited.

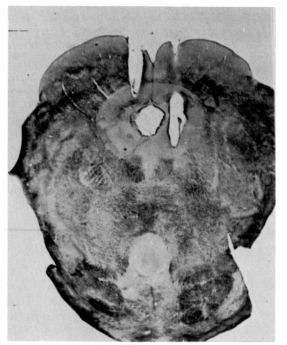

Fig. 7A

CAT 1 Ɡ

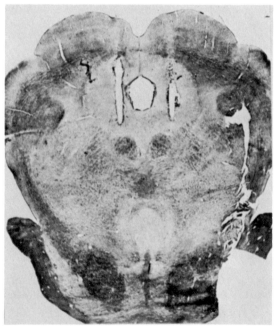

Fig. 7B

CAT 2 Ɡ,ₗ

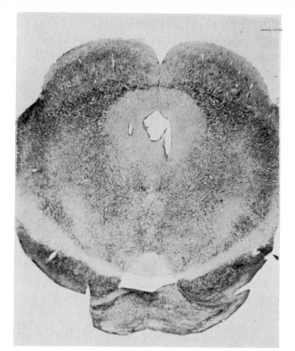

Fig. 7C

CAT 3ı

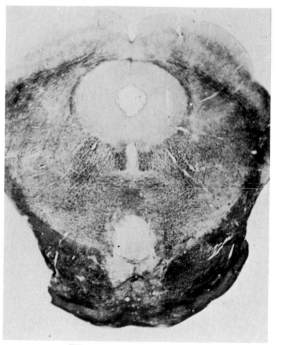

Fig. 7D

CAT 4 r

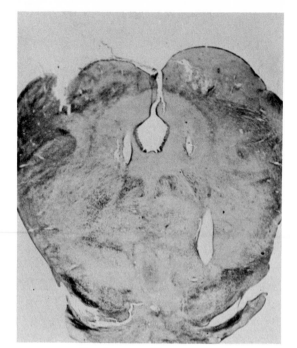

Fig. 7E

CAT 5 r,l

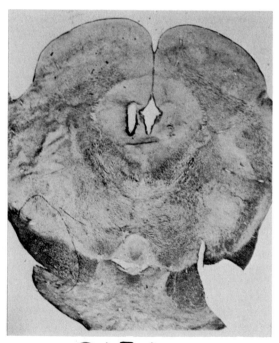

Fig. 7F

CAT 6l

The attack elicited from the central gray of the midbrain is marked by forceful and repeated striking, which is sometimes followed by a bite. Edwards has found in eleven cats, for each of which 80–100 trials were run, that the contralateral forelimb was always used in the strike, and the ipsilateral limb was not used at all for striking, although it was occasionally employed in positioning the rat. This finding of complete laterality of the behavior deserves emphasis. It is not the result of hand preference, for the unused limb can be readily brought into play by stimulating the contralateral central gray. Instead it implies that stimulation facilitates the use of the contralateral forelimb.

Evidence for facilitation of the motor system has been sought by Edwards. Action potentials were recorded from nerves going to the flexor and extensor muscles of the elbow (see Fig. 9). These nerves were selected since striking involves both flexion and extension. It begins with flexion at the elbow and paw, and extension at the shoulder (arm back). From this position close to the body, the forelimb then reaches out, the sequence being flexion at the shoulder (arm forward), extension at the elbow, then extension of the paw, and finally of the digits. In the case of multiple blows, the sequence is repeated. Since the action at the elbow is central to striking, evidence for direct activation of the nerves leading to the biceps (flexor) and triceps (extensor) muscle at the elbow on stimulation of the central gray was sought and found. On stimulating the central gray with short trains of pulses, action potentials were seen in these nerves in anesthetized cats immobilized with gallamine triethiodide. Furthermore, single shock stimulation of the central gray facilitates action potentials elicited in the nerve to the biceps muscle by single shocks to the motor cortex. Stimulation of the central gray increases the size of the action potentials due to stimulation of motor cortex.

Other experiments by Edwards indicate an interaction of the pyramidal tract with the activity due to central gray stimulation. Sectioning of the pyramidal tract brings about a loss of the normal flexion movements involved in the cat's strike and results in the cat's keeping its forelimb in a rigid semi-extended position during the attack elicited by stimulation. The laterality of the effect of stimulation is such that if the pyramidal tract is sectioned on one side only, the cat never resorts to the other forelimb to strike the rat. The unused forelimb, however, is regularly employed if the proper side of the central gray is stimulated. Illustrations of the strike prior to and after lesion of

---

Fig. 7. Sections from the brains of six of the twelve cats in which the behaviors listed in Fig. 8 were observed. The small letters following the number of the cat indicate the track of the electrode made in the superior colliculus and central gray of the aqueduct. The lowest position of the electrode is shown in each section.

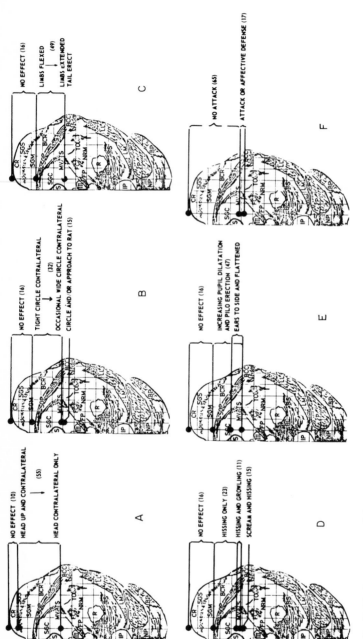

Fig. 8. Various aspects of the responses elicited in unanesthetized cats as a stimulating electrode is lowered along an axis 1 mm lateral to midline at a coronal plane 2 mm anterior to frontal zero are shown on a section taken from the atlas of Reinoso–Suarez. Note that affective displays and vocalization occur in the absence of attack. The numbers alongside the descriptions refer to the number of observations made. A: head position; B: body movement; C: stance; D: vocalization; E: affective display; F: attack.

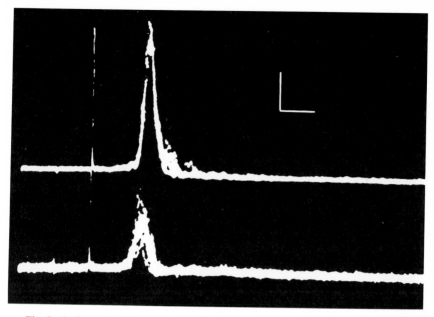

Fig. 9. Action potentials can be evoked in the nerves going to the biceps (upper tracing) and to the triceps (lower tracing) muscles of the forelimb of the cat by stimulation of sites in the central gray of the midbrain from which attack marked by striking with the paw can be elicited in unanesthetized cats. The cats used in the study of the action potentials were anesthetized with urethane, and immobilized with gallamine triethiodide. The nerves were severed close to the muscles. The horizontal line corresponds to 2 msec, and the vertical line to 200 μV for the upper tracing and 100 μV for the lower tracing. The line preceding the potential marks the end of the stimulus artifact.

the pyramidal tract are shown in Fig. 10. These data illustrate the influence of the patterning mechanism on a motor system directly involved in attack.

This set of experiments points clearly to involvement of specific parts of the motor system in the behavioral act of the cat's striking the rat.

Similar evidence of the influence of hypothalamic stimulation upon the motor nerves responsible for the closing movement of the jaw was presented earlier (Flynn, 1967). Jaw closure increased with concurrent stimulation of the hypothalamus, indicating a facilitation of the movement used in biting.

From these experiments one has evidence that stimulation produces effects upon motor systems that are concerned with striking and biting, as well as the general act of attacking.

There is corresponding evidence of the influence of stimulation upon sensory systems involved in attack. The behavioral evidence for the influence of stimulation on the sensory mechanisms comes from three sets of observations. First of all, stimulation at different sites within the brain can bring about

Fig. 10. On the left, a cat is shown just prior to striking the rat. The cat is being stimulated in the right central gray of the midbrain. Note that left forelimb is retracted and flexed at the elbow and wrist. On the right, this same cat is shown during a similar trial, but after a lesion had been made in the pyramidal tract. Note the extension and limited flexion in the forelimb.

attack on different kinds of objects. Second, the visual system appears to be gated by stimulation, in the sense that vision may suffice for opening the cat's mouth, or vision may be insufficient to do so, depending upon the site stimulated. Third, two reflexes come into play during the course of biting attack elicited by stimulation, and the sensory areas from which these reflexes, one for positioning the head, the other for opening the mouth, can be evoked are themselves a function of the intensity of stimulation to the brain.

Attack is directed at different objects depending upon which site within the brain is stimulated. Although a clear anatomical differentiation associated with the difference in objects attacked is not yet possible, not infrequently one finds that stimulation through one electrode elicits attack on one kind of object, stimulation through another electrode in the same animal gives rise to attack on other objects. For example, Cat F in the study by Adams and Flynn (1966), attacked a rat but not the experimenter if the brain was stimulated through electrode 1, while if the hypothalamus was stimulated through electrode 2, the cat would attempt to attack the experimenter, but not a rat. In other cases the range of objects attacked is increased. Some cats will attack a rat but not the experimenter on stimulation of one site, but will attack both on stimulation of another site (Chi & Flynn, 1968). Similarly both horsemeat and rat will be attacked by some cats, but only the rat will be attacked by others (see Fig. 3). Findings such as these suggest that stimulation influences the choice of objects attacked.

There is also evidence that the visual system may be gated by electrical stimulation of the brain. MacDonnell and Flynn (1966b) investigated the senses involved in a cat's attack on a rat. Vision and touch (particularly around the muzzle) were found to be of importance. Vision is required for locating the rat particularly if the experimental space is large. In investigating the role of the sensory branches of the trigeminal nerve, two branches, the infraorbital and the infraalveolar, were cut without impairment of the motor branch of the fifth nerve. The result of this operation was that cats, which prior to the sectioning of the nerves regularly approached and bit a rat, no longer bit the rat, even though they approached and rubbed their muzzles back and forth over the rat's back and neck. They failed to open their mouths to bite. Since we defined attack as striking or biting, the cats no longer attacked. This result is illustrated in Fig. 11. However, some of the cats, after the cutting of the nerves, still bit the rat (Fig. 12). It was only when these cats were blindfolded that they approached the rat but failed to bite it. In two of the cats, either result could be obtained, depending upon the site used in stimulating the brain. The data on these two cats are presented in Fig. 13.

We have also found in three of the cats that no longer attacked after the trigeminal branches were sectioned, that if the stimulus intensity was raised occasional biting could be obtained. When blindfolded, the behavior obtained at the higher intensity also disappeared. These facts indicate that in the one case vision was ineffective in opening the mouth, and that in the other case it was effective. One might think that the results obtained in the first instance could be due to the stimulus to the hypothalamus spreading to the optic tracts and effectively blinding the animal. If this were the case, stimulation at higher intensities should block the visual system more effectively, when in fact the contrary was found: Vision permitted opening the mouth, and blindfolding again abolished the effect.

In the light of these effects of stimulation on the choice of object attacked and the use of vision in opening the mouth, physiological evidence of the effect of hypothalamic stimulation on the visual system was sought (Chi & Flynn, 1968). There are no known direct pathways from the hypothalamus to the visual cortex. Furthermore if the hypothalamus had an effect upon the visual system, it might well be through the midbrain reticular formation, since the lateral hypothalamus can be regarded as a forward extension of the mesencephalic reticular formation. Potentials were evoked in the visual system by stimulating the optic tract or optic radiations in unrestrained unanesthetized cats.

Prior stimulation of the hypothalamus and of the midbrain altered the visual evoked potentials. However, the effect of the hyopthalamic stimulation differed from the effect of mesencephalic stimulation. This difference was most marked at higher intensities of stimulation. Hypothalamic stimulation decreased the magnitude of the response evoked in the visual cortex, whereas stimulation of the mesencephalic reticular formation induced an increase in the magnitude of the evoked response. Large lesions in the mesencephalic reticular formation did not abolish the effect of hypothalamic stimulation, an

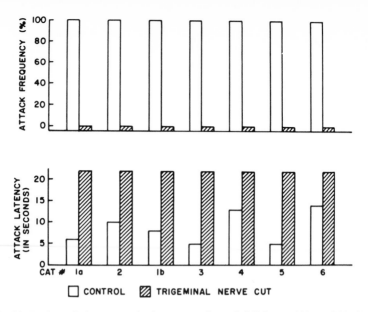

Fig. 11. In these six instances, the frequency of attack fell from 100% to 0% after the infraorbital and infraalveolar branches of the trigeminal nerve were cut. The motor branch of the same nerve was still functional. The number indicates the cat, and the letter refers to an electrode.

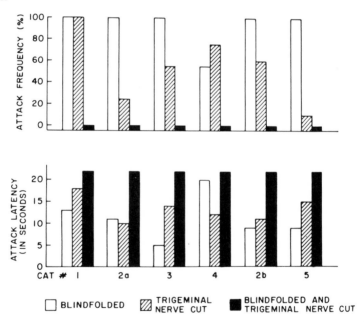

Fig. 12. In these five instances, cutting the infraorbital and infraalveolar branches of the trigeminal nerve did not abolish attack. When these animals were also blindfolded attack fell to zero. The number indicates the cat, the letter the electrode in the cat.

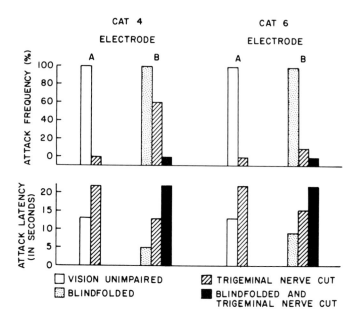

Fig. 13. After the infraorbital and infraalveolar branches of the trigeminal nerve were cut in these two cats, the cats' ability to bite a rat while being stimulated depended upon the electrode through which the animal was stimulated. If stimulated through electrode A, the attack was abolished after the trigeminal branches were severed. If stimulated through electrode B, attack was not abolished. If stimulated through electrode B blindfolding had to be added to cutting of the nerve to abolish attack.

indication that the hypothalamic effect was not dependent upon the mesencephalic reticular formation. The responses elicited under the various conditions are illustrated in Fig. 14.

Stimulation of the hypothalamus at sites from which quiet biting attack was elicited had the same effect on the evoked potentials as stimulation at sites from which affective attack was induced. No difference corresponding to the difference in object attacked was found. However, stimulation of the hypothalamus was shown to be capable of affecting responses in the visual system.

A second approach to the same problem of the effect of hypothalamic stimulation on the visual cortex has been undertaken in collaboration with H. Vanegas and W. Foote. This experiment is based on the work of Hubel and Wiesel (1962), who have found that individual cells in the visual cortex respond to complex stimuli. If one were to speculate that vision of patterned objects was mediated via the cells responding to stimuli, such as lines, slits, corners, and tongues, selection of attack objects might be a process of biasing the cells

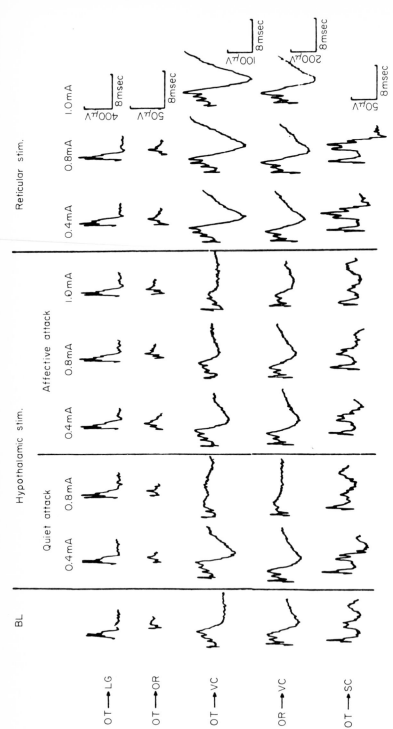

Fig. 14. Samples of averaged potentials evoked in the lateral geniculate (LG), optic radiations (OR), visual cortex (VC) and superior colliculus (SC) on stimulating the optic tract (OT) or optic radiations (OR) with an electrical shock. The baseline responses are shown under BL, and the effects of stimulating the hypothalamus and the midbrain reticular at various intensities (milliamperes) just prior to the electrical shock to the optic tract or radiations are shown. High intensity stimulation of the hypothalamus decreases the response at the visual cortex, whereas similar stimulation of the midbrain reticular formation increases it, indicating an influence of the hypothalamus apart from the midbrain reticular formation.

so that they respond optimally to particular patterns. In any case, the alteration of the response of single cells in the visual cortex as a result of hypothalamic stimulation is under study at the present time. The experiment is being done in acute preparations in which large mesencephalic lesions have been made, thus eliminating reticular influences. (In initial experiments, the cats were anesthetized with urethane and given gallamine triethiodide to immobilize them.) Hypothalamic stimulation has been found to alter the firing rate of the cells in the visual cortex. Some spontaneously active cells increase their rate of firing while other similar cells decrease it following stimulation to the hypothalamus. In addition, the response to turning a slit on and off or moving it can be increased in the presence of continuous hypothalamic stimulation (Fig. 15). Again, cells that are particularly sensitive to the movement of a slit respond less during hypothalamic stimulation while still others are more responsive during hypothalamic stimulation. The variety of alterations in response to hypothalamic stimulation seems more than sufficient at the present time to permit the sort of biasing that would enhance the perception of particular kinds of objects.

Further evidence of the direct influence of hypothalamic stimulation upon the sensory and motor mechanisms is provided by an experiment reported by MacDonnell and Flynn (1966a). After it was found that sectioning the trigeminal nerves abolished biting, the importance of these sensory nerves in the intact but stimulated cat was investigated. If a tactile stimulus, such as a narrow stick is applied to the cat's muzzle while no electrical stimulus is given to the brain, the cat tends to move its head away from the stick or to close its lips. In contrast to this, if electrical stimulation is delivered to the hypothalamus at a site from which biting attack is elicited, application of the same tactile stimulus to the muzzle gives rise to two responses. One is a rapid movement of the head in such a way as to bring the midline of the mouth to the stimulating object. The second is a rapid opening of the mouth, when the lip is touched. An important feature that serves to emphasize the effect of stimulation on the sensory systems is that the size of both of these sensory fields is a function of the intensity of the electrical stimulus to the hypothalamus. The size of the effective area increases with increasing stimulation (Fig. 16). This sensory motor mechanism that is brought into action through stimulation is an essential part of the quiet biting attack elicited by electrical stimulation of the hypothalamus.

In the experiment just cited, both sensory and motor components are altered by hypothalamic stimulation, with the result that a reflex mechanism, which probably has been suppressed gradually in the course of maturation, is reinstated in the service of attack behavior.

These findings with respect to the effects of stimulation on the motor and sensory senses involved in attack behavior have led us to formulate a general scheme which indicates how brain stimulation brings about attack behavior.

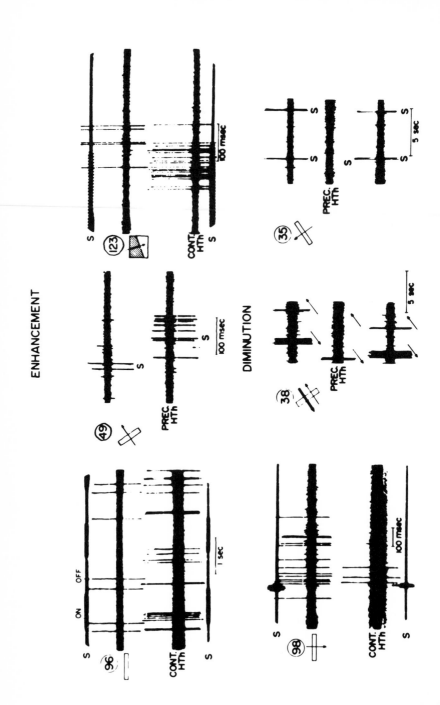

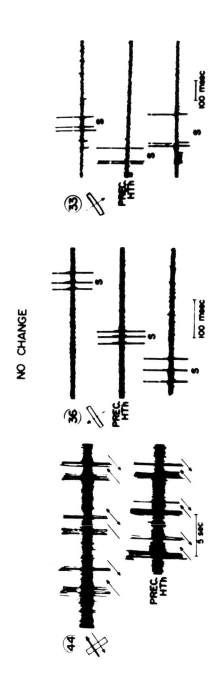

Fig. 15. Examples of the activity of cells which were found to respond optimally to slits, or moving slits or edges (the stimulus is just below the number of the cell), and the influence on this activity of hypothalamic stimulation (HTh) either while the visual stimulus was being presented (cont) or prior to its presentation (prec). The activity of some cells was enhanced, while that of others was diminished or unchanged.

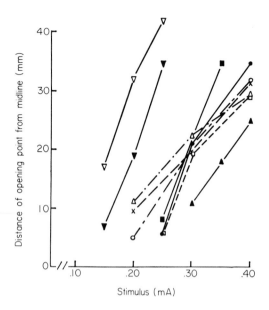

Fig. 16. The distance from the midline of a cat's mouth to the first point at which mouth opening occurs as a tactile stimulus is moved from the corner of the mouth toward the midline increases with the increase in intensity to the hypothalamus. The entire region from the midline to the opening point was effective for elicitation of jaw opening. In the absence of hypothalamic stimulation this response is not ordinarily present.

V. General Outline of the Neural Mechanisms Underlying Attack

In our view, when one stimulates the brain at a site from which a well-organized behavior such as attack is immediately elicited, the electrical stimulation excites an area of the brain whose activity influences both sensory and motor systems in such a way that if the environment contains appropriate objects complex behavioral patterns will be produced. Areas such as the lateral hypothalamus, the central gray, and reticular formation, from which one elicits attack, have multisynaptic connections with both sensory and motor systems and excitation of an effective area puts a particular bias on these neural systems that is of such a character as to facilitate the appearance of the behavior. These biases constitute a pattern, and we have therefore called those sites from which attack is elicited " patterning mechanisms." The patterning mechanism is placed at the core of Fig. 17, which is a general outline of the mechanisms involved in a cat's attack on a rat. The patterns vary from one site to another in the brain. Those in the thalamus for example seem less involved in movement that those in the hypothalamus. The patterns of excitation may also be quite different from those found in spontaneously

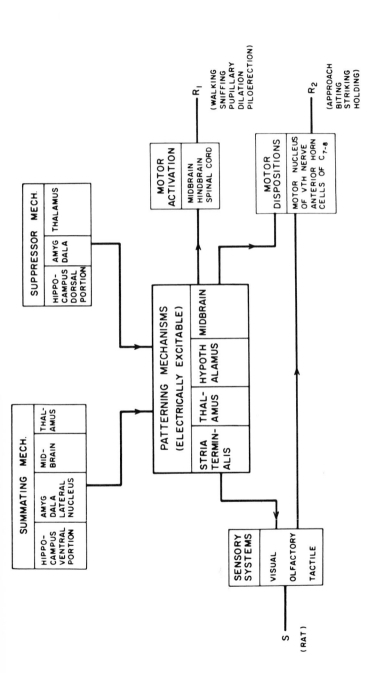

Fig. 17. The patterning mechanisms which are placed at the core of this figure are regarded as directly activating some motor systems, which give rise to specific responses (R_1), that are relatively independent of the environment. The patterning mechanisms also facilitate other motor systems, which bring about other activities (R_2) into being, provided suitable stimuli are found in the environment. The patterning mechanisms are also regarded as influencing sensory systems, so that specific stimuli in combination with a facilitated motor system give rise to the second category of responses (R_2). Other structures particularly of the limbic system can, when stimulated, summate with or inhibit the neural activities of the patterning mechanism.

occurring behavior. For example, there is little likelihood of a unilateral bias being established during naturally occurring behavior. Again an active electrode may excite adjacent fibers which normally are mutually inhibitory and thus give rise to behaviors that would never occur together normally. In any case we view a site from which a well-integrated behavior is elicited as a patterning mechanism influencing sensory and motor systems.

This view is not in conformity with the idea that brain stimulation elicits a drive that is free of specific sensory and motor involvement. According to this view, a drive is operationally defined by the performance of an arbitrary task in the course of obtaining some object. Even though cats stimulated to attack will perform arbitrary acts in the process of attacking, there is nonetheless a definite effect on the motor and sensory systems and these effects are central to the behavior elicited. The behavior elicited by electrical stimulation in an individual case is more limited than may be normal behavior, and may be only one subset of many subsets of behavior possible in spontaneously occurring attack. A concept such as drive, which at present has only a behavioral meaning, may eventually acquire neurophysiological and anatomical significance as well.

The motor system is regarded as being influenced in two ways by the patterning mechanism. In one case, the influence is more or less direct (motor activation) in the sense that elements of affective display for example are elicited independently of the environment. Even if the animal were lightly anesthetized, some of the elements would be seen on stimulation. In the second case (motor disposition), the motor system is regarded as being facilitated or suitably inhibited by the patterning mechanism, so that activities appropriate to a specific kind of behavior will occur provided that objects appropriate to this kind of behavior are in the environment.

The first kind of effect of stimulation (motor activation), namely a more or less direct one, has been known since the classical work of Karplus and Kreidl (1909), showing that the hypothalamus was of particular importance in activating the sympathetic nervous system. The sympathetic activation together with the facial components described by Kabat (1936) as a result of stimulating the hypothalamus constitute a large part of affective display. When the somatic responses resulting from stimulation of the hypothalamus (Hinsey, 1940) are added to sympathetic and facial components, all of which have been obtained even in anesthetized cats, one has strong reason for postulating a direct influence on the motor system. In fact, a large part of the general history of the physiological study of the hypothalamus attests to this first effect of stimulation.

The second kind of motor influence (motor disposition) is akin to that ascribed to the reticular formation. Just as certain parts of the reticular formation are regarded as having a general influence in terms of facilitating or inhibiting reflexes or motor responses, so the sites from which attack is elicited are regarded as capable of influencing specific systems intrinsic to the behavior. We have presented the evidence for this notion with respect to striking and biting in the previous section.

Again just as the reticular formation has an effect on the sensory system, so the notion proposed by us is that the patterning mechanisms for attack impose specific influences on the sensory system appropriate to attack behavior. The evidence for this has been given in terms of the effect of stimulation on the choice of object to be attacked, the gating of the visual system, and the appearance of the reflexes for opening the mouth and positioning the head.

In summary, electrical stimulation of the brain at sites from which one elicits attack activates certain motor systems directly, and in addition disposes sensory and motor systems to additional acts which are manifested in behavior, provided suitable objects are in the animal's environment.

REFERENCES

Adams, D. B. The activity of single cells in the midbrain and hypothalamus of the cat during affective defense behavior. *Archives Italiennes de Biologie*, 1968, **106**, 243–269.

Adams, D., & Flynn, J. P. Transfer of an escape response from tail shock to brain stimulated attack behavior. *Journal of the Experimental Analysis of Behavior*, 1966, **8**, 401–408.

Bard, P. A diencephalic mechanism for the expression of rage with special reference to the sympathetic nervous system. *American Journal of Physiology*, 1928, **84**, 490–515.

Bard, P. The hypothalamus and sexual behavior. *Research Publications, Association for Research in Nervous and Mental Disease*, 1940, **20**, 551–579.

Bard, P., & Rioch, D. McK. A study of four cats deprived of neocortex and additional portions of the forebrain. *Bulletin of the Johns Hopkins Hospital*, 1937, **60**, 73–147.

Chi, C. C., & Flynn, J. P. The effects of hypothalamic and reticular stimulation on evoked responses in the visual system of the cat. *Electroencephalography and Clinical Neurophysiology*, 1968, **24**, 343–356.

Delgado, J. M. R. Free behavior and brain stimulation. In C. C. Pfeiffer & J. R. Smythies (Eds.), *International review of neurobiology*, Vol. 6. New York: Academic Press, 1964. Pp. 349–449.

Ellison, G. D., & Flynn, J. P. Organized aggressive behavior in cats after surgical isolation of the hypothalamus. *Archives Italiennes de Biologie*, 1968, **106**, 1–20.

Fernandez de Molina, A., & Hunsperger, R. W. Organization of the subcortical system governing defence and flight reactions in the cat. *Journal of Physiology*, 1962, **160**, 200–213.

Flynn, J. P. In D. C. Glass (Ed.), *Neurophysiology and emotion*. New York: Rockefeller University Press & Russell Sage Foundation, 1967. Pp 40–60.

Fonberg, E. The motivational role of the hypothalamus in animal behavior. *Acta Biologiae Experimentalis, Polish Academy of Sciences*, 1967, **27**, 308–318.

Hess, W. R. Stammganglein-Reizversuche, 10. Tagung der Deutschen Physiologischen Gesellschaft, Frankfurt am Main. *Berichten über die Gesamte Physiologie*, 1928, **42**, 554–555.

Hess, W. R. *Hypothalamus and thalamus documentary pictures*. Stuttgart: Thieme, 1956.

Hess, W. R., & Akert, K. Experimental data on role of hypothalamus in mechanism of emotional behavior. *A.M.A. Archives of Neurology and Psychiatry*, 1955, **73**, 127–219.

Hess, W. R., & Brugger, M. Das subkortikale Zentrum der affecktiven Abwehrreaktion. *Helvetica Physiologica et Pharmacologica Acta*, 1943, **1**, 35–52.

Hinsey, J. C. In J. F. Fulton, S. W. Ranson, & A. M. Frantz (Eds.), *The hypothalamus and central levels of autonomic function. Research Publications, Association for Research in Nervous and Mental Disease*, 1940, **20**, 657–685.

Hinsey, J. C., & Ranson, S. W. A note on the influence of the hypothalamus on locomotion. *Journal of Comparative Neurology*, 1928, **46**, 461–463.

Hubel, D. H., & Wiesel, T. N. Receptive fields, binocular interaction and functional architecture in the cat's visual cortex. *Journal of Physiology*, 1962, **160**, 106–154.

Hunsperger, R. W. Affektreaktionen auf elektrische Reizung in Hernstamm der Katze. *Helvetica Physiologica et Pharmacologica Acta*, 1956, **14**, 70–92.

Hunsperger, R. W. Neurophysiologische Grundlagen des affecktiven Verhaltens. *Bulletin der Schweizerischen Akademie Medizinischen Wissenschaften*, 1965, **21**, 8–22.

Hutchinson, R. R., & Renfrew, J. W. Stalking attack and eating behaviors elicited from the same sites in the hypothalamus. *Journal of Comparative and Physiological Psychology*, 1966, **61**, 360–367.

Kabat, H. Electrical stimulation of points in the forebrain and mid-brain: The resultant alterations in respiration. *Journal of Comparative Neurology*, 1936, **64**, 187–208.

Kabat, H., Anson, B. J., Magoun, H. W., & Ranson, S. W. Stimulation of the hypothalamus with special reference to its effect on gastro-intestinal motility. *American Journal of Physiology*, 1935, **112**, 214–226.

Karplus, J. P., & Kreidl, A. Gehirn und Sympathicus. I. Mitteilung Zwischenhirnbasis und Halssympathicus. *Archiv für Gesamte Physiologie, Pflüger's*, 1909, **129**, 138–144.

Levison, P. K., & Flynn, J. P. The objects attacked by cats during stimulation of the hypothalamus. *Animal Behaviour*, 1965, **13**, 217–220.

MacDonnell, M. F., & Flynn, J. P. Control of sensory fields by stimulation of hypothalamus. *Science*, 1966, **152**, 1406–1408. (a)

MacDonnell, M. F., & Flynn, J. P. Sensory control of hypothalamic attack. *Animal Behaviour*, 1966, **14**, 339–405. (b)

MacDonnell, M. F., & Flynn, J. P. Attack elicited by stimulation of the thalamus and adjacent structures of cats. *Behaviour*, 1968, **31**, 185–202.

Masserman, J. H. Is the hypothalamus a center of emotion? *Psychosomatic Medicine*, 1941, **3**, 3–25.

Mitchell, C. L., & Kaelber, W. W., Unilateral vs. bilateral medial thalamic lesions and reactivity to noxious stimuli. *Archives of Neurology*, 1967, **17**, 653–660.

Nakao, H. Emotional behavior produced by hypothalamic stimulation. *American Journal of Physiology*, 1958, **194**, 411–418.

Ranson, S. W. The hypothalamus: its significance for visceral innervation and emotional expression. The Weir Mitchell Oration. *Transactions of the College of Physicians of Philadelphia, Series IV*, 1934, **2**, 222–242.

Ranson, S. W. Somnolence caused by hypothalamic lesions in the monkey. *A.M.A. Archives of Neurology and Psychiatry*, 1939, **41**, 1–23.

Richter, C. P. *Biological clocks in medicine and psychiatry*. Springfield, Ill.: Thomas, 1965.

Roberts, W. W., & Bergquist, E. H. Attack elicited by hypothalamic stimulation in cats raised in social isolation. *Journal of Comparative and Physiological Psychology*, 1968, **66**, 590–595.

Skultety, F. M. Stimulation of the periaqueductal gray and hypothalamus. *Archives of Neurology*, 1963, **8**, 608–620.

Ulrich, R. E., Wolff, P. C., & Azrin, N. H. Shock as an elicitor of intra- and inter-species fighting behaviour. *Animal Behaviour*, 1964, **12**, 14–15.

Urabe, M., & Tsubokawa, T. Stereotaxic thalamotomy for the relief of intractable pain. *Tohuku Journal of Experimental Medicine*, 1965, **85**, 286–300.

Wasman, M., & Flynn, J. P. Directed attack elicited from hypothalamus. *Archives of Neurology*, 1962, **6**, 220–227.

Woodworth, R. S., & Sherrington, C. S. A pseudaffective reflex and its spinal path. *Journal of Physiology*, 1904, **31**, 234–243.

HYPOTHALAMIC MECHANISMS FOR MOTIVATIONAL AND SPECIES-TYPICAL BEHAVIOR

W. W. ROBERTS

DEPARTMENT OF PSYCHOLOGY, UNIVERSITY OF MINNESOTA, MINNEAPOLIS, MINNESOTA

I. Introduction

A wide variety of motivational and species-typical (MST) behavior patterns can be induced in different species by localized stimulation of differentiated regions in the upper brainstem. These behaviors include attack (Roberts & Kiess, 1964; Roberts, Steinberg, & Means, 1967; von Holst & von Saint Paul, 1963; Wasman & Flynn, 1962), threat (Akerman, 1965b; W. R. Hess & Brugger, 1943; Roberts et al., 1967), male mating behavior (Akerman, 1965a; Roberts et al., 1967; Vaughan & Fisher, 1962), elements of maternal behavior including carrying and cleaning young (Fisher, 1956; Roberts, unpublished observations), fear-like escape and crouching (W. R. Hess, 1957; Putkonen, 1967; Roberts, 1958; Roberts, 1962; Roberts et al., 1967; von Holst & von Saint Paul, 1963), sleep (W. R. Hess, 1944; Roberts, Bergquist, & Robinson, 1969; Roberts & Robinson, 1968; Sterman & Clemente, 1962), investigatory behavior (Roberts & Carey, 1965; Roberts et al., 1967), grooming (W. R. Hess & Meyer, 1956; Roberts et al., 1967, 1969), gnawing (Roberts & Carey, 1965), components of nest building, including

This research was supported by Grant MHO6901 from the National Institute of Mental Health.

175

carrying and manipulating paper strips and burrowing (Fisher, 1956; Roberts & Carey, 1965), hoarding (Herberg & Blundell, 1967), eating (Brugger, 1943; Grossman, 1960; Larsson, 1954; Miller, 1957; Roberts *et al.*, 1967), and drinking (Andersson & McCann, 1955; Grossman, 1960). In some cases, these complex integrated responses may be accompanied by stereotyped motor movements, such as turning, circling, or rolling.

Most centrally induced responses are closely correlated temporally with the stimulation, beginning soon after the onset and terminating fairly promptly after extinction. Thus, they can be readily distinguished from spontaneous responses if the latter are naturally infrequent or if they have been reduced to a low level by satiation, exclusion of individuals displaying high rates of spontaneous performance, or employment of a test environment that inhibits spontaneous responses.

Centrally induced MST behavior patterns provide the most direct evidence that many complex behaviors having critical functions in homeostasis, nutrition, protection, or reproduction are produced by specific, localized, and probably innately organized brain mechanisms. The precise control over the onset, termination, and intensity of the responses permitted by electrical stimulation has made possible a variety of behavioral studies that have shown that the responses possess many of the cue, response, and reinforcement properties of normally induced behaviors. Identification of the effective anatomical zones for different responses has made feasible the selection and application of more physiological forms of local stimulation, such as warmth or neurohumoral transmitters, to test hypotheses regarding the normal input to the response mechanisms. Detailed analyses of the different components of the response patterns and their dependence on environmental stimuli have yielded evidence regarding the functional organization of the hypothalamic output and motor mechanisms that produce the responses, and the tracts conducting the critical hypothalamic output have been recently identified.

Our research program has concentrated on behavioral and neurophysiological studies of MST behaviors because of their critical role in the evolutionary adaptations of species and in the acquisition and performance of learned habits by individuals. We have also been encouraged by the hypothesis that it may be easier to decipher the brain mechanisms of complex behavior when it is produced by similar localized mechanisms in all members of a species than when it results from learned engrams that may vary widely between individuals and over time, and whose location in the brain is still unknown. We have used representative species from several different orders to test the generality of our findings, to sample a wider range of innately organized behaviors, and to make use of special experimental advantages offered by each species.

II. Behavioral Properties of Centrally Induced Motivational and Species-Typical Responses

Because of the unphysiological nature of electrical stimulation and the very limited size of the area directly excited by it, it is necessary to use behavioral tests to determine whether centrally induced responses have the same behavioral properties as the normal responses that they resemble. In a number of tests, hypothalamic responses have been shown to possess some of the principal properties of normal motivational responses. At the same time, a number of differences have been found that yield significant clues regarding the mode of organization of the mechanisms that produce the responses.

A. ADAPTIVE COMPOUNDS OF SIMPLER ELEMENTS

The movement patterns of most centrally induced MST responses are compounds of a number of simpler response elements that closely resemble normal responses of the species that have important adaptive functions in the health and survival of the individual or the production and survival of offspring. For example, the complete centrally induced male mating pattern in the opossum includes clicking the teeth together at intervals of 4 to 5 sec, nosing the genitalia of the female, mounting, rubbing the snout and cheeks in the fur of the female, relaxing for short periods on the back of the female, biting and tugging laterally on the neck of the female, and penile erection (Roberts *et al.*, 1967). All of these elements are also displayed in normal mating by opossums. Or in the cat, stimulation of a zone in the medial hypothalamus elicits all of the components of normal threat, including opening the mouth, retraction of the lips, hissing, growling, flattening of the ears, piloerection, striking, and biting (W. R. Hess & Brugger, 1943).

Even the finer interspecies differences in natural behavior are also present in centrally elicited responses. For example, vocalization during normal or centrally elicited threat in the cat is differentiated into two forms, hissing and growling, while the opossum displays only a single intermediate form under natural conditions or central stimulation. In normal or centrally induced attack, the opossum performs an elaborate head tossing response in a horizontal figure eight pattern just after seizing a prey object that moves in the opossum's mouth, while the cat never shows this component in either normal (Leyhausen, 1960) or centrally induced attack. And gnawing, which is a well-known natural activity of rats, but not of cats or opossums, can be induced readily by hypothalamic stimulation in rats, but not in the other two species.

While some electrodes elicit complete response patterns such as those described above, other electrodes that tend to be located nearer the borders of the same zone evoke incomplete subsets that differ in the number and identity of elements present. These cases and their significance for brain organization are discussed in Section IV,C,1.

B. Environmental Stimulus Control of Responses

Many (but not all) centrally induced MST behaviors are not performed automatically during every period of stimulation, but are strongly influenced by specific environmental stimuli. None of the responses that involve environmental objects, such as biting attack, mating, maternal responses, gnawing, burrowing, nest-building, hoarding, eating, and drinking, are performed in the absence of certain types of objects, which are fairly specific and differ for different responses. If the objects are absent, the animals typically engage in exploratory behavior and the consummatory responses related to the objects are not seen. This probably explains the failure of W. R. Hess (1957) and Hunsperger (1956) to detect the silent biting attack in cats that was later discovered by Wasman and Flynn (1962) when they tested their cats in the presence of rats. Thus, in these cases, the stimulation does not elicit the overt movements automatically, as would be expected if it were directly exciting part of the motor system for the responses, but instead it enhances the capacity of the object stimuli to elicit the responses.

Levison and Flynn (1965) have made a detailed study of the specificity of stimulus objects for centrally induced biting attack in cats. They found that an anesthetized rat was attacked more than a stuffed rat, which was attacked more than a stuffed toy dog, which was preferred to foam rubber or styrofoam blocks that were about the size of a rat. We have obtained similar preferences with centrally induced biting attack in the opossum (Roberts *et al.*, 1967) and in cats raised in normal environments, but not in cats raised in social isolation, who attacked a live rat and sponge equally (Roberts & Bergquist, 1968). Roberts and Carey (1965) and Roberts and Woodworth (1965) found that centrally induced gnawing in rats was not performed if the available objects were too soft (plastic sponges) or too solid (metal objects). Hardness by itself was not sufficient to prevent the gnawing, because it was performed repeatedly with a loose metal screw that was pulled out of its hole and then dropped like a gnawed wooden fragment, suggesting that the critical factor was the ability to pull a small object away from its initial site against moderate resistance.

In some cases, different components of response patterns are controlled by different stimulus aspects of the objects. In the biting attack pattern in the opossum (Roberts *et al.*, 1967), the head tossing component depended on the cues (probably tactile) of the rat's struggling and dropped out when it ceased. Head tossing did not appear at all if an anesthetized rat or a mouse that was too small to struggle was presented. In the absence of movement by the attack object, the opossum's biting was rhythmic and directed preferentially toward the head, which provided distinctive somesthetic, auditory, and possibly gustatory cues. In the mating pattern of the opossum, the mounting, rubbing, relaxing, and biting depended on the tactile cues supplied by the fur and were displayed even on a flat furry rug, while the anogenital nosing was evidenced only in the presence of a live female, indicating that other cues, probably olfactory, were essential for it. In the eating pattern of the opossum, seizing of pellets depended on the olfactory, visual, and tactile cues of pellets on the floor, chewing was associated with the cues of food in the mouth, and the paw movements that pushed the food back into the mouth appeared to be initiated by the cues of food on the edges of the mouth. The most detailed analysis of differentiated stimulus control of response elements is MacDonnell and Flynn's (1966) map of the sensory fields around the mouth of the cat where light touch elicits two specific reflexes for mouth orientation and opening during stimulation of the hypothalamic biting attack mechanism, but not in the absence of stimulation.

Some centrally induced responses are not controlled by the stimuli of specific objects, but by more general stimulus aspects of the environment. An escape-like response elicited from the preoptic area of opossums consisted of locomotion and pressing toward the transparent glass that formed one wall of the test box. This response was directed toward the visual stimuli that passed through the glass, since covering half the glass on the outside with an opaque board caused the animals to limit their activity to the half that remained transparent.

Other responses do not appear to require any specific environmental stimuli since we have been unable to prevent their performance by a variety of environmental manipulations, such as placing the animals in a quiet empty box with opaque walls or in total darkness, where they were observed with an infrared viewer. These responses include threat, investigatory behavior, and the clicking component of the male mating response in opossums.

C. Rewarding Effect of Performance of Responses

A third property of many centrally induced MST responses that require specific goal objects is that their performance is positively reinforcing. If the goal objects are not immediately available to the stimulated animal, but are contingent on a simple response, such as locomotion to a particular arm of a maze, the animal will learn to perform the response with increased speed and accuracy. For example, when cats that never attacked rats spontaneously were stimulated in the hypothalamic zone for biting attack, they learned a maze in which the only differential reward was a rat that they could assault (Roberts & Kiess, 1964). When a strong gnawing tendency was induced in

rats by hypothalamic stimulation, they learned a position habit and a black–
white visual discrimination in a metal-protected maze to obtain a wooden
board that they could gnaw (Roberts & Carey, 1965). Opossums stimulated
in the preoptic zone for male mating behavior learned a maze to obtain access
to a stuffed furry toy dog with which they could perform the preintromission
elements of mating (Roberts et al., 1967). Similar evidence has been reported
that centrally induced drinking and eating can produce learning of new instrumental responses rewarded with water or food (Andersson, Larsson, &
Persson, 1960; Coons, Levak, & Miller, 1965; Wyrwicka, Dobrzecka, &
Tarnecki, 1960). Mendelson (1966) found that centrally induced eating would
produce maze learning even if the onset of stimulation was delayed until after
the animals passed through the choice point into either one of the arms, suggesting that the rewarding effect of the eating was able to condition incentive
motivation (Logan & Wagner, 1965) to the cues of the maze that was able
to motivate the correct choice in the absence of stimulation.

The evidence that the performance (or resulting sensory feedback) of five
different centrally induced responses in four distantly related species is rewarding strongly suggests that rewarding properties are probably characteristic of many centrally elicited as well as natural MST responses in diverse
species. Positive reinforcement associated with the sensory feedback from
largely innately organized MST responses would contribute to their effectiveness by: (a) strengthening learned responses instrumental in obtaining
suitable goal objects; (b) reinforcing maximally efficient sequential chaining,
where one MST response is dependent on an earlier one, as in nest building;
(c) conditioning of MST responses (but not the *motivation* to perform them)
and incentive motivation to goal object and other environmental cues, so that
the responses would be performed more promptly when the motivation was
present; and (d) possibly improving some details of the innately organized
response itself.

The positive reinforcing effect of the performance of centrally induced responses probably explains Valenstein, Cox, and Kakolewski's recent reports
(1968, 1969) that experience in performing centrally induced responses with
particular objects in a particular environment increases the probability of
their subsequent performance under similar circumstances.

D. Habit Transfer between Natural and Centrally Induced
   Motivational States

Miller (1957) showed that hypothalamic stimulation that induced unconditioned eating caused satiated rats to perform a food-rewarded bar pressing
response previously acquired during natural hunger. Andersson and Wyrwicka

(1957) demonstrated a similar effect with centrally induced drinking in goats. Delgado, Roberts, and Miller (1954) found that stimulation of presumed pain mechanisms of the midbrain and thalamus in cats produced pain-like behavior, and elicited performance of a wheel-turning response that had been previously learned to initially escape and then avoid pain caused by electric shock through the floor. Adams and Flynn (1966) used a similar technique to test whether hypothalamic aggressive responses in the cat are accompanied by stimulus properties similar to pain. They found that a simple locomotor response originally learned to escape natural pain generalized to hypothalamic attack accompanied by vocal threat display, but did not generalize to silent biting attack that resembled predation. Generalization in the opposite direction, from learning during a centrally induced motivational state to a test under normal motivation, has been shown by Coons et al. (1965) and Wyrwicka et al. (1960) for centrally induced eating. These studies indicate that some centrally induced motivational states possess habit-eliciting capacities similar to the natural motivational states that they resemble, possibly through similar cue properties or possibly through a more direct access to habit storage mechanisms.

Some writers (e.g., Deutsch & Deutsch, 1966, pp. 191–192) have suggested that some centrally induced behaviors may be due to stimulation of sensory pathways rather than specific response integrating mechanisms. This is especially likely in the case of pain, which is less finely differentiated than other modalities. Roberts (1962) found that stimulation in the vicinity of the thalamic somatosensory nucleus, *ventralis posterior*, elicited affective display and escape responses that resembled responses to normal pain in that they varied from trial to trial and the escape component extinguished after a few trials. Stimulation of the optic tract and chiasm in opossums elicited growling that adapted much faster than when elicited from the hypothalamus, and may have resulted from a visual sensation, since opossums threaten very readily to moving visual stimuli (Roberts et al., 1967). Thus, the possibility of sensory causation must be considered for all centrally induced responses, especially when the brain stimulation is in or near a sensory system, and when relatively simple stimuli elicit the response promptly under natural conditions. However, it appears unlikely that many hypothalamic responses or response tendencies are due to simple sensory stimulation, because they lack the flexibility of normal sensorially induced responses in their constancy from trial to trial, absence of extinction, and closely graded relation to current intensity. Also, introspective reports from humans indicate that most stimulation in sensory systems produces paresthesias, and there is very little evidence that sensory input other than pain can elicit MST behaviors or behavior tendencies with the promptness characteristic of brain stimulation.

E. Interaction of Natural and Centrally Induced Responses

Centrally induced responses do not automatically override normal response tendencies, but are typically integrated with them on the basis of relative strength. For example, centrally induced mating and attack in the opossum and attack in the cat were often inhibited for varying durations by the defensive behavior of conspecifics or rats, and this could be overcome to some extent by increasing the stimulation current. Tenen and Miller (1964) have shown that the addition of quinine to food produces increasing inhibition of centrally induced eating as the quinine concentration is increased, that tolerance for quinine increases with stimulation current, and that normal hunger produced by deprivation summates with centrally induced eating.

F. Relation to Normal Motivational Processes

The preceding studies of the behavioral properties of centrally induced MST behaviors have shown that increased output from MST behavior mechanisms in the hypothalamus and related structures can act upon the rest of the nervous system to produce many behavioral changes usually attributed to motivation or drive (Hinde, 1959; Teitelbaum, 1967). Thus, variation in the output of these mechanisms under the influence of humoral or neural input can account for temporal variation in the effectiveness of rewards and in the probability of performance of unlearned MST behaviors in a constant stimulus environment. The possibility that these mechanisms may also account for temporal variation in the probability of performance of learned instrumental responses receives some support from evidence that object-procuring responses learned during stimulation decline (especially in latencies) when stimulation is withdrawn (Roberts & Carey, 1965; Roberts & Kiess, 1964). However, alternative explanations in terms of stimulus generalization decrement cannot be ruled out, and direct habit activation is confounded with learned incentive motivation in this type of test.

III. Development of Centrally Induced Motivational and Species-Typical Responses

It is usually assumed that the central mechanisms of complex behaviors produced by brain stimulation are innately organized, but there have been no direct tests of whether they can develop without experience with conspecifics or relevant goal objects. For this reason, a recent experiment in the author's laboratory (Roberts & Bergquist, 1968) investigated whether biting attack could be elicited by hypothalamic stimulation in cats raised in isolation from conspecifics and prey animals, and with reduced experience with other environmental stimuli. They were taken from their mothers and placed in individual cages at the age of five days, and hand fed for the first few weeks until they began to eat normally. When they reached an average age of one year, multiple electrodes were implanted. The best electrode point and voltage level were selected during a small number of stimulation trials with a dish of food or a small furry stuffed dog, which elicited much weaker biting than live rats and were barely adequate to detect attack responses. Next, the cats received five trials in a standard test situation with a rat followed by one to five trials with a plastic sponge. The rat and sponge were removed 9 sec before the stimulation was turned off to minimize the possibility that the attack might be rewarded by the termination of the stimulation. Motion pictures were made of all trials to provide a permanent record for later qualitative study and timing of latencies and duration of attack. A group of control cats obtained from local pounds and matched with the isolated cats by sex and approximate weight received the same surgical and test procedures.

The principal finding was that the cats raised in social isolation displayed during their first five trials with rats all of the components present in the attacks of the normal control animals. The isolated cats approached the rat with body lowered and neck extended. The main attack element was biting, and the paws were used to flatten, catch, or hold the rat. When the rats pawed or bit in self-defense, the isolated cats drew back their heads and increased their pawing. Some isolated cats pursued the rat when it was withdrawn before the end of the stimulation, and after the rat's removal, some animals searched the end where it had been tethered. The elicitation of these diverse response elements in the isolated cats indicates that a large part of the development of the brain mechanisms for hypothalamic attack does not require experience with prey animals or other cats. There was no evidence of improvement in latency, duration, or pattern of attack during the five trials with rats, which rules out the kind of rapid learning that may sometimes contaminate repeated test trials following experiential deprivation (Lorenz, 1965, pp. 94–97).

The possibility that the cats might have learned the attack pattern by playing with their tails, the food, or the food and water dishes was tested by giving additional stimulation trials with these objects. Since they were attacked very weakly or not at all, any attack habits previously acquired with these familiar objects were evidently not strong enough to account for the much stronger and more frequent attacks on the unfamiliar rats.

When compared with the normal control cats, the isolated animals were significantly inferior in the persistence and intensity of their attack on rats. Also, the controls attacked the sponge with significantly longer latencies and shorter durations than rats, but the isolates showed no evidence of discrimination, actually attacking the sponge with slightly faster latencies and longer

durations (Fig. 1). This indicates that some aspect of experience can modify
the functioning of the central attack mechanism. However, evidence is not
available as to whether these quantitative differences resulted from learned
habits, early malnutrition, disuse atrophy, interfering response tendencies, or

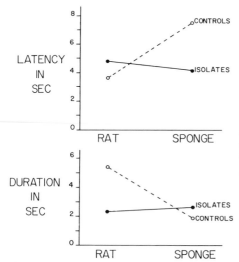

Fig. 1. Latency and duration of
attacks on rats and sponges elicited by
hypothalamic stimulation in normal cats
and cats raised without experience with
conspecifics or prey animals. The objects
were removed after the first 11 sec of
20-sec-stimulation trials.

other possible factors, so the interpretation of these differences is less clear
than the main finding that the development of the brain mechanism for most
elements of attack elicited from the hypothalamus does not require experience
with prey objects or conspecifics.

IV. Organization of Brain Mechanisms for Motivational and Species-Typical Responses

Studies of the functional organization of the MST behavior mechanisms
of the upper brainstem fall in three categories: (a) detailed localization of the
zones where the responses are elicited by stimulation; (b) determination of
the neural and humoral sources of excitatory and inhibitory input to the
zones; and (c) tracing the output from the zones to the motor mechanisms
where the responses are produced directly or as a result of interaction with
sensory input from relevant environmental stimuli.

A. LOCALIZATION OF RESPONSE ZONES

The locations from which male mating behavior, biting attack, defensive
threat, eating, grooming, investigation, and escape-like activity were elicited
in opossums (Roberts *et al.*, 1967) are shown on frontal diagrams through the

hypothalamus and preoptic region in Fig. 2. All response patterns were evoked from relatively specific and differentiated zones, except for the investigatory syndrome of sniffing, looking around, and locomotion, which was obtained throughout most of the preoptic area and hypothalamus, except for the ventromedial hypothalamus. There was some overlap between zones for different patterns, especially in the preoptic area, but most zones differed from others in at least part of their distribution. In general, the completeness, intensity, and duration of responses tended to be greatest for electrodes in the central portions of the zones and diminished toward the periphery, suggesting a center-to-periphery gradient in the density of hypothalamic efferents to the motor mechanisms for different response elements.

The anatomical distribution of points that elicited male mating behavior was similar in both males and females, and, except for penile erection, there were no significant sex differences in the threshold, form, intensity, degree of completeness, or persistence of responses. Thus, female opossums have a hypothalamic mechanism for male-type mating very similar to that of males. Fisher (1956) has induced components of female maternal behavior in male rats, including retrieving and pup cleaning, by the application of minute amounts of testosterone in the hypothalamus, and we have obtained similar responses by electrical stimulation. Thus, it appears that the brain mechanisms for male- and female-typical behaviors develop ontogenetically in both sexes, but are used much more by one sex than the other, perhaps because of differences in sensitivity to hormones or in input from other brain structures.

The anatomical locations of a number of response zones in the primitive marsupial opossum closely resemble those for similar behaviors in cats or rats, indicating that the phylogenetic continuity of some hypothalamic behavior mechanisms in carnivores and rodents extends back at least as far as early mammalian levels. The correspondence is closest for threat, which has a predominantly medial or ventromedial location in both cats and opossums (W. R. Hess, 1957; Roberts & Kiess, 1964), biting attack, which is located lateral or dorsolateral to the threat zone in cats and opossums (Roberts & Kiess, 1964; Wasman & Flynn, 1962), and eating, which is elicited from two zones in the opossum, the most posterior (F 12.5) having a similar location to eating zones in the cat and rat between the fornix and mammillothalamic tract (Brugger, 1943; Miller, 1960). Somewhat less precise parallels are apparent for mating, grooming, and eating evoked from the preoptic region in rats, cats or goats (Andersson & Larsson, 1961; Fisher, 1956; W. R. Hess & Meyer, 1956; Vaughan & Fisher, 1962), and upward looking elicited from the posterior hypothalamus above the mammillary bodies (W. R. Hess, 1957).

On the basis of evidence from cats that predominantly sympathetic responses are elicited from the posterior hypothalamus, and predominantly parasympathetic responses from the anterior hypothalamus and preoptic area,

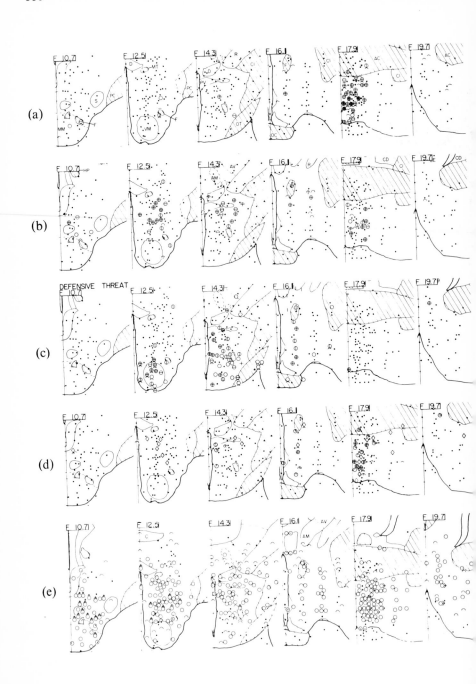

W. R. Hess (1957) proposed that the autonomic and behavior mechanisms of the hypothalamus may be organized into an anterior "trophotropic" component concerned with restorative and vegetative functions such as sleep and digestion, and a posterior "ergotropic" component concerned with active emergency functions such as defensive threat and escape-like locomotion. However, Fig. 3, which presents a sagittal reconstruction of the principal response zones in the opossum, shows that such general behavior categories are invalid for the opossum, since ergotropic and trophotropic behaviors are obtained from both anterior and posterior regions of the hypothalamus and preoptic area.

B. INPUT TO HYPOTHALAMIC–PREOPTIC RESPONSE ZONES

1. Neural Input

Evidence that the amygdala supplies excitatory input to the hypothalamic mechanism for threat behavior in the cat has been reported by de Molina and Hunsperger (1962), who found that threat elicited from the amygdala was blocked by lesions in the ipsilateral hypothalamic threat zone, and by Hilton and Zbrozyna (1963), who found that stimulation of the ventral amygdalofugal path between the amygdala and hypothalamus elicited threat, while destruction of the path blocked threat elicited from the amygdala. Flynn's (1967) evidence that attack elicited by stimulation of the hypothalamus is inhibited or facilitated by stimulation of different areas of the amygdala,

Fig. 2. *Locations of positive and negative points for motivational and species-typical responses in the opossum plotted on frontal plane diagrams of the hypothalamus and preoptic area located 10.7–19.7 mm anterior to the interaural axis.* Negative points are indicated by small filled circles (●). Plane F 10.7 corresponds to Bodian's (1939) Fig. 10; F 12.5 is slightly anterior to Fig. 8; F 14.3 corresponds to Fig. 5; and F 16.1 is slightly anterior to Fig. 3. AC: commissura anterior; AM: nucleus anterior medialis thalami; AV: nucleus anterior ventralis thalami; C: nucleus centralis; CD: nucleus caudatus; CI: capsula interna; D: nucleus dorsalis hypothalami; F: columna fornicis; H: hippocampus; HA: nucleus habenularis; HC: commissura hippocampi; HP: tractus habenulopeduncularis; LH: nucleus lateralis hypothalami; MM: corpus mammillare; MT: tractus mammillothalamicus; OC: chiasma opticum; OT: tractus opticus; PC: pedunculus cerebri; PV: nucleus filiformis pars paraventricularis; R: nucleus reticularis; S: nucleus subthalamicus; SE: area septalis; SM: stria medullaris; TH: thalamus; VM: nucleus ventromedialis hypothalami. From Roberts *et al.*, 1967. (a): male mating behavior (O, mounting; —, rubbing; |, biting; ×, penile erection; ∧, clicking). (b): biting attack (O, persistent biting; ∩, brief biting; |, head tossing; —, crunching dead rat). (c) defensive threat (O, mouth open; |, backing; —, head swinging; ∧, growling). (d) eating and grooming (◇, eating; ∧, generalized biting; O, persistent grooming; ∩, brief grooming; |, ∟, ⊦, +, number of areas groomed). (e) investigatory and escape-like activity (O, locomotion, sniffing, and looking; ∩, sniffing and looking; ↑, upward looking and climbing; →, pressing against glass cage front).

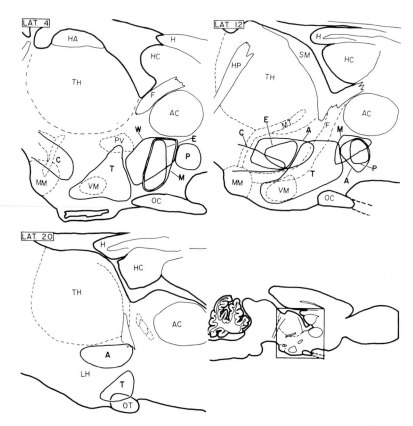

Fig. 3. The principal zones from which motivational responses were elicited in the opossum projected onto sagittal diagrams located .4, 1.2, and 2.0 mm lateral to the midline. (Lower right diagram shows a complete section 1.2 mm from the midline with a square indicating the portion enlarged in the other diagrams. Plane Lat. 0.4 corresponds to Bodian's (1939) Fig. 17; Lat. 1.2 is slightly medial to Fig. 15; and Lat. 2.0 corresponds to Fig. 13. Response zone abbreviations: A, biting attack; C, upward looking and climbing; E, eating; M, male mating behavior; P, pressing against glass side of cage; T, defensive threat; W, grooming. For structure abbreviations, see Fig. 2. From Roberts *et al.*, 1967.)

hippocampus, dorsomedial thalamus, and midbrain indicates that a variety of structures send excitatory or inhibitory input to the hypothalamic attack zone or structures that mediate its output.

2. *Humoral Input*

Evidence for humoral input to hypothalamic motivational mechanisms has been offered by Harris, Michael, and Scott (1958) and Michael (1966) for estrogenic control of the female mating mechanism in the cat, by Fisher

(1956) for androgenic control of the male mating mechanism in the rat, by Andersson (1953) for osmotic control of the drinking mechanism, and by Andersson and Larsson (1961) for thermal control of the drinking and eating mechanisns.

The preoptic zone where grooming was elicited by electrical stimulation in the opossum (Roberts *et al.*, 1967) was very similar to the area where thermoreceptors have been found in the cat (Nakayama, Hammel, Hardy, & Eisenman, 1963; Eisenman & Jackson, 1967), and where local warming induces thermoregulatory responses of panting and sweating in cats (Magoun, Harrison, Brobeck, & Ranson, 1938). Also, grooming or spreading saliva over the fur is a prominent thermoregulatory response in the opossum (Higginbotham & Koon, 1955). These facts suggested that blood temperature acting through thermoreceptors might be one of the normal sources of input to the grooming mechanism identified by electrical stimulation. To test this possibility, a quadruple electrode array was implanted in the medial preoptic area or surrounding regions in opossums so that a 2 × 2 × 2 mm cube would be warmed when radiofrequency (RF) current (2 MHz) was passed between the tips (Roberts *et al.*, 1969).

Warming of the medial preoptic region induced grooming, panting, and, somewhat unexpectedly, sleep-like relaxation. All three components were very similar to the spontaneous behavior displayed when the animals were exposed to natural environmental heating at 44 to 48°C (Fig. 4). The central warming was probably exciting thermoreceptor neurons selectively, because electrical stimulation through the same electrodes using 60-Hz sine wave current elicited a variety of nonthermoregulatory responses in addition to grooming,

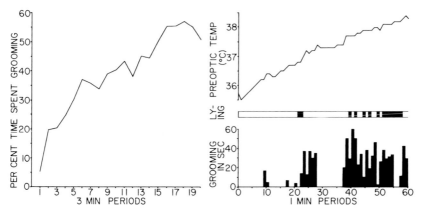

Fig. 4. *Responses of opossums to natural environmental warming at 44 to 48°C.* Left graph shows average percentage of time eight opossums groomed during 23 one-hour test sessions. Right diagram shows preoptic temperature, occurrence of lying stretched out, and amount of grooming during one test session. From Roberts *et al.*, 1969.

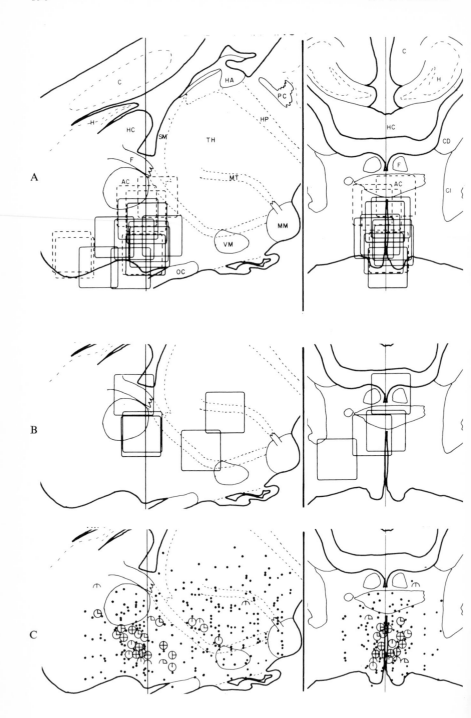

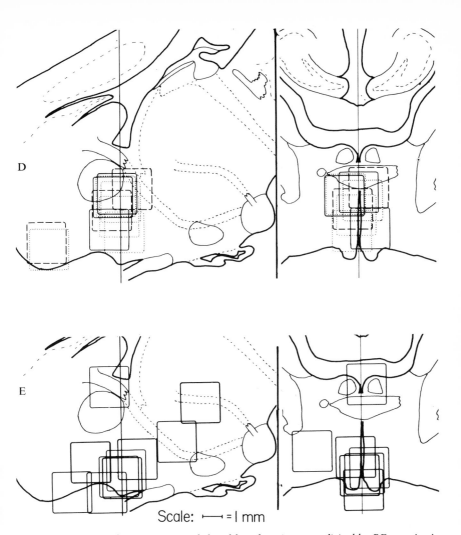

Fig. 5. *Region where grooming and sleep-like relaxation were elicited by RF warming in opossums compared with region where grooming was evoked by electrical stimulation in study of Roberts et al. (1967).* Sagittal diagrams located .6 mm from midline show positive and negative electrodes within 1.2 mm of midline. Frontal diagrams through vertical line on sagittal diagram show warming electrodes that overlapped plane of diagram or electrodes from electrical stimulation study that were located within 1.2 mm of plane. Squares indicate size of 2-mm cube enclosed by warming electrode. AC: commissura anterior; C: cortex cerebri; CD: nucleus caudatus; CI: capsula interna; F: columna fornicis; H: hippocampus; HA: nucleus habenularis; HC: commissura hippocampi; HP: tractus habenulopeduncularis; MM: corpus mammillare; MT: tractus mammillothalamicus; OC: chiasma opticum; PC: pedunculus cerebri; SM: stria medullaris; TH: thalamus; VM: nucleus ventromedialis hypothalami. A: grooming elicited by warming (—, persistent grooming; – – –, brief grooming). B: no grooming from warming. C: grooming elicited by electrical stimulation (○, persistent grooming; ∩, brief grooming; |, ∟, ⊦, +, number of areas groomed; •, no grooming). D: sleep-like lying down (···, lying on side, curled; – – –, lying on side, back straightened; —, lying on side, back straightened, waving legs); E: no lying down. From Roberts *et al.*, 1969.

such as looking around, sniffing, locomotion, mouth opening, climbing, mating, attack, and various stereotyped motor responses. Since radio frequency warming inside or outside of the effective area for grooming, panting, and relaxation never elicited any other responses throughout a series of current values that ranged up to lesion-making levels, it may be concluded that even the highest noninjurious levels of RF warming do not have a general excitatory effect like electric current.

The grooming induced by preoptic warming consisted of licking the legs and accessible parts of the trunk, washing the face with wet forepaws, and combing the ear, neck, and shoulder with wet hindpaws. The percentage distribution over different body areas was very similar to grooming induced by natural environmental warming, with which it correlated .94 (Pearson r). The elements of grooming elicited by electrical stimulation were similar to those induced by central or natural warming, but the components directed toward the anterior part of the body were relatively more frequent and those directed toward the posterior part were relatively less frequent than when the stimulus was warming. This indicates that the electrical stimulation was acting somewhat differently from the warming, perhaps by nonspecifically exciting nonthermal as well as thermal input and output components of the grooming mechanism. The more anterior distribution of the grooming elicited by the electrical stimulation is also characteristic of the grooming that follows eating, which suggests that the preoptic grooming mechanism may produce different types of grooming in response to different sources of input.

Figure 5 shows the location of effective and ineffective electrodes for elicitation of grooming and sleep-like lying down. The distribution of electrodes that evoked grooming when RF heating current was applied overlapped considerably with the zone where electrical stimulation through smaller electrodes elicited grooming in the preceding study, which confirms the hypothesis that thermoreceptors are probably one of the normal sources of input to the grooming mechanism. The effective zones were not precisely the same, perhaps because of the more specific action of the warming.

Although grooming and sleep-like lying down were induced by warming similar zones, grooming was more consistently obtained from the lower three-fourths of the preoptic area and lying down from the upper two-thirds. Thus, the five most dorsal electrodes in the preoptic region induced lying down with little or no grooming, and the five most ventral electrodes produced grooming without lying down. This indicates that the warming was not producing general excitation of a unitary mechanism for heat dissipation, nor was it eliciting a general "heat drive," but instead was activating different groups of thermoreceptors that in some cases, if not all, have outputs to different sensory–motor mechanisms.

The similarity between the area where sleep-like relaxation was induced by warming in the opossum and the area where Sterman and Clemente (1962) elicited sleep behavior with bilateral electrical stimulation in the cat suggests that preoptic thermoreceptors may supply one of the normal inputs to the sleep mechanism of the cat. This has been confirmed recently (Roberts & Robinson, 1970) by the finding that localized warming of the preoptic area causes cats to lie down in a sleep posture, develop a synchronized EEG (Fig. 6), and pant. Grooming like that displayed by opossums was not obtained, but under normal environmental heating, it has a higher threshold than relaxation and panting in cats (Robinson & Lee, 1941).

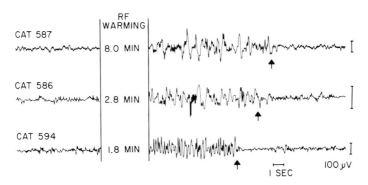

Fig. 6. *Cortical EEG of three cats before and after radiofrequency warming of preoptic region.* The arrow indicates where cats were awakened by auditory and visual stimuli. Upper two cats show deep sleep pattern of 1 to 3 Hz waves and occasional spindles. Lower cat, which received a shorter duration of warming, shows relaxed rest pattern of 5 to 8 Hz waves (R. Hess, Koella, & Akert, 1953). From Roberts & Robinson, 1968.

C. OUTPUT OF HYPOTHALAMIC–PREOPTIC RESPONSE ZONES

1. *Evidence from Analysis of Responses*

a. Incompleteness of Responses. Most descriptions of centrally induced MST responses have tended to emphasize the complete patterns of normally related response elements that are elicited by some electrodes in the effective zones. However, such complete sets of elements are actually evoked by only a minority of brain electrodes, while the majority produce incomplete combinations of elements that differ in degree of completeness and the particular elements present. For example, in W. R. Hess and Brugger's (1943) study of the threat response in the cat, only about 6% of the electrodes evoked complete combinations of growling, hissing, piloerection, and flattening of the ears, and 94% elicited incomplete subsets that included every possible combination of the four elements (Fig. 7). In the opossum, Roberts *et al.* (1967)

found that only 20% of the 212 points that elicited mating, attack, threat, and grooming produced complete patterns, while the remainder evoked a wide variety of incomplete patterns. For mating, attack, and threat almost all conceivable subsets of elements were produced, except for those that included very rare elements, such as erection, or physically difficult or impossible combinations, such as growling without mouth opening in the threat pattern, head tossing or crunching without biting in the attack pattern, or rubbing or biting without mounting in the mating pattern. For grooming, the incomplete combinations were less varied (4), but nevertheless comprised 80% of the total number of points.

Whether the eating and drinking responses are also made up of separate elements that can be obtained in different combinations is not clear from the available data. However, occasional electrodes in opossums (Roberts *et al.*, 1967) and rats (personal observations) elicited biting or gnawing on food that resembled eating, but a large amount was allowed to fall out of the mouth, suggesting that the swallowing and perhaps the chewing elements may have been missing.

The differences between electrodes in the completeness of responses were not due to unreliable test procedures because the responses were typically highly repeatable from trial to trial and session to session. The possibility, suggested by von Holst and von Saint Paul's (1963) paper, that the incomplete response patterns may have resulted from weak or ineffective stimulation combined with consistent ordered series of thresholds for response elements is ruled out by the numerous cases in Fig. 7 in the right-hand boxes that are incompatible with an ordered threshold hypothesis. The possibility that the stimulation was too weak is also unlikely because the range of thresholds for elements elicited by individual electrodes was narrow, averaging less than ± 10% of the mean threshold, and further increases that averaged 50% above the mean threshold failed to elicit additional elements. The possibility that the varied incomplete responses might be due to consistent differences in learned or unlearned behavior patterns of individual animals was ruled out by an analysis of the opossum data that disclosed that interelectrode differences in the completeness of responses were approximately equal for electrodes located in the same animal or in different animals.

Because of the variation in the completeness of responses and the additional finding that some electrodes evoked elements belonging to more than one pattern, a further analysis was made of the opossum data to determine whether the response patterns were genuine clusters of elements that tended to occur together or were merely artifacts of efforts to relate the responses to normal behavior patterns. For every possible pair of response elements, an index of association was calculated, I being equal to the number of electrodes that elicited both elements divided by the number of electrodes that elicited the less frequent element. This index ranged from .00, when two elements were

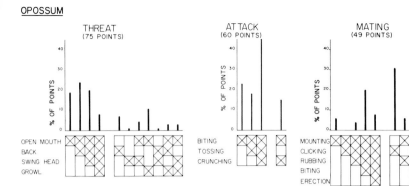

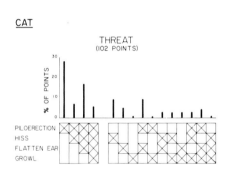

Fig. 7. *Percentage of electrode points that elicited different combinations of elements of the mating, threat, and attack patterns in the opossum* (Roberts *et al.*, 1967) *and in the threat pattern in the cat* (W. R. Hess & Brugger, 1943). Response elements are listed in descending order of frequency. The left-hand box below each graph contains the combinations that would result if differences in the frequency of response elements and in the completeness of the response patterns were due to consistent differences in response thresholds. The right-hand box contains combinations incompatible with this hypothesis.

never evoked by the same electrode, to 1.00, when the less frequent was always accompanied by the other element. Figure 8 presents the average indexes for the mating, attack, threat, and grooming patterns. When the two elements in a pair belonged to the same pattern, the index was consistently high, but when they were drawn from different patterns, it was generally low [except for mating and grooming, which also had the greatest anatomical overlap, but could be dissociated by applying more physiological stimulation (Roberts *et al.*, 1969)]. This indicates that although the completeness of response patterns differed widely, the anatomical separation of the mechanisms for different patterns was great enough so that elements belonging to the same pattern were much more likely to occur with each other than with elements of other patterns.

In behavioral terms, the interelectrode variability in the completeness of response patterns and in the particular elements elicited indicates that stimulation of hypothalamic–preoptic motivational mechanisms does not typically evoke unitary "drives" for mating, attack, or threat. Instead, it increases the probability of performance of specific response elements which form complete behavior patterns in only a minority of cases. In physiological terms,

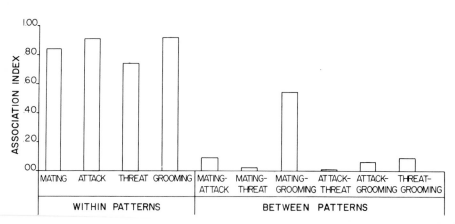

Fig. 8. Average index of association for pairs of elements drawn from the same response pattern compared with that for pairs drawn from different patterns. I is the number of electrodes eliciting both elements per the number of electrodes eliciting less frequent element of pair.

the incompleteness of centrally induced behaviors means that electrical stimulation probably excites directly only a small fraction of the neurons in a response zone, and there is relatively little synaptic spread between neurons controlling different response elements within the hypothalamic zones or efferent to them. The smallness of the region of direct and transynaptic excitation in the hypothalamic zones is also supported by the considerable differences that were often found between responses elicited by electrodes separated by 1 mm or less. For example, the deepest point on the anterior electrode of Opossum 20 produced grooming, the next point eating, the third point eating plus the clicking component of mating, and the top point looking around.

The number and variety of incomplete responses evoked by stimulation strongly suggests that the small region excited by each electrode is a probabilistic sample of efferent neurons that send independent projections to separate lower-order sensory–motor mechanisms for different response elements. This concept of divergent hypothalamic–preoptic projections to fractional response mechanisms is similar to that of Bard (1950), and the present evidence provides convergent support for Bard's original inferences from brainstem transections. The finding of Roberts et al. (1969) that warming the dorsal part of the preoptic thermoreceptor area can produce lying down without grooming, and warming the ventral part can produce grooming without lying down indicates that the separateness of some hypothalamic–preoptic efferent channels is continuous from the humoral receptor neurons that initiate activity in the channels to the final motor neurons that produce the overt responses.

A possible objection to a probabilistic interpretation of the incompleteness of hypothalamic–preoptic responses is that so many neurons were in contact with the relatively large uninsulated tips of Hess's and the author's electrodes (about 50–2000 neurons, depending on electrode size and neuron density) that even the smallest zone of excitation would be expected to elicit complete responses in almost all cases, if the hypothalamic efferents that produce behavioral responses are a high percentage of hypothalamic neurons and are randomly mixed within zones. However, the multiplicity of functions performed by the hypothalamus suggests that behavioral efferents may be a relatively small fraction of the population, and the number excited by a given electrode may be even further reduced by differences in excitability resulting from different orientations in the electric field (Terzuolo & Bullock, 1956). Also, the efferents may not be completely randomly mixed within zones, but may be aggregated in larger homogeneous groups or clumps that are randomly distributed within zones.

The dependence of many hypothalamic responses on specific environmental stimuli means that the mechanisms influenced by hypothalamic output are not purely motor, but sensory–motor in nature. The effect of hypothalamic output on the mechanisms is to increase the capacity of specific sensory input to elicit specific motor output as, for example, would be the case if presynaptic inhibition were withdrawn from sensory endings on motor neurons.

b. Exaggerated Intensity of Responses. A prominent difference between centrally induced responses and the natural behaviors that they resemble is the exaggerated intensity of the former at medium and high levels of stimulation. When we compared centrally induced and normal mating and attack in opossums, we found that the centrally induced behavior had a more rapid onset, greater intensity, and less susceptibility to interference when the females threatened or the prey rats counterattacked. In our study of gnawing (Roberts & Carey, 1965) some animals gnawed so vigorously that they caused their gums to bleed or loosened their lower incisors. Since the stimulation in these cases was unilateral and was probably exciting only a portion of the response zone on that side, the magnified intensity of the responses suggests that the excited efferents were driven at a much higher rate than normal, and were few relatively synapses from the final motor mechanism.

2. Evidence from Combinations of Lesions and Stimulation

Hunsperger (1956) and Carli, Malliani, and Zanchetti (1963) have reported that threat behavior elicited by hypothalamic stimulation in the cat is blocked by lesions in the midbrain, which suggests that the hypothalamicofugal pathways that produce the response descend at least as far as the midbrain. MacLean, Denniston, and Dua (1963) have mapped a pathway for penile erection in the squirrel monkey that descends through the ventral midbrain to the pons, and has very short latencies and a low frequency response, suggesting that it is relatively close to the final motor mechanism. On the other hand, Grossman (1967, pp. 607–614; 1968) has emphasized the relations of the hypothalamus with higher limbic and neocortical structures and has suggested that the motivational functions of the hypothalamus may be mediated via its ascending connections with these higher structures.

Dr. Ernest H. Bergquist has recently completed a dissertation in my laboratory designed to determine the direction and location of the critical output paths for hypothalamic motivational mechanisms in the opossum (Bergquist, 1970). In 32 opossums, he implanted chronic stimulation electrodes in the preoptic and anterior hypothalamic zones for male mating behavior, attack, threat, eating, grooming, and investigation and lesion electrodes posterior, anterior, or lateral to them. After a week of convalescence, current thresholds were obtained for the responses, a radio frequency lesion was made around the lesion electrode, and the thresholds were remeasured.

The only lesions that raised response thresholds were posterior hypothalamic lesions that interrupted connections between the hypothalamus and midbrain. The thresholds were unaffected by larger lesions in the anterior medial forebrain bundle rostral to the stimulating electrodes or by larger lesions lateral to the lateral hypothalamus that interrupted hypothalamic connections with the amygdala and basal ganglia. This indicates that the connections of the hypothalamus and preoptic area with the midbrain are necessary for the elicitation of hypothalamic–preoptic responses, and sufficient in the absence of anterior and lateral connections. It strongly suggests that hypothalamic efferents produce motivational behavior in the opossum via descending projections to structures in the midbrain or lower brainstem.

The posterior lesions raised thresholds only for responses elicited by ipsilateral electrodes, and had no effect on responses evoked by contralateral electrodes. For example, attack and eating elicited in Opossum 244 by electrodes in the right hypothalamus were abolished by a right ventrolateral posterior lesion, even for currents up to 7 × and 34 × the prelesion thresholds, while thresholds for the same responses elicited from the left hypothalamus actually decreased slightly, but not significantly. Following a left ventrolateral posterior lesion, the responses elicited by the left electrode were abolished, even for currents up to 5 × and 18 × the prelesion levels. This evidence indicates that the efferent path is unilateral as far as the mammillary bodies, and rules out the possibility that the threshold elevations may have been due to nonspecific impairment caused by lethargy or interfering responses, such as circling.

Detailed planimetric and statistical analyses of the posterior lesions, which differed in location and size of effect on thresholds, disclosed that increases in the thresholds for grooming, attack, mating, eating, and investigatory behavior were maximally correlated with the amount of destruction in the ventrolateral quadrant of the posterior hypothalamus, which contains the medial forebrain bundle (Fig. 9, top row). However, threshold increases for threat were unrelated to ventrolateral damage, but were maximally correlated with destruction in the dorsomedial quadrant containing part of the periventricular system. These findings were confirmed in the graphical analysis shown in Fig. 9, where it is seen that the densest overlap of lesions that raised thresholds for grooming, attack, mating, eating, and investigation was in the vicinity of the medial forebrain bundle, while lesions that did not affect these responses were located medially, and left most of the ventrolateral region intact. The lesions that raised thresholds for threat were located medially and differed from the ineffective lesions chiefly in greater dorsomedial extension. This indicates that the medial forebrain bundle is the critical hypothalamicofugal path for most motivational responses, but that a more medial pathway, perhaps the posterior periventricular system, is critical for the threat response.

V. Summary and Conclusions

Recent studies using localized brain stimulation in conscious animals have demonstrated that specific localized brain mechanisms exist for a wide variety of motivational and species-typical behaviors, including attack, threat, mating, maternal behavior, flight, crouching, investigatory behavior, grooming, gnawing, nest building, hoarding, eating, and drinking.

Most of these centrally induced behaviors consist of a number of separate elements that together form ecologically adaptive response patterns that closely resemble natural responses of the species. Although some responses are performed relatively automatically whenever the stimulation is administered, most responses that are directed toward particular objects or aspects of the environment are not performed unless sensory input from the critical object or environmental stimulus is also present. In some cases, different elements of a pattern require different kinds of sensory input.

In addition to facilitating specific sensory–motor mechanisms, the brain stimulation also causes the performance (or accompanying sensory feed-back) of a variety of object-directed responses to be positively reinforcing, since animals that show no spontaneous tendency to perform the responses without stimulation will learn a maze during stimulation to obtain the goal objects

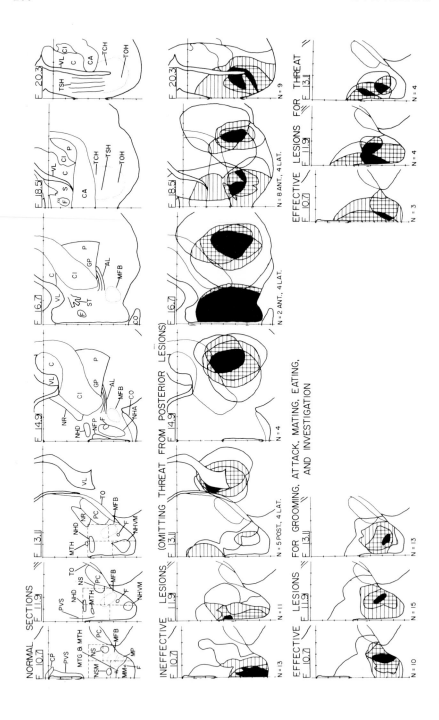

Fig. 9. *Posterior lesions that were effective in raising thresholds for hypothalamic–preoptic responses in opossums are compared with ineffective posterior, lateral and anterior lesions in composite drawings on representative frontal diagrams located 10.7–20.3 mm anterior to the interaural axis.* Anatomical structures are identified in the top row. The effective posterior lesions for grooming, attack, mating, eating, and investigation are located in the left half of the third row, and the ineffective posterior lesions for these responses are shown in planes 10.7–13.1 of the second row. The effective posterior lesions for threat are indicated in the right half of the third row, and the ineffective posterior lesions below in the fourth row. The ineffective lateral lesions are shown in planes 13.1–18.5 of the second row, and the ineffective anterior lesions in planes 16.7–20.3. Terminology based on Bodian (1939, 1940) and Loo (1931). Frontal plane 10.7 corresponds approximately to Bodian's (1939) Fig. 10, plane 11.9 to Fig. 9, plane 13.1 to Fig. 7, plane 14.9 to Fig. 4, and plane 16.7 to Fig. 2. AL: ansa lenticularis; C: nucleus caudatus; CA: commissura anterior; CI: capsula interna; CP: commissura posterior; CO: chiasma opticum; F: fornix; GP: globus pallidus; MFB: medial forebrain bundle; MM: mammillary body; MP: pedunculus corporis mammillaris; MTG: tractus mammillotegmentalis; MTH: tractus mammillothalamus; NFP: nucleus filiformis pars paraventricularis; NHA: nucleus hypothalamicus anterior; NHD: nucleus hypothalamicus dorsalis; NHVM: nucleus hypothalamicus ventromedialis; NR: nucleus reticularis; NS: nucleus subthalamicus; NSM: nucleus supramammillaris; P: putamen; PC: pedunculus cerebri; PVS: periventricular system; S: septal area; ST: stria terminalis; TCH: tractus caudohypothalamicus; TO: tractus opticus; TOH: tractus olfactohypothalamicus; TSH: tractus septo-hypothalamicus; VL: ventriculus lateralis. From Bergquist, 1968.

necessary for their performance. Some centrally induced motivational states are similar enough to natural motivational states that habits learned under one condition transfer effectively to the other. Centrally induced responses are typically integrated with normal response tendencies on the basis of comparative strength. Thus, centrally induced motivational and species-typical responses resemble their natural counterparts in many respects, and their central mechanisms can account for many of the behavioral properties of normal motivational and species-typical behavior.

The question of the innateness of the organization of central behavior mechanisms has been investigated for one response, biting attack in cats. Hypothalamic stimulation of adults raised from infancy without experience with prey animals or conspecifics produced all of the components elicited in normal cats, indicating that the mechanisms are probably largely innately organized.

In the cat and the opossum, the only two species in which an appreciable number of responses have been thoroughly mapped, most responses are elicited from relatively specific and differentiated zones that partially overlap in some areas, but differ significantly in their overall distribution. Male sexual behavior and female maternal behavior can be elicited from the hypothalamus of both sexes, indicating that brain mechanisms for sex-specific behaviors develop in both sexes, but are differentially utilized in adulthood.

Relatively little is known about the sources of input to hypothalamic–preoptic behavior mechanisms. Evidence has been offered for neural input from the amygdala to the attack and threat mechanisms in the cat, and local humoral input to the mating, eating, and drinking mechanisms in cats, rats, and goats. Very recently, it has been found that local thermoreceptors are probably one source of normal input to the preoptic zones where electrical stimulation induces grooming in opossums and sleep in cats.

The variability in the completeness of response patterns elicited by different electrodes and in the particular elements present strongly suggests that hypothalamic efferents follow divergent and independent paths to separate mechanisms for the different elements of a response pattern. The exaggerated intensity of centrally induced responses indicates that the stimulation is able to drive the response mechanisms more strongly than normal, and is probably not very many synapses from the final motor mechanism. In the opossum, it has been shown that the hypothalamic efferents that produce a variety of motivational and species-typical behaviors follow a descending path to the midbrain. Those for male mating behavior, attack, grooming, eating, and investigation descend in the medial forebrain bundle, while those for threat follow a more dorsomedial path, possibly the descending component of the periventricular system.

ACKNOWLEDGMENTS

Grateful acknowledgment is made to Eunice Roberts for assistance with the histology and many other aspects of the research.

REFERENCES

Adams, D., & Flynn, J. P. Transfer of an escape response from tail shock to brain stimulated attack behavior. *Journal of the Experimental Analysis of Behavior*, 1966, **9**, 401–408.

Akerman, B. Behavioural effects of electrical stimulation in the forebrain of the pigeon. I. Reproductive behaviour. *Behaviour*, 1965, **26**, 323–338. (a)

Akerman, B. Behavioural effects of electrical stimulation in the forebrain of the pigeon. II. Protective behaviour. *Behaviour*, 1965, **26**, 339–350. (b)

Andersson, B. The effect of injections of hypertonic NaCl solutions into different parts of the hypothalamus of goats. *Acta Physiologica Scandinavica*, 1953, **28**, 188–201.

Andersson, B., & Larsson, B. Influence of local temperature changes in the preoptic area and rostral hypothalamus on the regulation of food and water intake. *Acta Physiologica Scandinavica*, 1961, **52**, 75–89.

Andersson, B., Larsson, S., & Persson, N. Some characteristics of the hypothalamic "drinking centre" in the goat as shown by the use of permanent electrodes. *Acta Physiologica Scandinavica*, 1960, **50**, 140–152.

Andersson, B., & McCann, S. M. Drinking antidiuresis, and milk ejection from electrical stimulation within the hypothalamus of the goat. *Acta Physiologica Scandinavica*, 1955, **35**, 191–201.

Andersson, B., & Wyrwicka, W. The elicitation of a drinking motor conditioned reaction by electrical stimulation of the hypothalamic drinking area in the goat. *Acta Physiologica Scandinavica*, 1957, **41**, 194–198.

Bard, P. Central nervous mechanisms for the expression of anger in animals. In M. L. Reymert (Ed.), *Feelings and emotions*. New York: McGraw-Hill, 1950. Pp. 211–237.

Bergquist, E. H. Output pathways of hypothalamic mechanisms for sexual, aggressive, and other motivational behaviors in opossums. Unpublished doctoral dissertation, University of Minnesota, 1968.

Bergquist, E. H. Output pathways of hypothalamic mechanisms for sexual, aggressive, and other motivational behaviors in opossum. *Journal of Comparative and Physiological Psychology*, 1970, **70**, 389–398.

Bodian, D. Studies on the diencephalon of the Virginia opossum. I. The nuclear pattern in the adult. *Journal of Comparative Neurology*, 1939, **71**, 259–323.

Bodian, D. Studies on the diencephalon of the Virginia opossum. II. The fiber connections in normal and experimental material. *Journal of Comparative Neurology*, 1940, **72**, 207–297.

Brugger, M. Fresstrieb als hypothalamisches Symptom. *Helvetica Physiologica et Pharmacologica Acta*, 1943, **1**, 183–198.

Carli, G., Malliani, A., & Zanchetti, A. Midbrain course of descending pathways mediating sham rage behavior. *Experimental Neurology*, 1963, **7**, 210–223.

Coons, E. E., Levak, M., & Miller, N. E. Lateral hypothalamus: learning of food-seeking response motivated by electrical stimulation. *Science*, 1965, **150**, 1320–1321.

Delgado, J. M. R., Roberts, W. W., & Miller, N. E. Learning motivated by electrical stimulation of the brain. *American Journal of Physiology*, 1954, **179**, 587–593.

de Molina, A. F., & Hunsperger, R. W. Organization of the subcortical system governing defence and flight reactions in the cat. *Journal of Physiology*, 1962, **160**, 200–213.

Deutsch, J. A., & Deutsch, D. *Physiological psychology*. Homewood, Ill.: Dorsey Press, 1966.

Eisenman, J. S., & Jackson, D. C. Thermal response patterns of septal and preoptic neurons in cats. *Experimental Neurology*, 1967, **19**, 33–45.

Fisher, A. E. Maternal and sexual behavior induced by intracranial chemical stimulation. *Science*, 1956, **124**, 228–229.

Flynn, J. P. The neural basis of aggression in cats. In D. C. Glass (Ed.), *Neurophysiology and emotion*. New York: Rockefeller University Press, 1967. Pp. 40–60.

Grossman, S. P. Eating or drinking elicited by direct adrenergic or cholinergic stimulation of hypothalamus. *Science*, 1960, **132**, 301–302.

Grossman, S. P. *A textbook of physiological psychology*. New York: Wiley, 1967.

Grossman, S. P. Drive centers and a drive state. *Neuroscience Research Progress Bulletin*, 1968, **6**(1), 50–57.

Harris, G. W., Michael, R. P., & Scott, P. P. Neurological site of action of stilboestrol in eliciting sexual behavior. In G. E. Wolstenholme & C. M. O'Connor (Eds.), *Neurological basis of behavior*. London: Churchill, 1958. Pp. 236–254.

Herberg, L. J., & Blundell, J. E. Lateral hypothalamus: Hoarding behavior elicited by electrical stimulation. *Science*, 1967, **155**, 349–350.

Hess, R., Koella, W. P., & Akert, K. Cortical and subcortical recordings in natural and artificially induced sleep in cats. *Electroencephalography and Clinical Neurophysiology*, 1953, **5**, 75–90.

Hess, W. R. Das Schlafsyndrom als Folge diencephaler Reizung. *Helvetica Physiologica et Pharmacologica Acta*, 1944, **2**, 305–344.

Hess, W. R. *The functional organization of the diencephalon*. New York: Grune & Stratton, 1957.

Hess, W. R., & Brugger, M. Das subkortikale Zentrum der affektiven Abwehrreaktion. *Helvetica Physiologica et Pharmacologica Acta*, 1943, **1**, 33–52.

Hess, W. R., & Meyer, A. E. Triebhafte Fellreinigung der Katze als Symptom diencephaler Reizung. *Helvetica Physiologica et Pharmacologica Acta*, 1956, **14**, 397–410.

Higginbotham, A. C., & Koon, W. E. Temperature regulation in the Virginia opossum. *American Journal of Physiology*, 1955, **181**, 69–71.

Hilton, S. M., & Zbrozyna, A. W. Amygdaloid region for defence reactions and its efferent pathway to the brain stem. *Journal of Physiology*, 1963, **165**, 160–173.

Hinde, R. A. Unitary drives. *Animal Behaviour*, 1959, **7**, 130–141.

Hunsperger, R. W. Affektreaktionen auf elektrische Reizung im Hirnstamm der Katze. *Helvetica Physiologica et Pharmacologica Acta*, 1956, **14**, 70–92.

Larsson, S. On the hypothalamic organization of the nervous mechanism regulating food intake. *Acta Physiologica Scandinavica, Supplementum*, 1954, **115**, 8–63.

Levison, P. K., & Flynn, J. P. The objects attacked by cats during stimulation of the hypothalamus. *Animal Behaviour*, 1965, **13**, 217–220.

Leyhausen, P. *Verhaltenstudien an Katzen*. (2nd ed.) Berlin: Parey, 1960.

Logan, F. A., & Wagner, A. R. *Reward and punishment*. Boston: Allyn & Bacon, 1965.

Loo, Y. T. The forebrain of the opossum, *Didelphis virginiana*. II. Histology. *Journal of Comparative Neurology*, 1931, **52**, 1–148.

Lorenz, K. *Evolution and modification of behavior*. Chicago: University of Chicago Press, 1965.

MacDonnell, M. F., & Flynn, J. P. Control of sensory fields by stimulation of hypothalamus. *Science*, 1966, **152**, 1406–1408.

MacLean, P. D., Denniston, R. H., & Dua, S. Further studies on cerebral representation of penile erection: caudal thalamus, midbrain, and pons. *Journal of Neurophysiology*, 1963, **26**, 273–293.

Magoun, H. W., Harrison, F., Brobeck, J. R., & Ranson, S. W. Activation of heat loss mechanisms by local heating of the brain. *Journal of Neurophysiology*, 1938, **1**, 101–114.

Mendelson, J. Role of hunger in T-maze learning for food by rats. *Journal of Comparative and Physiological Psychology*, 1966, **62**, 341–349.

Michael, R. P. Action of hormones on the cat brain. In R. A. Gorski & R. E. Whalen (Eds.), *Brain and behavior*. Vol. III. *The brain and gonadal function*. Berkeley: University of California Press, 1966. Pp. 82–98.

Miller, N. E. Experiments on motivation. *Science*, 1957, **126**, 1271–1278.

Miller, N. E. Motivational effects of brain stimulation and drugs. *Federation Proceedings*, 1960, **19**, 846–854.

Nakayama, T., Hammel, H. T., Hardy, J. D., & Eisenman, J. S. Thermal stimulation of electrical activity of single units of the preoptic region. *American Journal of Physiology*, 1963, **204**, 1122–1126.

Putkonen, P. T. S. Electrical stimulation of the avian brain. *Annales Academiae Scientiarum Fennicae, Series A, II*, 1967, **130**, 1–95.

Roberts, W. W. Rapid escape learning without avoidance learning motivated by hypothalamic stimulation in cats. *Journal of Comparative and Physiological Psychology*, 1958, **51**, 391–399.

Roberts, W. W. Fear-like behavior elicited from dorsomedial thalamus of cat. *Journal of Comparative and Physiological Psychology*, 1962, **55**, 191–197.

Roberts, W. W., & Bergquist, E. H. Attack elicited by hypothalamic stimulation in cats raised in social isolation. *Journal of Comparative and Physiological Psychology*, 1968, **66**, 590–595.

Roberts, W. W., Bergquist, E. H., & Robinson, T. C. Thermoregulatory grooming and sleep-like relaxation induced by local warming of preoptic area and anterior hypothalamus in opossum. *Journal of Comparative and Physiological Psychology*, 1969, **67**, 182–188.

Roberts, W. W., & Carey, R. J. Rewarding effect of performance of gnawing aroused by hypothalamus stimulation in the rat. *Journal of Comparative and Physiological Psychology*, 1965, **59**, 317–324.

Roberts, W. W., & Kiess, H. O., Motivational properties of hypothalamic aggression in cats. *Journal of Comparative and Physiological Psychology*, 1964, **58**, 187–193.

Roberts, W. W., & Robinson, T. C. Sleep-like relaxation induced by warming of hypothalamic and preoptic thermoreceptors in cats. *Experimental Neurology*, 1969, **25**, 282–294.

Roberts, W. W., Steinberg, M. L., & Means, L. W. Hypothalamic mechanisms for sexual, aggressive, and other motivational behaviors in the opossum, *Didelphis virginiana*. *Journal of Comparative and Physiological Psychology*, 1967, **64**, 1–15.

Roberts, W. W., & Woodworth, C. H. Gnawing behavior aroused by hypothalamic stimulation in rats. 1965. Motion picture film available from University of Minnesota Audio-Visual Extension Service, 2037 University Ave. S.E., Minneapolis, Minnesota.

Robinson, K., & Lee, D. H. K. Reactions of the cat to hot atmospheres. *Proceedings of the Royal Society of Queensland*, 1941, **53**, 159–170.

Sterman, M. B., & Clemente, C. D. Forebrain inhibitory mechanisms: sleep patterns induced by basal forebrain stimulation in the behaving cat. *Experimental Neurology*, 1962, **6**, 103–117.

Teitelbaum, P. The biology of drive. In G. C. Quarton, T. Melnechuk, & F. O. Schmitt (Eds.), *The neurosciences: A study program*. New York: Rockefeller University Press, 1967. Pp. 557–567.

Tenen, S. S., & Miller, N. E. Strength of electrical stimulation of lateral hypothalamus, food deprivation, and tolerance for quinine in food. *Journal of Comparative Physiological Psychology*, 1964, **58**, 55–62.

Terzuolo, C. A., & Bullock, T. H. Measurement of imposed voltage gradient adequate to modulate neuronal firing. *Proceedings of the National Academy of Sciences, U. S.*, 1956, **42**, 687–694.

Valenstein, E. S., Cox, V. C., & Kakolewski, J. W. Modification of motivated behavior elicited by electrical stimulation of the hypothalamus. *Science*, 1968, **159**, 1119–1121.

Valenstein. E. S., Cox, V. C., & Kakolewski, J. W. The hypothalamus and motivated behavior. In J. Tapp (Ed.), *Reinforcement and Behavior*. New York: Academic Press, 1969.

Vaughan, E., & Fisher, A. E. Male sexual behavior induced by intracranial electrical stimulation. *Science*, 1962, **137**, 758–760.

von Holst, E., & von Saint Paul, U. On the functional organisation of drives. *Animal Behaviour*, 1963, **11**, 1–20. (Translated from *Naturwissenschaften*, 1960, **47**, 409–422.

Wasman, M., & Flynn, J. P. Directed attack elicited from hypothalamus. *Archives of Neurology*, 1962, **6**, 220–227.

Wyrwicka, W., Dobrzecka, C., & Tarnecki, R. The effect of electrical stimulation of the hypothalamic feeding centre in satiated goats on alimentary conditioned reflexes, Type II. *Acta Biologiae Experimentalis, Polish Academy of Sciences*, 1960, **20**, 121–136.

Questions for Dr. Flynn and Dr. Roberts

Question: Does stimulation-induced attack lead to the onset of spontaneous attack?

Answer: (FLYNN) There is certainly a possibility of a great deal of conditioning to occur in the situation in which we examine these animals. Occasionally, we find that after a large number of trials the cat will attack the rat more or less spontaneously, but this is a rarity.

Question: Would you speculate why so very few cats will attack spontaneously?

Answer: (FLYNN) I think we can activate this system in other ways (other than by electrical stimulation), but I'm unsure just exactly what the stimuli are, I don't think any are specified at the present time.

Question: Does the ease of elicitation of attack vary with food deprivation state?

Answer: (FLYNN) Normally our cats are not hungry, but we have tried depriving the cats for as long as 72 hr. If after 72-hr deprivation, you put the cat in the cage with food and with a rat the cat starts eating. If you then stimulate, the cat leaves the food and goes over and attacks the rat.

Question: Do you have any difficulty in finding " positive " points?

Answer: (ROBERTS) No. For example, we get gnawing with the best coordinates at least one out of two times.

Question: To what degree are your thermal probes actually warming the tissues?

Answer: (ROBERTS) Less than is required to cook it because the effects of thermal stimulation are highly repeatable week to week. This is a difficult problem because the area is so small that it is difficult to place a thermistor to measure local temperature.

Question: Most of the people who do electrical stimulation work like your own use monopolar stimulation. Why is this used in preference to bipolar stimulation?

Answer: (ROBERTS) The main reason is that the field around a semi-hemispherical monopolar tip is easier to understand. You can assign a given point in space to the region of maximal current density.

LEARNING AND MEMORY

The neural basis of learning, the elusive "engram," is one of the most classical and fundamentally important aspects of the neural control of behavior. We are extremely fortunate to have leading authorities here representing different strategies and approaches to the problem. Dr. Bureš utilizes the methods of spreading depression and the split brain, Dr. Weiskrantz employs the lesion-behavior approach, Dr. Olds explores single neuron correlates, and Dr. John examines evoked potential correlates of learning. We do not yet know the nature of the engram; however, the work reported here provides a highly significant advance in our knowledge of the neuronal mechanisms of learning.

—Richard F. Thompson

THE REUNIFIED SPLIT BRAIN

J. BUREŠ AND O. BUREŠOVÁ

INSTITUTE OF PHYSIOLOGY, CZECHOSLOVAK ACADEMY OF SCIENCES, PRAGUE

I. Introduction

While most attempts to localize specific engrams were not successful, the ablation technique yielded some useful results, indicating which parts of the central nervous system are necessary and sufficient for the storage and retrieval of a particular type of information (Lashley, 1950; Sperry, 1959). On the other hand, permanent mutilation of the nervous system caused by surgical intervention prevents engrams from forming or maintaining normal connections with other brain areas. Perhaps this is why so little is known about engram development.

Is the information stored in the form of single or multiple traces? Is the engram formed during the actual learning stationary or does it grow or shrink after the termination of training (e.g., during consolidation or forgetting)? Can the initially localized engram spread to other brain structures?

These questions, essential for an understanding of the intimate mechanisms of memory, cannot be fully answered by classical ablation methods. Their solution is possible only when the experimental procedure employed for localizing the engram formation during learning does not interfere with later growth or multiplication of the memory trace. Functional ablation techniques, particularly the functional decortication by repeated waves of cortical spreading depression (CSD), recently became a powerful experimental tool well suited for analyzing some of the above problems (Bureš, 1959; Bureš & Burešová, 1956, 1960a, 1960b; Bureš, Burešová, & Záhorová, 1958; Burešová, 1956).

Convincing evidence for the duplicate storage of information was obtained from the split brain experiments perfected by Sperry (1961, 1964) and other investigators. Results of these experiments can be summarized in the following points:

(1)   When, during learning, relevant information is channeled through lateralized inputs to one hemisphere, engrams are formed not only there, but also in the contralateral hemisphere.

(2)   Formation of the duplicate trace is prevented when corpus callosum and other commissural pathways are interrupted prior to learning.

(3)   In the split brain preparation, lateralized inputs generate lateralized independent engrams; the two hemispheres behave as two separate minds competing for control of the undivided portion of the brain.

It is obvious that the problem of engram growth could be easily studied in a preparation in which the lateralized memory trace can interact with the other hemisphere through intact commissural pathways. This is possible with the functional ablation technique which achieves lateralization of memory traces by eliminating one hemicortex from learning while leaving the brain functioning normally for later use. While lateralized input and sections of commissures are necessary for producing lateralized engrams in the surgical split brain, in the so called "reversible split brain," memory traces are formed only in the normally functioning hemisphere, the other hemicortex being impaired by CSD (Fig. 1). Thus, although the two methods for trapping the

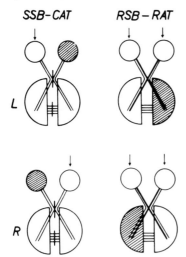

Fig. 1. The surgical split brain (SSB) and reversible split brain (RSB). L is learning; R is retention testing. For details see text.

engram and confining it to one hemisphere are different, they should give the same results within certain limits. However, because different species (predominantly cats or monkeys for the surgical split brain; almost exclusively rats for the functional decortication) and different time scales (commissurotomy requires a long recovery; CSD acts immediately) are used, the results obtained by the two techniques are not necessarily identical. Careful checking of the degree of engram lateralization is the necessary prerequisite for the application of the functional ablation technique in the re-unified split brain studies.

II. Lateralization of Engrams Acquired during Unilateral CSD

Engram lateralization in both surgical and reversible split brain animals is estimated by retention testing with the hemisphere which did not participate in the original learning. This is achieved by using the input connected to the untrained hemisphere in the first case or by eliciting CSD in the trained hemisphere in the second case (Fig. 1).

Both methods revealed complete lateralization of engrams, the acquisition of which required the processing of complex sensory information and the mastery of difficult motor reactions. Learning and relearning curves for the two hemispheres were usually found to be strikingly similar, as was the number of to-criterion trials. Figure 2 summarizes data on comparable avoidance learning obtained in seven different laboratories using the functional decortication technique.

On the other hand, memory storage of simple tasks cannot be completely lateralized by section of the neocortical commissures or by unilateral CSD. Thus, obvious brightness discrimination can be interocularly transferred (Meikle & Sechzer, 1960), whereas the more difficult threshold discrimination fails to transfer in chiasma and callosum sectioned cats. Similarly, relearning of the emotional and vegetative components of a conditioned reaction proceeds in the untrained hemisphere faster than the original unilateral acquisition (Meikle, Sechzer, & Stellar, 1962). Learning under unilateral CSD does not result in complete lateralization of passive avoidance (Bureš, Burešová, Fifková, 1964; Carlson, 1967; Schneider, 1967) or its extinction (Bureš & Burešová, 1966). Retention tests performed after unilateral training with the contralateral untrained hemisphere reveal retention of the classically conditioned vegetative reactions (Ross & Russell, 1967) and habituation to a new environment (Squire, 1966) (Fig. 3).

The degree of transfer may vary also according to the testing procedure used. With the relearning to-criterion technique, Albert (1966), Carlson (1966),

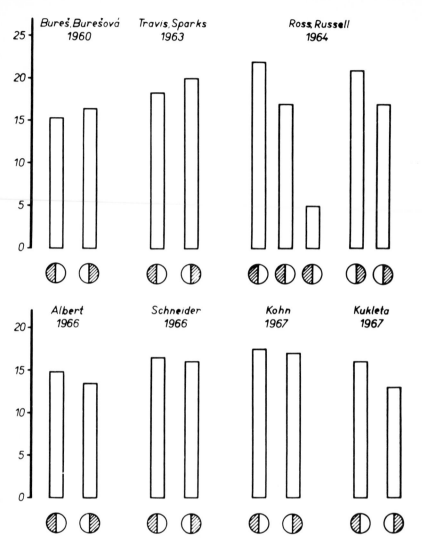

Fig. 2. Lack of interhemispheric transfer of active avoidance reactions acquired during unilateral CSD and tested during contralateral CSD. Depressed hemisphere is indicated by shading. Ordinate: number of to-criterion trials. Retention was tested after three acquisition sessions in the experiments by Ross and Russell (1964) and after a singe learning session in the other studies.

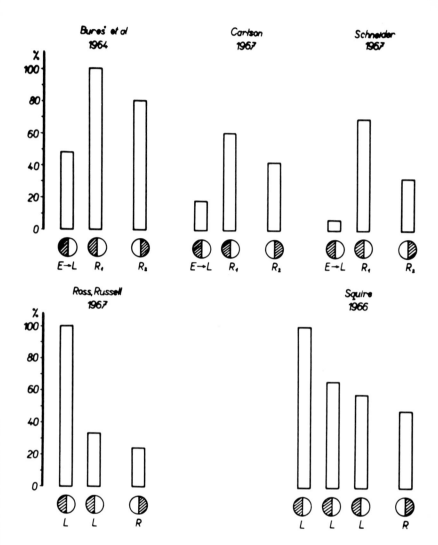

Fig. 3. *Examples of conditioned reactions which cannot be lateralized by using the split brain technique.* Above: passive avoidance tasks. Spontaneous preference for one part of the apparatus expressed as percentage of the total exploration time (E), is changed by learning (L). Retrieval of the new preference is better with the same (R_1) than with the opposite hemisphere (R_2). Different two-compartment tests were used by Bureš et al. (1964) and Carlson (1967); a step-down test by Schneider (1967). Below: to-criterion learning (L) and relearning (R) of a conditioned respiratory response (Ross & Russell, 1967). Habituation of the orienting response in a maze expressed by the number of entered alleys (Squire, 1966).

and Kohn (1967) demonstrated full lateralization of visual discrimination of two compartments, whereas Carlson (1966, 1967) found, with preference testing under similar conditions, partial retention in the untrained hemisphere. Kukleta (1967) showed that contralateral retention of unilaterally acquired runway avoidance improved with overtraining of the original habit. Only insignificant improvement was found with relearning to criterion, while marked savings were observed in escape latencies and in the preference for one of two available escape pathways. These findings indicate that tasks may differ according to the relative strength of the lateralized and nonlateralized engrams formed during acquisition and recovered during retrieval.

Some types of learning are impossible to lateralize in the anatomical split brain, evidently because the unilateral input induces formation of bilateral engrams (probably at subcortical levels) or of unilateral engrams available for contralateral readout.

In the CSD experiments an alternative possibility must be taken into account: the unilateral engram may spread to the contralateral hemisphere after the latter has recovered from the CSD impairment. This mechanism was ruled out in experiments in which the two hemispheres were never simultaneously functioning during the learning–retrieval interval (Bureš et al., 1964). Because the contralateral retention of a unilaterally acquired passive avoidance reaction was the same irrespective of whether both hemispheres were normal (allowing for transfer at the cortical level) or depressed (excluding such transfer) during the learning–retention interval, a bilateral engram was obviously formed during acquisition (Fig. 4).

The statement that engrams formed during learning do not spontaneously grow afterward is still more clearly supported by experiments with fully lateralized memory traces. Although up to two weeks of intact brain function were available for transfer of the lateralized engram to the untrained hemisphere, the latter consistently displayed no retention (Russel & Ochs, 1963).

Thus, the first conclusion derived from the reversible split brain studies is that unilateral engrams formed during learning in one hemisphere do not spontaneously spread during the learning–retrieval interval to the untrained hemisphere. This is intuitively rather unexpected as introspection makes us believe that especially highly emotional experiences are repeatedly subjected to internal rehearsal. The lack of spontaneous interhemispheric transfer of lateralized engrams in rats may, therefore, indicate either that such internal recall mechanisms are poorly developed in this species or that the internal rehearsal alone is inadequate for multiplying and expanding the original memory trace. This distinction becomes important in the light of further experiments in which the conditions of interhemispheric transfer were specified.

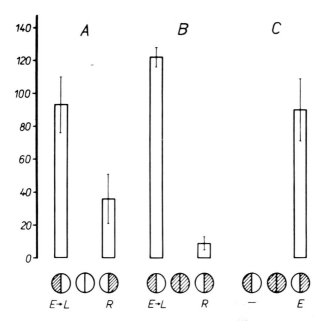

Fig. 4. *Evidence for subcortical storage of a passive avoidance task.* Out of 180-sec exploration time (E) naive rats with unilateral CSD spent 90–120 (ordinate) sec in the small dark compartment connected with a large light enclosure. After receiving electric shocks in the small compartment for 1 min (L) the animals display significant avoidance of this part of the apparatus with the contralateral hemisphere (A). The same result was obtained even when CSD was evoked in the trained hemisphere before the recovery of the naive hemisphere and maintained until the retention (R) test (B). Similar CSD treatment does not influence exploratory behavior of naive animals (C).

III. Interhemispheric Transfer of Lateralized Engrams

Lateralized memory traces may facilitate formation of the same engram in the opposite hemisphere when several transfer trials are performed with an intact brain in the period between unilateral acquisition and contralateral retrieval. Since its first demonstration (Bureš, 1959; Bureš & Burešová, 1960b) this phenomenon was repeatedly confirmed using both appetitive and aversive tasks and different testing methods (Albert, 1966; Beach, 1966; Bivens & Ray, 1965; Burešová & Bureš, 1968; Kohn, 1967; Ray & Emley, 1965; Ross & Russell, 1964; Russell & Ochs, 1961; Schneider, 1966; Travis, 1964). These studies made it possible to examine more systematically some factors involved in the interhemispheric transfer and to contribute to a better understanding of the underlying physiological mechanisms.

A typical interhemispheric transfer experiment consists of three phases
which are separated by intervals of various lengths: unilateral learning, intact
brain transfer trials, and contralateral relearning. One can assume that
during the transfer (interdepression) trials, information is passed from the
originally trained hemicortex to the untrained one. According to this assumption, the two hemispheres are termed transmitting and receiving respectively.

A. STRENGTH OF THE TRANSMITTED ENGRAM

It is obvious that with increasing amounts of interdepression training the
result of the retention test becomes independent from the original learning
and asymptotically approaches the bilateral acquisition–unilateral retention
situation. On the other hand, transfer is best expressed when elicited by a
single transfer trial (Albert, 1966; Bivens & Ray, 1965; Kohn, 1967; Ray &
Emley, 1965; Russell & Ochs, 1961) which alone does not significantly
facilitate the subsequent unilateral learning. Under these conditions, the
strength of the unilateral engram in the transmitting hemisphere is the most
important variable. Both factors were systematically examined by Travis
(1964) who used three levels of original learning (accumulation of 0, 3, 15
avoidances) and four levels of interdepression learning (accumulation of 0,
1, 5, or 10 avoidances). Relearning with the recipient hemisphere 30 min after
the interdepression training indicated that with one or five trials, transfer is
best expressed in rats who received 15 avoidances in the original learning.
With ten interdepression trials, performance of the recipient hemisphere was
no longer significantly influenced by the original learning. Data by other
authors (Bureš & Burešová, 1960b; Schneider & Hamburg, 1966) fit well into
the same picture (Fig. 5).

B. TIME FACTORS

Another important variable is the time required for the completion of
transfer. It is possible that formation of the transferred trace involves influences originating in the trained hemisphere and outlasting the actual performance of the interdepression trials. Elimination of the transmitting
hemisphere by CSD before the transmission of information to the untrained
hemisphere is completed may thus interfere with transfer. In most transfer
experiments, however, 30 or more minutes elapsed between the interdepression
trials and relearning under CSD in the trained hemisphere. This seems to
exceed many times the minimum transmitting time. Using a successive brightness discrimination, Ray and Emley (1965) evoked CSD in the transmitting
hemisphere 15 sec of 10 min after a single transfer trial and tested retention
with the recipient hemisphere 24 hr later. The transfer was absent in the

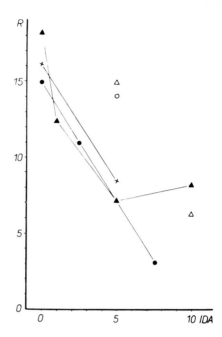

Fig. 5. *Interhemispheric transfer of active avoidance induced by interdepression training*. Ordinate: number of to-criterion trials during relearning with the recipient hemisphere (R). Abscissa: number of interdepression avoidances (IDA). Approximately equal to-criterion training of the transmitting hemisphere preceded the interdepression trials in the experimental groups (▲, ●, ×), while no such training was applied in the control groups (○, △). [○, Bureš & Burešová (1960); △, Travis (1964); ×, Schneider & Hamburg (1966)].

15-sec group and complete in the 10-min group. Albert (1966), in simple runway avoidance experiments, established complete transfer after 3 min, but only minimal signs of transfer after 30 sec. Transmitting times shorter than 5 min were also reported for a delayed spatial alternation habit by Burešová and Bureš (1968).

Time plays a still more important role in the consolidation of the transferred trace. The memory disturbing effects of bilateral CSD were described by Black, Suboski, and Freedman (1967), Bureš and Burešová (1963), Kupfermann (1966). Pearlman (1966), Pearlman and Jarvik (1961), and Schneider (1967). In the interhemispheric transfer experiments, CSD can be applied more specifically to interfere with consolidation of memory traces in the recipient hemisphere alone. Using this approach, Ray and Emley (1965) reported complete or partial disruption of the transferred trace when CSD in the untrained hemisphere was evoked 15 sec or 10 min after the transfer trial. Bivens and Ray (1965) found no transfer when CSD was elicited in the recipient hemisphere 1 hr after the interdepression trial, and Albert (1966) reported disruption of transfer when less than 2 hr was allowed for consolidation. Interhemispheric transfer of delayed spatial alternation (Burešová & Bureš, 1968) is suppressed when CSD is evoked in the recipient hemisphere 15 min or 1 hr but not 2 hr after the transfer trials (Fig. 6). Under these conditions CSD seems to evoke prolonged retrograde amnesia similar to or even exceeding that described with bilateral functional decortication. Rapid

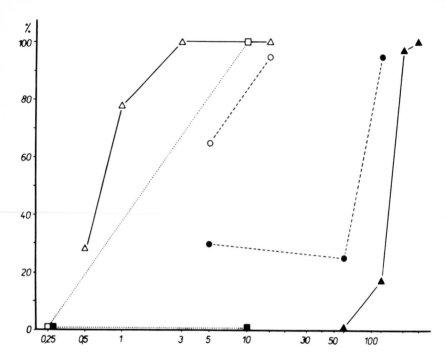

Fig. 6. *Transmitting time* (O, △, □) *and consolidation time* (●, ▲, ■) *in the interhemispheric transfer experiments.* Ordinate: percentage of performance during retention test. Performance of animals not subjected to CSD within 24 hr after the transfer trials correspond to 100%. Abscissa: time (in minutes) from the last transfer trial to KCl application onto the transmitting (O, △, □) or recipient (●, ▲, ■) hemisphere. For detail see text. [□, Ray & Emley (1965); △, Albert (1966); O, Bureš & Burešová (1968)].

formation of the transferred trace makes it possible to use this method to examine the early consolidation phase of complex tasks which cannot be otherwise trained in a few trials. More important for the general mechanisms of learning is the possibility of subdividing the total transfer time into the time component required for the recipient hemisphere to develop an independently maintained trace (transmitting time, about 1 min) and the time component required for formation of a permanent engram (consolidation time, approximately one hour).

C. STIMULI INDUCING TRANSFER

Interhemispheric transfer induced by several interdepression trials can be interpreted in different ways. Besides the straightforward transfer hypothesis which assumes transcallosal facilitation of the formation of the duplicate trace in the symmetrical region of the contralateral hemisphere, other mechanisms must also be taken into account. The trained hemisphere may simply guide the animal to the correct solution of the task and thus considerably shorten the trial and error phase of learning in the naive hemisphere. The transfer would not be mediated through commissural pathways in this case, but through an extracerebral event recorded by the sensory channels of the recipient hemisphere. Such an hypothesis implies, however, that only correct responses can induce interhemispheric transfer. Although this was originally believed to be the case (Bureš & Burešová, 1960b; Russell & Ochs, 1963), later experiments attempting to determine which components of the learning situation are relevant to the transfer proved that correct performance is not an obligatory condition of transfer.

Russell and Ochs (1963) considered reinforcement crucial for transfer. In their experiments, rats were trained to bar-press for food with one hemisphere and then tested under extinction conditions either with the trained or untrained hemisphere. A single reinforced trial performed with both hemispheres intact raised the subsequent extinction score of the recipient hemisphere high above the basal operant level. On the other hand, 10–25-nonreinforced bar-presses with intact brain did not induce any signs of transfer.

The interhemispheric transfer interpretation of these experiments was recently questioned by Schneider (Schneider, 1967; Schneider & Ebbesen, 1967) who found in a similar situation considerable increase of bar-pressing with the recipient hemisphere, not only when a unilaterally trained rat was given a bilateral transfer trial, but also when it was allowed to perform a single reinforced bar-press with the recipient hemisphere alone. The unilateral one-trial learning explanation does not apply, however, to experiments in which this possibility was checked by adequate controls or in which transfer was induced by nonreinforced trials.

Ray and Emley (1964, 1965) failed to find a difference in transfer of a successive brightness discrimination for animals rewarded or not rewarded on the interdepression trial. Still more interesting is their observation that although the recipient hemisphere never experienced the second cue, bilateral exposition to one of the two cues induced transfer of the total discrimination pair. Also, Kohn (1967) reported good transfer to appetitively motivated simultaneous brightness discrimination by a single nonreinforced trial.

The possibility of achieving transfer by application of the isolated unconditioned stimulus was examined by Schneider and Hamburg (1966). After unilateral elaboration of a runway avoidance, he applied either five avoidances or 3 min of unescapable shocks to the intact animal. As transfer was the same in both groups, it seems that activation of the emotional component of the task may induce transmission of the engram. Similar results were also obtained, however, when the unescapable shocks were applied prior to the first unilateral training. Although the latter finding is interpreted by Schneider as supporting his generalization hypothesis (see below), it may simply indicate that the nonlateralized subcortical component of the memory trace formed by unescapable shocks constitutes a bridge between the two hemispheres mediating later transmission of more specific unilaterally acquired engrams.

This conclusion is supported by Kukleta's (1967) finding that 15 escape trials given in a simple runway under bilateral CSD facilitated subsequent interhemispheric transfer of a more complex avoidance task (Fig. 7).

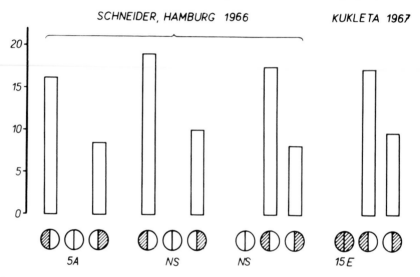

Fig. 7. *Interhemispheric transfer induced by nonspecific interdepression or predepression experience.* Ordinate: number of to-criterion trials during learning and relearning of a simple runway avoidance. Conditions of transfer: 5A: 5 avoidances; NS: unescapable electric shocks applied between or prior to the two CSD's; 15E: 15 escape trials applied under bilateral CSD prior to the first unilateral training.

The most detailed analysis of the conditions required for successful transfer was performed by Kohn (1967). This author elaborated a simultaneous brightness discrimination with one hemisphere and then exposed the intact animal to a single transfer trial. Transfer occurred not only when the animal was allowed to make a correct reinforced response, but also when it was exposed to locked positive, negative, or unpainted doors, and even when the passage through this unlocked negative door was reinforced by food. Significant transfer was also observed when the animal found no goal box (and no reinforcement) after opening the correct panel. On the other hand, transfer was not induced by an interdepression trial in which the stimulus panels were removed and the rat had free access to the reinforcement in the goal box or one in which the stimulus panels as well as the goal box were removed. In another experiment, Kohn (1967) trained unilaterally depressed rats to avoid a black compartment and go to a white compartment or vice versa. Twenty-four hours after learning to criterion with one hemisphere, the intact rat was given a single transfer trial during which the escape or avoidance either corresponded to the original learning or to its reversal. In both cases retraining of the original task with the recipient hemisphere was facilitated. On the other hand, reversal training with the recipient hemisphere was considerably impaired by a positive and unaffected by a reversed transfer trial.

The above experiments indicate that interhemispheric transfer occurs even when there is considerable difference between the conditions of the initial training and those of the transfer trials. Some minimum resemblance to the original situation appears to be necessary, however, for activation of the experience stored in the transmitting hemisphere. Further study of the selectivity of this reminder effect, which is remotely analogous to the perceptual activation of human reminiscences, may shed light on the role played in the mechanism of recall by the stimulus generalization phenomenon, i.e., by the ability of the animal trained under a definite set of stimuli to respond with the same reaction to more or less different sets of stimuli.

D. STIMULUS GENERALIZATION HYPOTHESIS

The stimulus generalization phenomenon was used in a different context by Schneider (1967) to interpret some of the reversible split brain results. In a series of papers (Schneider, 1966, 1967; Schneider & Ebbesen, 1967; Schneider & Hamburg, 1966; Schneider & Kay, 1968), Schneider advocated a point of view according to which learning under unilateral CSD leads to formation of bilateral subcortical engrams. The absence of savings in retention tests performed with the contralateral hemisphere is not due to the unavailability of the engram but to a generalization decrement, i.e., to the inability of the brain to recognize the old cues in the new context. According to this interpretation, the transfer trials helped to bridge the gap between the two unilateral CSD states by facilitating the transfer of the conditioned response from one set of stimuli to another via a stimulus generalization process. Although the generalization decrement may play a role in some CSD experiments (it may explain why after unilateral learning, retrieval with the same hemisphere may be better than bilateral retrieval—Burešová, Bureš, & Lukaszewska, 1966a; Schneider, 1966), it hardly seems possible that this phenomenon would account for a complete absence of savings. On the contrary, perfect interocular transfer (Sheridan, 1965) in rats makes the generalization decrement hypothesis extremely improbable. It may even be guessed from the easy generalization and difficult differentiation between stimuli applied to symmetrical receptors (Bykov, 1924) that unilateral CSD would resemble contralateral CSD more than bilateral decortication or intact brain. Schneider and Kay (1968) reached a similar conclusion after experiments in which they reinforced bar-pressing during unilateral CSD, but not during bilateral CSD or with intact brain.

Schneider's hypothesis does not explain why the same cues are correctly recognized by the untrained hemisphere when used as CS during unilateral training of a classically conditioned vegetative reaction (Ross & Russell, 1967), of a passive avoidance task (Carlson, 1966), or of habituation (Squire, 1966); but why they remain lateralized when associated with active avoidance or approach conditioning. Examples of transfer between intact and bilaterally decorticated brain and vice versa (Bureš & Burešová, 1967; Thompson, 1964), and between unilateral or bilateral decortication states (Carlson, 1967) are also at variance with the generalization–decrement hypothesis.

While stressing the purely behavioral side of the problem, Schneider ignores the physiological arguments against his position. The generalization–decrement hypothesis does not account for the disruption of transfer by CSD evoked shortly after the transfer trials in the transmitting, and particularly in the receiving hemisphere (see above). As the latter disruptive effect is evidently caused by CSD interference with engram consolidation in the recipient hemisphere, it is scarcely possible to maintain that the transfer is due to stimulus generalization at the subcortical level. Schneider's arguments were subjected to a critical analysis by Squire and Liss (1968).

E. Imperative and Facultative Transfer

Another interesting approach to the problems of interhemispheric transfer is offered by a combination of the unilateral CSD with lateralized sensory input. In a recent project (Nadel & Burešová, 1968, 1969), rats were trained under unilateral CSD to perform a simultaneous pattern discrimination task. On the next day, ten transfer trials were given with both hemispheres intact, but with vision restricted to one eye. As the optic nerves in rats are nearly completely crossed (Lund, 1965), the eye contralateral to the trained hemisphere has direct access to the original engram, which is available to the ipsilateral eye only indirectly through the visual cortex of the untrained hemisphere and through callosal fibers. It is obvious that the transfer trials performed with the contralateral eye do not directly involve the recipient hemisphere which is not indispensable for correct performance. Participation of the recipient hemisphere in the transfer process is, therefore, a facultative one. On the other hand, the use of the ipsilateral eye in the transfer experiments makes the participation of the recipient hemisphere an imperative condition. Retention testing with the untrained hemisphere on Day 3 revealed an excellent transfer in the imperative transfer group, but practically no savings in the facultative transfer conditions. Neither group deviated significantly from randomness during the transfer trials, but when no training was given during CSD on the first day the interdepression trials alone did not significantly influence the relearning on Day 3. Similar results were obtained with a black–white discrimination.

The striking difference between imperative and facultative transfer can be due to various mechanisms. First of all, it is possible that formation of the transferred engram requires simultaneous matching of the transcallosally mediated image with the sensory input. Only when the two sets of information agree is a memory trace recorded in the recipient hemisphere. Such a mechanism may be of general biological importance as it would enable the brain to ignore false information generated by the spontaneous neural activity (e.g., during dreaming). It is well known, however, that in animals with completely lateralized visual input, transcallosal engrams are formed during monocular learning (Myers, 1957; Myers & Sperry, 1958). Thus, the failure of transfer under the facultative transfer conditions is more probably due to the difference between the processes taking place in the transmitting visual cortex during learning and retrieval. Although the received visual information is currently communicated to the recipient hemisphere in both cases, during learning it is also accompanied by "write-in" signals which are necessary for the formation of the engram. It may be argued that this does not explain the imperative transfer which is also triggered by read-out trials. It seems, therefore, that transcallosal readout, as distinguished from direct readout, initiates an active plastic process in the transmitting hemisphere (matching of the incoming visual information with the available trace) which, in turn, starts transcallosal information flowing in the reverse direction, i.e., from the transmitting to the recipient hemisphere. The latter process takes place because direct readout of the transferred engram is evidently more efficient than the transcallosal communication, and the principle of parsimony requires the brain to employ the simplest solution available.

The conclusion that new engrams are only formed by active brain processes different from those which take place during routine performance may have broader implications for the general learning theory. This is illustrated by other experiments with monocular learning in rats (Nadel & Burešová, 1968, 1969). During monocular learning to criterion of a pattern discrimination, a primary trace in the hemisphere contralateral to the active eye and a weaker secondary trace in the ipsilateral hemisphere are formed. Retention testing under unilateral CSD reveals that the primary trace equals

in strength the engram transferred by ten interdepression trials under conditions of imperative transfer, while the secondary trace is much weaker
(Fig. 8). When the monocular habit is overtrained during five days, the

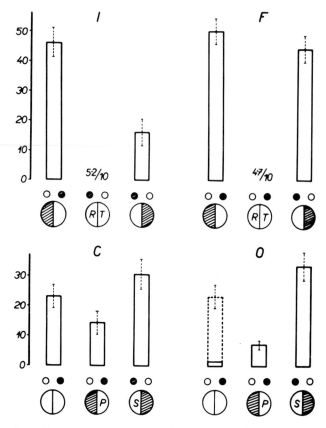

Fig. 8. *Lateralizarion of pattern discrimination acquired during monocular learning*
(C, O) *and the imperative* (I) *or facultative* (F) *conditions of interhemispheric transfer.*
Ordinate: number of to-criterion trials. Shading indicates the covered eye or depressed
hemisphere. R: recipient hemisphere; T: transmitting hemisphere; P: primary trace; S:
secondary trace. The numbers indicate the ratio of correct responses to all interdepression
trials. In group O the discrimination was overlearned by applying 25 trials on five consecutive days. The dashed and solid columns indicate the number of to-criterion trials with both
hemispheres intact on the first and last training day, respectively.

primary trace is further strengthened, but the secondary one is not improved
(Fig. 8). This is not unexpected since the overlearning trials resemble the
facultative transfer; the hemisphere ipsilateral to the trained eye is not
engaged in the performance which fosters the primary trace but which does

not stimulate and may even inhibit formation of parallel engrams, the existence of which now seems to be superfluous.

Similar processes may account for the physiological blindness of the eye which permanently yields information inconsistent with the messages received from other receptors as in cases of strabism. Also, concentration of verbal behavior in the dominant hemisphere in man may be due to the increasing use of the minor hemisphere after the influences of the right-handed world have made the storage of the verbal engrams asymmetric.

IV. Interhemispheric Synthesis of Lateralized Engrams

The analysis of lateralized engram formation under unilateral CSD and of the conditions for interhemispheric transfer of such engrams leads logically to the problem of interhemispheric synthesis. In the preceding chapters, a single experience was examined, but the split brain technique makes it possible to store two independent memory traces, one in each hemisphere. Mutual interference of the separately stored experiences is prevented by the absence of commissures in the surgical split brain (Sperry, 1964; Trevarthen, 1962) and by the lack of spontaneous interhemispheric transfer in the reversible split brain (Bureš & Burešová, 1960a, b). Either of the two engrams can be separately used later when read out through lateralized sensory inputs in the first case, or during unilateral CSD in the second case. A different situation arises, however, when the split brain animal with two independent sets of information is exposed to stimuli simultaneously activating both engrams. As pointed out by Sperry (1967), the only means remaining in the bisected brain for interhemispheric communication "are indirect and not unlike those by which one person informs another of something that he has experienced." In addition to this mechanism, the reversible split brain also has all commissural pathways available for an internal interhemispheric information flow and internal synthesis of the separated engrams into a new integrated entity. The main objective of the interhemispheric synthesis experiments is to contribute to a better understanding of the architecture of the logically constructed engram assemblies by studying the differences between intrahemispheric and interhemispheric integration.

The typical interhemispheric synthesis experiment proceeds in three stages: (1) acquisition of Experience A with the first hemisphere; (2) acquisition of Experience B with the second hemisphere; (3) synthesis of A and B with intact brain. According to the character of Tasks A and B and to the synthesis situation, the experiments may be classified as a synthesis of antagonistic and synergistic experiences.

A. Synthesis of Antagonistic Experiences

Although the possibility of using the CSD technique to store conflicting experiences in both hemispheres and to maintain their separate coexistence in the intact brain was already described in the first interhemispheric transfer experiments (Bureš, 1959; Bureš & Burešová, 1960a); the results of the collision of the two opposite tendencies were not experimentally analyzed until much later (Burešová *et al.*, 1966a; Gerbrandt, Burešová, & Bureš, 1968).

In the simplest case, rats are taught with the left hemisphere to go left and 24 hr later with the right hemisphere to go right in a T maze. On Day 3 both arms of the T maze are open and the animals are allowed to choose between them freely. When the two engrams are well balanced in strength, the left and right choices occur at random as in a naive animal. This randomness is not due, however, to mutual annihilation, but rather to mutual equilibration of the two engrams. If on Day 3 retention is tested, not by free choice but by relearning one of the tasks, considerable savings are found as compared with naive animals.

The relearning experiments clearly demonstrate the essential difference between interhemispheric synthesis and normal learning. In intact brain, learning Task B, directly opposing previously acquired Task A necessarily results in reversal, i.e., the animal learns not only to go right on Day 2, but also to inhibit the tendency to go left. Relearning of Task A on Day 3 is then a new reversal which usually requires more trials to criterion than the original learning (Fig. 9).

With lateralized learning, acquisition of Task B does not implicate inhibition of Task A, both engrams remaining equally available for the synthesis experiment. The sequence of Task A–B–A on Days 1–3 does not lead, therefore, to reversal learning on Day 3 but to relearning of Task A with considerable savings. Of the two engrams, that which corresponds better to the requirements of the synthesis test is used. However, the advantages of the separate memory storage are lost by the completion of synthesis. A new switching to Task B already requires many more trials and does not differ from reversal of the bilaterally learned Task A (Fig. 9).

The absence of reversal learning in the reversible split brain can be interpreted as due to substitution of common sequential or successive learning by parallel learning. Under normal conditions, each experience is given a definite time label. This is not only important for chronological ordering of events, but also for evaluating their significance in decision making. When there are different possible solutions of the problem, the simple hypothesis is usually adopted, namely, that the response which was correct the last time will also be correct the next time. Thus, of two conflicting experiences, the recent one will have a decisive influence on the behavior of the animal. This is not the case when learning is lateralized by CSD. It seems that the time

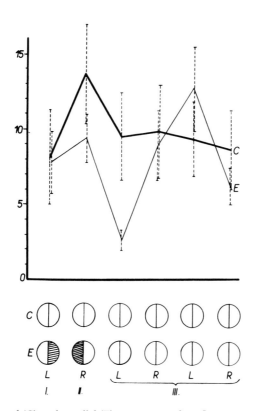

Fig. 9. *Sequential* (C) *and parallel* (E) *acquisition of conflicting experiences.* Ordinate: number of to-criterion trials in acquisition and reversal of a left–right discrimination in a simple T maze. I,II,III: days 1,2,3; R,L: right or left channel open. The schematic drawing indicates the conditions of the experiment in Groups C and E. Vertical bars denote the standard errors of the mean.

labeling of the unilaterally acquired engrams is lost or at least so weakened that, as far as the animal is concerned, they cannot be distinguished. The engrams are there, but the bonds connecting them with the whole system of memories are loose and waiting for a more definite integration.

When the conflicting tendencies are not well balanced, the behavior of the animal is determined by the more powerful experience. The interhemispheric synthesis can be used for testing the strength of memory traces acquired under different conditions of learning and with different motivational backgrounds. Figure 10 illustrates a comparison of the strength of appetitive and aversive memory traces. Rats learned with the left hemisphere to escape electric shocks through the left arm of a T maze and with the right hemisphere to get water in the right arm of the same maze. Each habit was mastered to a different extent: criterion of nine correct choices out of ten consecutive

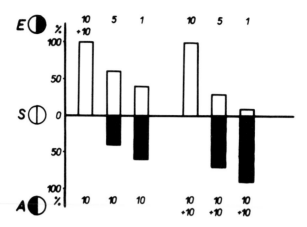

Fig. 10. *Competition between aversively and appetitively motivated conflicting experiences, stored separately in the left and right hemisphere.* Columns indicate the percentage of left (white) or right (black) choices in the T maze during the synthesis stage of the experiment (S). The numbers above and below the columns indicate the amount of escape or avoidance training to the left (E) and of appetitive training to the right (A) previously given to the left and right hemispheres, respectively. For details see text.

trials (10) in some groups followed by ten overlearning trials (10 + 10), criterion of four correct choices out of five consecutive trials (5) or one reinforced trial (1) in others. On the next day, with both hemispheres intact, the animal was placed on start of the T maze and its behavior at the choice point was recorded. The results clearly indicate that aversive learning is much more efficient than appetitive learning, one to five aversively reinforced trials being equivalent to approximately 15 appetitively reinforced trials.

In evaluating such experiments, many factors must be taken into account which may influence the final result, e.g., motivation during acquisition and motivation during retention. If the rats are given 5 ml of water immediately before the retention test, the strength of the appetitive engram is significantly decreased (Fig. 11). Also, the sequence of acquisition of the two tasks is not negligible—the more recent experience being less affected by forgetting. Tasks with partially unlateralized subcortical storage (simple escape learning) may even induce weakening of the previously formed contralateral engrams by a mechanism akin to reversal.

The interhemispheric conflict is not necessarily resolved by the prevalence of one partial task. If an intermediate solution is available, the two memory traces may be synthesized into a behavioral act which was never before performed by the animal. Burešová *et al.* (1966c) taught rats to avoid the white painted left side of a rectangular apparatus with the left hemisphere and the black painted right side with the right hemisphere (Fig. 12). When

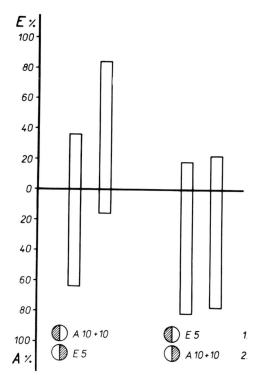

Fig. 11. *Competitive synthesis of lateralized engrams:* The role of the sequence of the partial experiences and of motivation level during retrieval. Columns indicate the percentage of left (upwards) or right (downwards) choices during the synthesis stage of the experiment. The conditions of training on Days 1 and 2 are given at the bottom (A 10 + 10: appetitive training to the right, E 5: escape training to the left). The left columns of each pair represent groups which were allowed to drink 5 ml of water before the retention testing.

allowed to explore the apparatus with both hemispheres intact, approximately 40% of the animals preferred to stay in the center. This behavior, distinctly different from that of naive animals who display a marked preference for corners, is evidently due to some kind of subtraction of the two opposing avoidance gradients. In the remaining animals, one of the engrams was clearly prevalent with a significant bias for the black side.

V. Synthesis of Synergistic Experiences

Not only antagonistic, but also synergistic engrams can be used for interhemispheric synthesis (Burešová & Bureš, 1965; Burešová, Lukaszewska, & Bureš, 1966b; Burešová, Votava, & Bureš, 1966c). To discover whether new

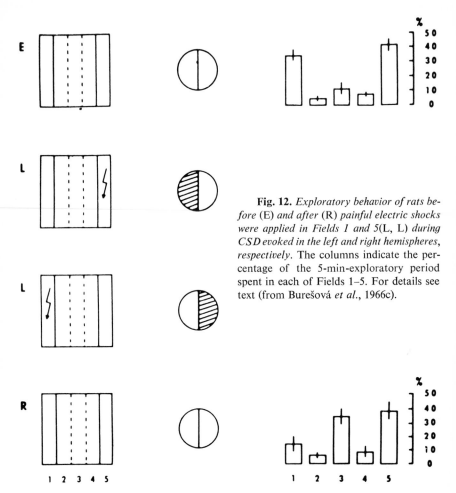

Fig. 12. *Exploratory behavior of rats before* (E) *and after* (R) *painful electric shocks were applied in Fields 1 and 5*(L, L) *during CSD evoked in the left and right hemispheres, respectively.* The columns indicate the percentage of the 5-min-exploratory period spent in each of Fields 1–5. For details see text (from Burešová *et al.*, 1966c).

complex behavior can be directly synthesized from partial information independently stored in the left and right hemisphere, an escape reaction (jumping on an elevated platform) was elaborated with the left hemisphere. On the next day a conditioned emotional response was established in the right hemisphere (an acoustic signal of 10-sec duration delivered during the last 5 sec with unescapable electric shocks). On the third day the above partial habits were used to synthesize an avoidance reaction (jumping on the elevated platform on the sound alone). Synthesis in control Group A (Fig. 13) which learned both the escape and the conditioned emotional reaction with the intact brain was slightly better expressed than in control Group B which learned both partial tasks with the same hemisphere. Essentially similar results were obtained from the interhemispheric synthesis in Group C which

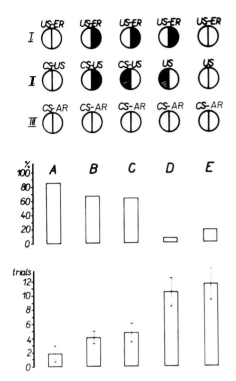

Fig. 13. *Interhemispheric synthesis of memory traces.* Top: experimental arrangement in Groups A–E. ER: escape reaction; AR: avoidance reaction, I,II,III: experimental Days 1,2,3. Middle incidence of the avoidance reactions in three nonreinforced synthesis trials. Below: number of to-criterion trials in avoidance learning (from Burešová and Bureš, 1965).

performed in the avoidance task much better than animals in which no conditioned emotional reaction was elaborated (Groups D and E).

Unfortunately, the above experiments cannot be regarded as a conclusive proof of interhemispheric synthesis, the most important prerequisite of which is complete lateralization of the partial engrams. This condition is not satisfied in the case of the conditioned emotional reactions (see above). Only strictly lateralized instrumental reactions were used, therefore, in further experiments (Burešová *et al.*, 1966b, 1966c) which lead to the rather unexpected conclusion that under certain conditions interhemispheric synthesis may be more efficient than the usual intrahemispheric synthesis. In one of these experiments (Burešová *et al.*, 1966c), rats learned with one hemisphere to avoid or escape electric shocks in a U-shaped runway (Fig. 14). On the next day the animals were trained with the contralateral hemisphere in another apparatus to escape from the grid floor compartment into the safe compartment by passing through a curtain covered door. On the third day the animals were again placed in the U-shaped runway in which the partition separating the two alleys was provided with a curtain covered opening. By passing through this opening the animals could shorten the escape pathway by about 70%. Animals having received no curtain training ignored the opening in the

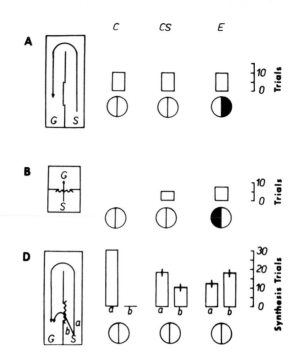

Fig. 14. *Interhemispheric synthesis of complementing experiences.* A,B,D: schematic drawings of the apparatus employed in the three phases of the experiment. C,CS: control groups; E: experimental group. The columns indicate mean to-criterion trials (top and middle) and mean numbers of trials in which the animals used either route "a" or "b" during the synthesis experiments (bottom). G: goal, S: start. (from Burešová *et al.*, 1966c).

partition completely. The interhemispheric synthesis group used the short cut 17.1 times and the control group (learning the partial tasks sequentially with both hemispheres intact) only 11.2 times out of 30 synthesis trials. It seems that under conditions of interhemispheric transfer the animal may use the independent engrams more efficiently than a normal animal can use the same but sequentially acquired experiences.

The fact that the synthesis situation highly resembles Task A probably induces in normal animals with sequentially structured memory some inhibition of B engrams and decreases the probability of their readout. Absence of such quasiantagonistic relationships between the undated and independent partial engrams and their loose fitting into the memory system of the individuum thus creates, at least in some behavioral situations, better conditions for a "creative," unusual combination of previous experiences than does the common sequential learning. True interhemispheric synthesis is restricted, however, to the first few trials performed with both hemispheres intact. After transferred secondary engrams are formed in the contralateral hemisphere, the synthesis may adopt intrahemispheric rather than inter-hemispheric character. The first interhemispheric synthesis trials are therefore the most important ones since their result may considerably influence the further course of the experiment.

VI. Conclusion

Although the functional ablation by CSD has been used in different behavioral applications (transfer of information from decorticate to normal state, interference with consolidation, transient elimination of subcortical centers, etc.), the reversible split brain studies were most successful in opening new avenues of research. The relevant information obtained by the CSD technique in this area can be summarized in the following points:

(1) Memory traces are only formed during learning and do not spon-taneously spread to other areas afterwards.

(2) Interhemispheric transfer of a lateralized engram can be induced by one or several transfer trials performed with both hemispheres intact before the retention testing with the contralateral hemisphere.

(3) Interhemispheric transfer can be induced by interdepression trials in which the animal is exposed only to a part of the transferred experience.

(4) Formation of the duplicate trace in the recipient hemisphere re-quires, after the interdepression trials, a brief support from the transmitting hemisphere (transmitting time) and a longer availability of the recipient hemisphere (consolidation time).

(5) Combination of unilateral input with unilateral CSD makes it possible to differentiate between the role of learning (imperative transfer) and performance (facultative transfer) in the formation and preservation of engrams.

(6) Replacing the usual sequential learning by independent lateralized acquisition of different experiences weakens the dating of engrams and loosens the internal relationships within the system of memories.

(7) Interhemispheric synthesis of lateralized engrams may, under definite experimental conditions, prove to be more efficient than the usual intra-hemispheric synthesis.

Most of the above points are statements of possible lines of research rather than complete answers. Schneider's (1967) generalization decrement hypothesis shows that even the basic results of the interhemispheric transfer experiments can be interpreted from an entirely different theoretical position. The possibilities offered by the reversibility of CSD are not yet fully exploited by the investigators who are not prepared to deal with phenomena un-precedented in the normal brain functions. Further improvement of the CSD technique and application of other functional ablation procedures is another prerequisite for progress in this area of research.

REFERENCES

Albert, D. J. The effect of spreading depression on the consolidation of learning. *Neuro-psychologia*, 1966, **4**, 49–64.

Beach, F. A. Spreading depression and interhemispheric transfer of an avoidance response. *Psychonomic Science*, 1966, **5**, 9–10.

Bivens, L. W., & Ray, O. S. Memory trace disruption by cortical spreading depression. *Psychological Reports*, 1965, **17**, 175–178.

Black, H., Suboski, M. D., & Freedman, N. L. Effect of cortical spreading depression and ether following one-trial discriminated avoidance learning. *Psychonomic Science*, 1967, **9**, 597–598.

Bureš, J. Reversible decortication and behavior. In M. A. B. Brazier (Ed.), *The central nervous system and behavior*. Transactions of the Second Conference. New York: Josiah Macy, Jr. Found., 1959. Pp. 207–248.

Bureš, J., & Burešová, O. A study on the metabolic nature and physiological manifestations of the spreading EEG depression of Leao. *Physiologia Bohemoslovenica*, 1956, **5**(Suppl.), 4–6.

Bureš, J., & Burešová, O. The use of Leao's spreading depression in the study of inter-hemispheric transfer of memory traces. *Journal of Comparative and Physiological Psychology*, **53**, 1960, 558–563. (a)

Bureš, J., & Burešová, O. The use of Leao's spreading cortical depression in research on conditioned reflexes. *Electroencephalography and Clinical Neurophysiology*, 1960, Suppl. 13, 359–376. (b)

Bureš, J., & Burešová, O. Cortical spreading depression as a memory disturbing factor. *Journal of Comparative and Phsyiological Psychology*, 1963, **56**, 268–272.

Bureš, J., & Burešová, O. Interhemispheric transfer of extinction of the passive avoidance reaction in rats. *Journal of Comparative and Physiological Psychology*, 1966, **62**, 459–461.

Bureš, J., & Burešová, O. Spreading depression and cortico-subcortical interrelations in the mechanism of conditioned reflexes. *Progress in Brain Research*, 1967, **22**, 378–387.

Bureš, J., Burešová, O., & Fifková, E. Interhemispheric transfer of a passive avoidance reaction. *Journal of Comparative and Physiological Psychology*, 1964, **57**, 326–330.

Bureš, J., Burešová, O., & Záhorová, A. Conditioned reflexes and Leao's spreading cortical depression. *Journal of Comparative and Psychological Physiology*, 1958, **51**, 263–268.

Burešová, O. Influence of spreading EEG depression on unconditioned and natural conditioned alimentary reflexes. (In Russian.) *Physiologia Bohemoslovenica*, 1956, **5**, 350–358.

Burešová, O., & Bureš, J. Interhemispheric synthesis of memory traces. *Journal of Comparative and Physiological Psychology*, 1965, **59**, 211–214.

Burešová, O., & Bureš, J. The role of the transmitting and receiving hemispheres in the interhemispheric transfer of T-maze alternation acquired during unilateral cortical spreading depression in rats. *Communications in Behavioral Biology, Part A*, 1968, **1**, 115–119.

Burešová, O., Bureš, J., & Lukaszewska, I. Strain differences in retrieval of unilateral and bilateral engrams. *Physiology and Behavior*, 1966, **1**, 331–333. (a)

Burešová, O., Lukaszewska, I., & Bureš, J. Interhemispheric synthesis of goal alternation and jumping escape reactions. *Journal of Comparative and Physiological Psychology*, 1966, **62**, 90–94. (b)

Burešová, O., Votava, J., & Bureš, J. Interhemispheric synthesis of competing and complementing experiences. *Physiology and Behavior*, 1966, **1**, 59–63. (c)

Bykov, K. M. Experiments on paired functions of cerebral hemispheres. (In Russian.) *Russkiĭ Fiziologicheskiĭ Zhurnal*, 1924, **7**, 294–295.

Carlson, K. R. Aspects of avoidance learning stored subcortically. Paper presented at the meeting of the Eastern Psychological Association, New York, April 1966.

Carlson, K. R. Cortical spreading depression and subcortical memory storage. *Journal of Comparative and Physiological Psychology*, 1967, **64**, 422–430.

Gerbrandt, L. K., Burešová, O., & Bureš, J. Discrimination and reversal learning followed by a single electroconvulsive shock. *Physiology and Behavior*, 1968, **3**, 149–153.

Kohn, B. Spreading depression and stimulus control of interhemispheric transfer. *Neuropsychologia*, 1967, **5**, 275–286.

Kukleta, M. The use of unilateral cortical spreading depression in the study of subcortical storage of memory traces in rats. *Physiology and Behavior*, 1967, **2**, 301–304.

Kupfermann, I. Is the retrograde amnesia that follows cortical spreading depression due to subcortical spread? *Journal of Comparative and Physiological Psychology*, 1966, **61**, 466–467.

Lashley, K. S. In search of the engram. *Symposia of the Society for Experimental Biology*, 1950, **4**, 454–482.

Lund, R. D. Uncrossed visual pathways of hooded and albino rats. *Science*, 1965, **149**, 1506–1507.

Meikle, T. H., & Sechzer, J. A. Intercular transfer of brightness discrimination in "split brain" cats. *Science*, 1960, **132**, 734–735.

Meikle, T. H., Sechzer, J. A., & Stellar, E. Interhemispheric transfer of tactile conditioned responses in corpus callosum-sectioned cats. *Journal of Neurophysiology*, 1962, **25**, 530–543.

Myers, R. E. Corpus callosum and interhemispheric communication: Enduring memory effects. *Federation Proceedings*, 1957, **16**, 398.

Myers, R. E., & Sperry, R. W. Interhemispheric communication through the corpus callosum. *A.M.A. Archives of Neurology and Psychiatry*, 1958, **80**, 298–303.

Nadel, L., & Burešová, O. Monocular input and interhemispheric transfer in the reversible split-brain. *Nature*, 1968, **220**, 914–915.

Nadel, L., & Burešová, O. Interocular transfer in the hooded rat. *Physiology and Behavior*, 1969, **4**, 613–619.

Pearlman, C. A. Similar retrograde amnesia effects of ether and spreading cortical depression. *Journal of Comparative and Physiological Psychology*, 1966, **61**, 306–308.

Pearlman, C. A., & Jarvik, M. E. Retrograde amnesia produced by spreading cortical depression. *Federation Proceedings*, 1961, **20**, 340.

Ray, O. S., & Emley, G. Time factors in interhemispheric transfer of learning. *Science*, 1964, **144**, 76–78.

Ray, O. S., & Emley, G. Interhemispheric transfer of learning. *Life Sciences*, 1965, **4**, 271–279.

Ross, R. B., & Russell, I. S. Lateralization and one-trial interhemispheric transfer of avoidance conditioning. *Nature*, 1964, **204**, 909–910.

Ross, R. B., & Russell, I. S. Subcortical storage of classical conditioning. *Nature*, 1967, **214**, 210–211.

Russell, I. S., & Ochs, S. One-trial interhemispheric transfer of a learning engram. *Science*, 1961, **133**, 1077–1078.

Russell, I. S., & Ochs, S. Localization of a memory trace in one cortical hemisphere and transfer to the other hemisphere. *Brain*, 1963, **86**, 37–54.

Schneider, A. M. Retention under spreading depression: a generalization-decrement phenomenon. *Journal of Comparative and Physiological Psychology*, 1966, **62**, 317–319.

Schneider, A. M. Control of memory by spreading cortical depression: a case for stimulus control. *Psychological Review*, 1967, **74**, 201–215.

Schneider, A. M., & Ebbesen, E. Interhemispheric transfer of lever pressing as stimulus generalization of the effects of spreading depression. *Journal of the Experimental Analysis of Behavior*, 1967, **10**, 193–197.

Schneider, A. M., & Hamburg, M. Interhemispheric transfer with spreading depression: a memory transfer or stimulus generalization phenomenon? *Journal of Comparative and Physiological Psychology*, 1966, **62**, 133–136.

Schneider, A. M., & Kay, H. Spreading depression as a discriminative stimulus for lever pressing. *Journal of Comparative and Physiological Psychology*, 1968, **65**, 149–151.

Sheridan, C. L. Interocular transfer of brightness and pattern discrimination in normal and corpus callosum-sectioned rats. *Journal of Comparative and Physiological Psychology*, 1965, **59**, 292–294.

Sperry, R. W. Preservation of high-order function in isolated somatic cortex in callosum-sectioned cats. *Journal of Neurophysiology*, 1959, **22**, 78–87.

Sperry, R. W., Cerebral organization and behavior. *Science*, 1961, **133**, 1749–1757.

Sperry, R. W. The great cerebral commissure. *Scientific American*, 1964, **210**, 42–52.

Sperry, R. W. Split-brain approach to learning problems. In G. C. Quarton, T. Melnechuk, & F. O. Schmitt (Eds.), *The neurosciences: A study program*. New York: Rockefeller University Press, 1967. Pp. 714–722.

Squire, L. R. Transfer of habituation using spreading depression. *Psychonomic Sciences*, 1966, **5**, 261–262.

Squire, L. R., & Liss, P. H. Control of memory by spreading cortical depression: A critique of stimulus control. *Psychological Review*, 1968, **75**, 347–352.

Thompson, R. W. Transfer of avoidance learning between normal and functionally decorticate states. *Journal of Comparative and Physiological Psychology*, 1964, **57**, 321–325.

Travis, R. P. The role of spreading cortical depression in relating the amount of avoidance training to interhemispheric transfer. *Journal of Comparative and Physiological Psychology*, 1964, **57**, 42–46.

Travis, R. P., & Sparks, D. L. The influence of unilateral and bilateral spreading depression during learning upon subsequent relearning. *Journal of Comparative and Physiological Psychology*, 1963, **56**, 56–59.

Trevarthen, C. B. Double visual learning in split-brain monkeys. *Science*, 1962, **136**, 258–259.

VISUAL MEMORY AND THE TEMPORAL LOBE OF THE MONKEY

L. WEISKRANTZ

INSTITUTE OF EXPERIMENTAL PSYCHOLOGY, OXFORD, ENGLAND

I would like to discuss a problem that relates quite specifically to one region of the primate brain, the so-called inferotemporal cortex. My reasons for doing so stem not only from the inherent interest of the research itself, but also because some more general methodological issues emerge. In fact, the point that will be made is that it is by no means a straightforward matter to decide whether an alteration in behavior is or is not the result of an alteration in memory processes. That general point, of course, is not unique to temporal lobe studies but has been made in a number of connections, as, for example, in the analysis of the effects of electroconvulsive shock (ECS). However, the temporal lobe material does, I think, raise some new points.

The starting point for this particular problem of the monkey temporal lobe comes from the study of the effects of damage to the temporal lobe in man. It is well known that bilateral damage to the inferior and mesial portions of the temporal lobes in human clinical material is associated with a severe condition of anterograde amnesia (Milner, 1966; Milner & Teuber, 1968). It appears that such patients have normal spans of attention, and can have normal intelligence as assessed by standard tests. Their memory for events that occurred prior to the lesion is normal, although there is some variable degree of retrograde amnesia for events that occurred in the months just before the surgery. But they have a striking difficulty in retaining new information for more than a brief period of seconds or minutes, unless they have the opportunity to continue to rehearse the material. Retention for acquired motor skills, on the other hand, appears to be unaffected. The most obvious interpretation is that such patients have normal short-term memory, but suffer from a reduced ability to introduce information into their long-term store.

The consideration of the defect in man will be discussed later in the paper. Some years ago an attempt was made to see whether a similar interpretation could be placed upon the effects of bilateral inferotemporal cortex lesions in monkeys. It has been known since the mid-1950's that monkeys subjected to such lesions are deficient in visual discrimination learning (Chow, 1952; Mishkin & Pribram, 1954). Since the defect in the monkey is apparently limited to the visual modality, whereas the human defect is multimodal, the interpretation could not be identical in all respects. But the question was asked whether the visual discrimination learning defect in monkeys could be akin to a reduced ability to introduce new information into a long-term visual store.

Before one can embark on such an endeavor, of course, it is necessary to rule out simpler interpretations, such as that the lesioned monkey is not able to see as well, i.e., that he has a reduced sensory capacity. To review all the evidence here would be impracticable and in any case one can never demonstrate the universal negative. Briefly, it can be stated that the infero-temporal lesioned monkey has normal visual acuity (Weiskrantz & Cowey, 1963), normal shapes of its visual fields, and normal sensitivity to brief flashes of light in all regions of the fields (Cowey & Weiskrantz, 1967). A convincing demonstration has been made by Wilson & Mishkin (1959) that the inferotemporal deficit is qualitatively dissimilar from that produced by direct damage to the visual cortex, since double dissociation was obtained between the two lesions, the temporal lobe one being more associated with "visual learning" tasks, the striate lobe lesion being more associated with tasks of "visual capacity." On the other hand, it is worth noting that some rather striking effects of inferotemporal lesions on size constancy, visual generalization and other visual performance have been discovered. Some of these effects will be returned to later. To avoid becoming trapped (here, at least) in the quagmire of a distinction between sensation and perception, the author merely indicates that at least there were not strong grounds for delaying making an approach to the monkey temporal lobe defect in terms of a change in the capacity by the animal to introduce visual material into long term storage. The analysis by Wilson and Mishkin, in fact, insofar as it linked the inferotemporal region with "visual functions related to learning," could be said to have given an impetus to such an approach. An animal with defective input to long-term storage will obviously have difficulty in learning conventional visual pattern discriminations involving, as they do, hundreds of trials.

The line of reasoning used by Iversen and the author was that if the inferotemporal lesioned monkey has normal short-term memory but a defective input into long-term memory, then it ideally ought to learn tasks at a normal rate provided the learning can be made to take place quickly. But retention for such acquired tasks ought to be defective after an interval of hours. Accordingly, the animals were trained in a "learning set" procedure for three-dimensional objects, so that they could eventually learn any new task in a few trials. Their retention of a large number of such acquired tasks was tested, according to various paridigms, after intervals of 15 min or 24 hr, by determining whether there was any savings in their subsequent relearning. Some of the results have been published (Iversen & Weiskrantz, 1964) and have been discussed in another symposium (Weiskrantz, 1967), and so will not be repeated in detail here. They can be summarized as follows: (a) The initial learning of simple visual object discriminations was generally but not necessarily slower (this point was made especially clear in a study by Buffery, 1964) by temporal lobe lesioned monkeys than by control operates or normal monkeys; (b) The retention of such acquired discriminations was markedly impaired after 24 hr, or indeed even after 15 min. Monkeys with inferotemporal plus hippocampal damage required about as many trials to relearn a problem, on the average, as they had done initially. Monkeys with damage restricted to inferotemporal cortex were impaired, but not so severely as those with the more extensive lesions, but even they showed zero savings after intervals of 24 hr in Buffery's study; (c) The retention impairment was apparently restricted to the visual modality; at least, retention of tactile discriminations tested in the same way as the visual tasks was normal (in fact, somewhat better than normal); (d) Finally, the retention impairment was clearly strongly influenced by retroactive interference, in that "forgetting" occurred far more dramatically when the animal learned another new but similar visual problem in the interval between original learning and subsequent retention. With an intervening tactile problem or just an interval of darkness, retention of the originally acquired visual problem was reasonably good. In comparison, the interference effects in control animals were virtually negligible.

These results offered, we felt, strong support for the view that an inferotemporal lesioned monkey suffers from an impairment in the long-term memory of visual information. But some aspects of the results, particularly those relating to interference effects, led to a closer consideration of the matter. Given that there was, empirically speaking, a retention defect, to what might it have been due? There seem to be four main possibilities: (a) Visual information might enter the long-term store in a normal form, but subsequently decay abnormally rapidly; (b) Another possibility yielding a similar prediction to (a) is that the information does not enter the long-term store at all, and therefore that it decays at a rate determined by the decay of short-term memory traces (cf. Weiskrantz, 1966); (c) Alternatively it could be that information enters the long-term store freely, without abnormal impediment, but is cast in the wrong form, i.e., it is miscoded or categorized incorrectly; (d) Information enters the long-term store with abnormal difficulty, but such information as does enter is correctly categorized and is not subject to abnormal decay.

It is not easy to construct critical tests to decide among these alternatives. But one type of study is clearly relevant to the first two possibilities, (a) and (b), namely the plotting of forgetting curves for the same types of object discrimination tasks as we have just been considering. In fact, we already had good reason to believe, from Prisko's (1963) analysis of a human bi-temporal case, that rapid forgetting characterized the human material and therefore might also apply to the monkey. Prisko used a variation of the Konorski (1959) technique of delayed paired comparison (see Milner & Teuber, 1968). In this method, two stimuli are presented successively, separated by a short interval, and the subject has to report whether the two stimuli were identical or not. Prisko found that with visual stimuli her subject deteriorated very rapidly with increasing intervals, falling to chance within a minute. Normal control subjects showed no decline over a 1-min interval. [Some years ago, in fact, Mingay and the author (unpublished) tested infero-temporal and other operated monkeys in this type of situation. We found no difference between operated and normal controls, but we also found that performance deteriorated very rapidly in controls with delays up to 10 sec. It seems as though the normal monkey might be like the operated human.] Given Prisko's results, together with our own results showing poor savings after 24 hr or less, and given our own preconceptions, we confidently expected to find rapid forgetting curves for previously acquired object discriminations in the temporal lobe operated monkeys. In fact, we *did* in our first analysis of the results, but subsequent analyses made us more sceptical.

The experiment itself was peformed as follows: Each animal was trained on an object discrimination to a criterion of 18 out of 20 successive trials correct. He was then kept in darkness (to minimize interference) in the testing apparatus for a variable interval, and then retrained until the same criterion was achieved. The intervals used were zero seconds (i.e., immediate retesting without a break), 1 min, 6 min 36 sec, 23 min 40 sec, and 2 hr 22 min. The intervals were presented in a random balanced order, and each animal received ten problems for each interval. The operate groups included monkeys with inferotemporal cortex plus hippocampus lesions or inferotemporal cortical lesions. There was a normal control group. The intertrial interval during testing and retesting was not rigidly controlled, but averaged about 10 sec.

When we plotted the results using a conventional savings measure, we found that the animals with large temporal lesions showed more rapid forgetting than the unoperated controls, declining to zero savings in about 2 hr, whereas the controls showed virtually no forgetting over that interval (Fig. 1). The inferotemporal group fell in between the controls and the large temporal lesioned animals.

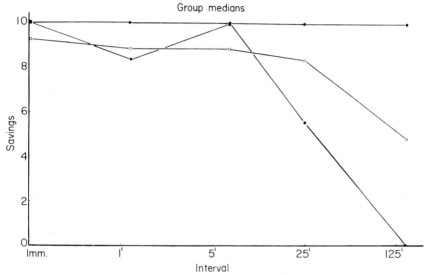

Fig. 1. Savings as a function of the interval between learning and relearning for group medians. Savings score calculated by the following formula: (Errors to criterion in learning − Errors in relearning)/(Errors to criterion in learning + Errors in relearning). Scores based on median of each group taken as a whole. ●, N; □: IT; ■: IT + H. (N = normal; IT = inferotemporal; IT + H = inferotemporal + hippocampus)

One aspect of the results troubled us, and that was that one of the temporal group's results showed a drop in savings even with immediate retention. This is even more evident when the individual median savings scores were averaged (Fig. 2). This led us to examine the trial-to-trial performance in the relearning sessions, and quickly made us realize that a simple savings measure fails to separate two different features of the relearning performance: the initial starting point of the first relearning trial, and the subsequent rate of growth of the relearning curve. Poor savings could be due to either factor alone, and yet one's interpretation would be quite different in each case. In order to separate these two factors and plot them both as a function of the interval following initial acquisition, it is helpful to use a three-dimensional plot. The results for the three groups are shown in Figs. 3, 4, and 5.

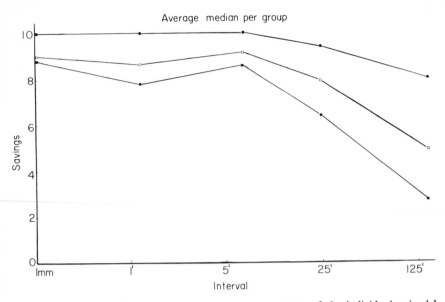

Fig. 2. Same as Fig. 1 but scores based on an average of the individual animals' medians for each group.

It will be seen that the slopes of the three surfaces are roughly parallel, but that the whole surfaces of the temporal groups seem to be displaced downwards. In Figs. 6 and 7 the left-hand edges of the surfaces of the temporal groups' results are roughly matched with an equivalent performance level in the control group surface. On casual inspection, at least, it is hard to reject the hypothesis that they form continuous surfaces. If that is the case, it means that the forgetting curves and relearning curves of the temporal groups are normal, given an adjustment for initial starting point. These surfaces are for the groups as a whole, individual results being rather variable. Occasionally, however, we found an animal whose rate of forgetting did appear to be genuinely faster than the control rate (cf. Fig. 8). The histology for this animal has not been completed, and the results are awaited with interest.

If, then, we are cautious and reject the hypothesis that there is abnormally fast forgetting over this time scale in the temporal lobe operated monkeys, that would appear to eliminate the first two alternatives, (a) and (b), discussed above. The immediate puzzle that requires explanation is why the immediate retention of the temporal group should be defective. Five possibilities have occurred to us. The first stems from a simple statistical consideration. If the initial learning by the temporal group is slower, then as the performance approaches the criterion level it may by chance slip above the level, yielding a premature achievement of the criterion. This is more likely to happen for a curve that approaches the criterion slowly than one that approaches it rapidly. The immediate retention performance of the operated groups would simply reflect the fact that the animals really had never reached a proper level of learning. As it happens, in the present experiment the temporal groups were slower in their initial learning. But it seems unlikely that this can be a general explanation of poor retention in such animals. We have already cited Buffery's study (1964; cf. Weiskrantz, 1967) showing that a severe retention impairment over 24 hr can be demonstrated even with normal initial learning scores. Also, the savings scores in the Iversen and Weiskrantz (1964) study were analyzed as a function of the initial learning scores, and when the latter were matched between groups, the temporal lobe operates were still deficient in savings over 24 hr (in fact, the difference in savings between groups was enhanced, cf. Weiskrantz, 1967).

A second explanation might be that the short-term retention by temporal lobe operates is defective, i.e., that they tend to forget from trial to trial and so can never achieve an adequate level of learning. This possibility seems rather unlikely. Such monkeys are normal in delayed response, delayed matching from sample, and delayed paired comparison, bridging gaps longer than the intertrial interval in the tasks with which we have been concerned here. Riopelle and Churukian (1958) studied visual learning as a function of intertrial interval in a number of operated groups of monkeys, including inferotemporals, and found no interaction between type of lesion and interval.

The third possibility is that the objects themselves are somehow misperceived by the inferotemporal lesioned monkeys, in such a way that they are not remembered as well. There are a number of lines of evidence that favor such a view. The most dramatic comes from Humphrey (unpublished), who found that monkeys with inferotemporal cortex lesions were deficient in size constancy. He found that such animals tended to use either retinal size or distance singly as cues, but not the two in combination, as is necessary for accurate discriminations of real size with real distance variable, and as was displayed by normal and control operates. It could be argued convincingly that perception lacking constancy might also be perception that is poorly remembered. Another well-known line of attack comes from Butter and his colleagues. Butter and Gekoski (1966), for example, found that inferotemporal operates perceive fewer subparts than normal monkeys of pattern discriminanda, as inferred from transfer experiments. Iversen and the author (1967) also reported a similar finding. Butter, Mishkin, & Rosvold (1965) also have reported that inferotemporal operates show broader generalization gradients than controls. Buffery (1964) found in a study of nondelayed matching from sample that inferotemporal monkeys, even after they had learned the matching rule, took longer on each individual trial to select the correct matching stimulus.

NORMAL

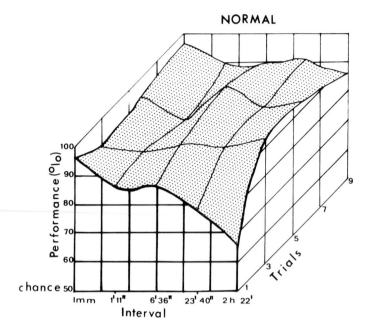

Fig. 3

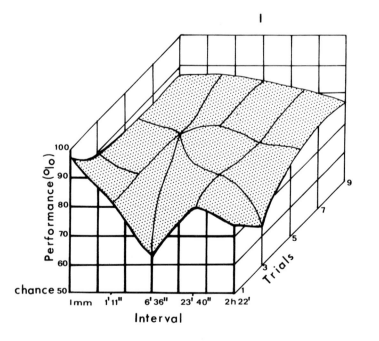

Fig. 4

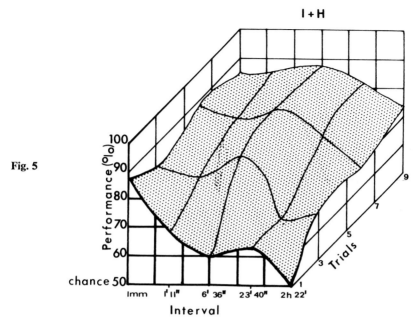

Fig. 5

Fig. 3. Relearning curves of normal monkeys plotted as a function of the interval following original learning to criterion, including immediate (Imm) relearning after no interval. Performance scores during relearning (y-axis) are plotted separately for odd-numbered trials from 1 to 9 (z-axis). Intervals between achievement of criterion in original learning and beginning of relearning are shown on the x-axis. Scores of three monkeys on 50 problems each are averaged.

Fig. 4. Same as Fig. 3 except that monkeys had bilateral inferotemporal cortex lesions.

Fig. 5. Same as Fig. 4 for three monkeys with inferotemporal cortical lesions plus deep temporal tissue, including (presumably) hippocampus (Histological verification of lesions not yet available).

There is, unfortunately, one difficulty with all these types of studies, and it involves us in what might appear to be a vicious circle. All of them require that the animal be trained on a particular discrimination or a particular rule. It is well known that generalization gradients, say, typically become sharper as training proceeds. Humphrey found that normal monkeys at an earlier stage of learning, before they had reached criterion, showed a pattern of imperfect size constancy almost identical to that shown by the inferotemporal monkeys postoperatively. We have seen that inferotemporal monkeys generally take longer to reach a criterion of learning, and we have also seen that they do not maintain that level even after having apparently reached it. The difficulty that now arises is in separating cause from effect. Do they learn slower and maintain lower levels of performance because they misperceive, or is their apparent misperception simply a reflection of their having mastered

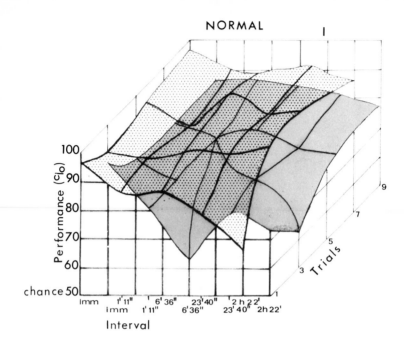

NORMAL   I

Performance (%)

100
90
80
70
60
chance 50

Imm   1' 11"   6' 36"   23' 40"   2 h 22'
   Imm   1' 11"   6' 36"   23' 40"   2h 22'

Interval

Trials
1 3 5 7 9

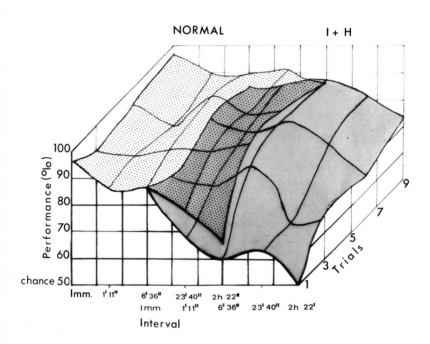

NORMAL   I + H

Performance (%)

100
90
80
70
60
chance 50

Imm.   1' 11"   6' 36"   23' 40"   2h 22"
   Imm   1' 11"   6' 36"   23' 40"   2h 22'

Interval

Trials
1 3 5 7 9

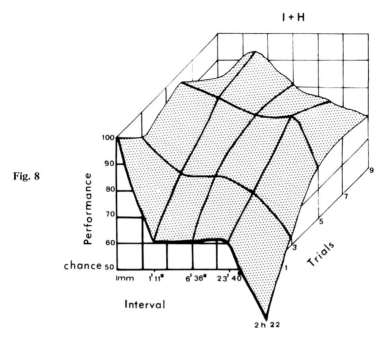

I + H

Fig. 8

Performance

100
90
80
70
60
chance 50

Imm   1'11"   6' 36"   23' 40

Interval

2 h 22

Trials

1
3
5
7
9

Fig. 6. Partial superimposition of Figs. 3 and 4, so that immediate relearning scores of the operated group are approximately matched to appropriate region of surface representing the normal group.

Fig. 7. Partial superimposition of Figs. 3 and 5, so that immediate relearning scores are approximately matched.

Fig. 8. Same as Fig. 3 for one monkey with bilateral lesions of inferotemporal cortex plus deep temporal lesions.

the particular tasks less effectively (for some other reason)? It is interesting, in this connection, that Butter (personal communication) found, in a follow-up of the transfer experiments already referred to above (Butter & Gekoski, 1966), that with more and more training the inferotemporal operated monkeys became more and more like controls in their transfer dispositions. There is a logical way out of this dilemma, but no one has applied it systematically to the present problem experimentally: It must be ensured that both experi-mental and control groups are matched to the same level of acquisition before performance measures are compared. In practice, that probably means reducing the level of the control group. A related strategy is the use of "probes" or "spot checks" of transfer, generalization, matching, and perceptual constancy at different stages of training. If a brain lesion yields qualitative rather than merely quantitative differences from control conditions one can then be quite sure of having broken the vicious circle.

If, as I believe, the dilemma has not yet been resolved, then we must weigh judgment about this third possible explanation. But for those who are predisposed to accept the view that the inferotemporal monkey misperceives, and therefore retains information less adequately, it must be stressed once again that this type of animal *can* learn simple discriminations at a normal rate, and at the same time demonstrate markedly poor retention of them after a gap of hours. If the entire syndrome is to be reduced to one of misperception, then it must be of a type of misperception that allows for normal rates of discrimination learning under certain conditions.

The fourth possible explanation assumes that perception is, or at least can be, normal in the inferotemporal lesioned monkey, but that the information is miscoded or misclassified in long-term memory. One version of this would argue that the categories in long-term memory are overly broad and inclusive. This, of course, brings us full circle to one of the original hypotheses suggested earlier to account for the poor savings by inferotemporal monkeys. It seems to be the most parsimonious explanation of Iversen's finding that retention of visual discrimination tasks was so sensitive to interference by intervening visual tasks. Dr. Elizabeth Warrington, of the National Hospital, Queen Square, and the author have been studying various aspects of memory in amnesic patients, including one documented case of temporal lobe damage. We have found that such patients appear to show strikingly greater forgetting under conditions of interference. Of some significance for the present argument, we also found a high rate of intrusions from earlier tests and false positive responses (Warrington & Weiskrantz, 1968b). A highly instructive finding has been published by Talland (1965, pp. 188–189) among his studies of amnesic patients suffering from Korsakoff psychosis. When he gave all subjects, patients and controls, highly structured instructions about the identity of specific features of visual stimuli, the difference in the subsequent retention of such stimuli between patients and controls disappeared.

Such results tempt one to reexamine the common claim regarding the general amnesic syndrome that it represents a failure, or at least a severe impairment in the introduction of material into long-term storage. When Dr. Warrington and the author used fairly conventional learning and retention procedures, we certainly found poor retention even after a few minutes. But, when we used series of fragmented pictures (Gollin, 1960) and words that became gradually more complete as the series progressed until the subject could make correct identification, we found significant long-term retention by the amnesic group, even over weeks (Warrington & Weiskrantz, 1968a) (Figs. 9–12). Such retention was inferred from the fact that subjects could correctly identify less and less complete pictures and words as their experience of the specific series increased. An explanation in terms of a simple nonspecific practice effect was ruled out. This is not to say that the patients were

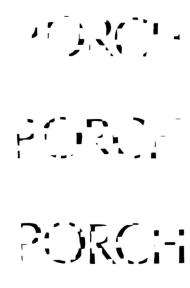

PORCH

Fig. 10. Example of incomplete word.

Fig. 9. Example of incomplete picture (from the series of Gollin, 1960). [Reprinted with permission of author and publisher: Gollin, E. S. Developmental studies of visual recognition of incomplete objects. *Perceptual and Motor Skills*, 1960, **11**, 289–298.]

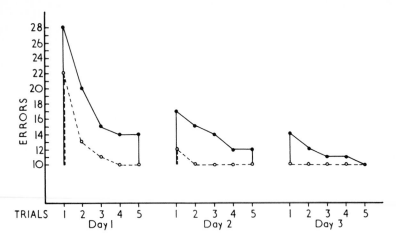

Fig. 11. Mean error scores for each trial for each patient group on the incomplete picture test. (●—, patients, O——, controls)

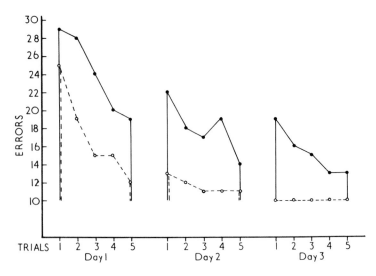

Fig. 12. Mean error score for each trial for each patient group on the incomplete word test.

as good as normals: After a fixed number of trials they had not reached the same level of proficiency as the controls in their initial acquisition. Therefore, we cannot say whether their retention is normal or not until both experimental and control groups are trained to the same criterion; we are just in the process of doing that experiment now.

These various lines of evidence are supportive, rather than conclusive. They are consistent with the view that the impaired retention in human and monkey temporal lobe cases may reflect a miscoding of information in the long-term store, rather than a failure of storage as such. But the same dilemma exists for this fourth alternative as for the third, namely the issue of cause and effect. If subjects cannot as quickly or as reliably achieve or maintain success in initial acquisition, then their subsequent heightened sensitivity to interference effects in retention, for example, may be a secondary consequence of that fact. The logical way out of the dilemma is precisely the same as outlined earlier, but it remains to be implemented experimentally.

The distinction between the third and fourth possible explanations of the unreliable postcriterion performance in the temporal lobe lesioned monkeys is between perception and long-term classification. Quite aside from the particular logical difficulty in which the work finds itself, there are some other difficulties in drawing such a distinction in experiments of this kind. The first stems from the properties of the surgical approach itself. When a treatment can be introduced quickly after the perceptual stage, then one can separate these two stages more clearly. And when the treatment is reversible, it becomes possible to separate failures in storage from failures in retrieval. Preliminary work by Roger Ward at Cambridge, using polarizing electrodes implanted over the inferotemporal cortex, suggests both a retrograde and an anterograde effect of polarization on retention. The former effect clearly rules out an explanation of these results, at least, in terms of perceptual phenomena. But another source of uneasiness about drawing a useful distinction lies in the constant dynamic interplay between perception and classification. What we see is undoubtedly influenced by our past categorization of previous perceptions, and our categories are themselves derived from our perceptual experience. Given this close interplay, it might seem foolhardy even to attempt to dissociate these two processes through any procedure as crude as brain lesions. A cynic might say that one is trying to deal with not a simple straightforward question like, "How many angels can fit on the head of a pin?" but with one more like, "How many angels have wings?"

One reply to such cynics takes us, in fact, to our fifth possibility, which is that the inferotemporal cortex is carrying out both a perceptual and a mnemonic role, separately. Perhaps we have been looking for a distinction that certainly exists logically and functionally but that fails to occur in our lesioned material because, in fact, both processes are independently affected by the same lesion. Some evidence in favor of this line of argument comes from unpublished work by Mishkin and Iwaii at Bethesda and also by Gross and Cowey at Harvard, who have found that posterior inferotemporal cortex lesions (bordering on the foveal projection of the striate cortex) produce the traditional, well-known pattern discrimination learning defect. Anterior inferotemporal lesions also do, but to a significantly lesser extent. In contrast, anterior lesions yield a greater impairment than posterior ones on a task in which several discrimination tasks are taught concurrently, with their trials interspersed. Mishkin and Iwaii refer tentatively to their anterior defect as one in "memory or associative learning." The particular tasks involved in these studies do not really allow one to conclude as yet that a dissociation between perceptual and mnemonic processes has been achieved. But just as double dissociation between striate cortex and inferotemporal demonstrated by Wilson and Mishkin gave us an important clue about inferotemporal function, so perhaps this latest example of double dissociation will achieve equal importance. At the very least it demonstrates that the conventional inferotemporal lesion produces a compound effect.

If one is allowed to speculate about the organization of the temporal lobe when it is in the brain rather than what happens when it has been removed, perhaps the story might go something like this. One knows from single unit recordings in the striate and parietal cortex of the cat that a progression from simple to complex and from complex to hypercomplex can be plotted (Hubel & Wiesel, 1960, 1965). This is a progression whereby certain configurational and orientational features of retinal inputs become more and more abstracted, and information about the locus of the configuration in the visual field as a whole is lost. Perhaps, by the time information has reached the temporal lobe (via the route suggested by the anatomical studies of Kuypers, Szwarzbart, Mishkin, and Rosvold (1965), information about locus is eliminated altogether. There is good reason to suppose, in fact, that information about locus finds its way to the frontal eye fields and superior layers of the superior colliculus.

Given such a configuration processor in the temporal lobe, it seems most reasonable to identify it with Mishkin and Iwaii's and Gross and Cowey's posterior subdivision of the inferotemporal strip. With posterior lesions leaving an imperfect configurational abstracting mechanism, perhaps the locational aspects of stimuli become more heavily relied upon by the animal. The fact that Butter's monkeys tended to concentrate largely on one spatial locus of stimuli may be significant. Weiskrantz and Mingay (1967) have published a study that can be interpreted as showing that monkeys with inferotemporal lesions are *more* anchored to a particular spatial locus and those with frontal lesions are *less* anchored than normal controls when they are presented with an array of equally rewarded objects spread out in front of them.

Visual information that has been abstracted achieves significance through its associations, particularly with reward and punishment. It is nowadays fashionable, but even so it is not unreasonable, to assume that such associations are mediated via the limbic system. We assume that the flow of information proceeds in a forward direction in the inferotemporal region and from there makes its way to the anteromedial portions of the lobe, including amygdala, uncus, and pyriform cortex, and thence on to hypothalamus. In the course of its forward movement, it is assumed that yet another abstraction takes place which allows for an economical classification for purposes of further handling by the limbic system. In this sense, the anterior temporal lobe is not a store or a gate to the store, but simply a processor that determines the size and labels of files in which information will ultimately be stored. Of course, the flow of information need not be undirectional, and the system probably would be inefficient if it were, and therefore there is little point in trying to arbitrate between input and output theories of temporal lobe function.

The speculation is embarrassingly woolly, but it has the virtue of being commendably brief and at least puts the temporal lobe in a comprehensible perspective. One situation that has always been rather puzzling is that, for a brain in which the store apparently has not a well-defined locus, lesions in one specific region should, in man at least, block the input to that store. The puzzle is reduced if the temporal lobe is considered to be simply a by-station, in an already existing hierarchical system, that imposes its operation upon information passing through it, and by altering the character of the information itself, alters its retrievability. But the whole line of speculation could be put to flight by the next round of experimental work, which would not tell us how many angels have wings, but at least that they can fly.

REFERENCES

Buffery, A. W. H. The effects of frontal and temporal lobe lesions upon the behaviour of baboons. Unpublished doctoral dissertation, Cambridge University, 1964.

Butter, C. M., Mishkin, M., & Rosvold, H. W. Stimulus generalization in monkeys with inferotemporal and lateral occipital lesions. In D. J. Mostofsky (Ed.), *Stimulus generalization*. Stanford: Stanford University Press, 1965. Pp. 119–133.

Butter, C. M., & Gekoski, W. Alterations in pattern equivalence following inferotemporal and lateral striate lesions in rhesus monkeys. *Journal of Comparative and Physiological Psychology*, 1966, **61**, 309–312.

Chow, K. L. Further studies on selective ablation of association cortex in relation to visually mediated behavior. *Journal of Comparative and Physiological Psychology*, 45, 1952, 109–118.

Cowey, A., & Weiskrantz, L. A comparison of the effects of inferotemporal and striate cortex lesions on the visual behavior of rhesus monkeys. *Quarterly Journal of Experimental Psychology*, 1967, **19**, 246–253.

Gollin, E. S. Developmental studies of visual recognition of incomplete objects. *Perceptual and Motor Skills*, 1960, **11**, 289–298.

Hubel, D. H., & Wiesel, T. N. Receptive fields of single neurons in the cat's striate cortex. *Journal of Physiology*, 1960, **150**, 91–104.

Hubel, D. H., & Wiesel, T. N. Receptive fields and functional architecture in two nonstriate visual areas (18 and 19) of the cat. *Journal of Neurophysiology*, 1965, **28**, 229–289.

Iversen, S. D., & Weiskrantz, L. Temporal lobe lesions and memory in the monkey. *Nature*, 1964, **201**, 740–742.

Iversen, S. D., & Weiskrantz, L. Perception of redundant cues by monkeys with inferotemporal lesions. *Nature*, 1967, **214**, 241–243.

Konorski, J. A new method of physiological investigation of recent memory in animals, *Bulletin de l'Academie Polonaise des Sciences, Serie des Sciences, Biologiques*, 1959, **7**, 115–117.

Kuypers, H. G. J. M., Szwarzbart, M. K., Mishkin, M., & Rosvold, H. E. Occipitotemporal connections in the rhesus monkey. *Experimental Neurology*, 1965, **11**, 245–262.

Milner, B. Amnesia following operation on the temporal lobes. In C. W. M. Whitty & O. L. Zangwill (Eds.), *Amnesia*. London: Butterworth, 1966. Pp. 109–133.

Milner, B., & Teuber, H. L. Alteration of perception and memory in man: Reflections on methods. In L. Weiskrantz, (Ed.), *Analysis of behavioral change*. New York: Harper & Row, 1968. Pp. 268–375.

Mishkin, M., & Pribram, K. H. Visual discrimination performance following partial ablations of the temporal lobe. I. Ventral vs. lateral. *Journal of Comparative and Physiological Psychology*, 1954, **47**, 14–20.

Prisko, L. Short-term memory in focal cerebral damage. Unpublished doctoral dissertation, McGill University, 1963.

Riopelle, A. J., & Churukian, G. A. The effect of varying the intertrial interval in discrimination learning by normal and brain-operated monkeys. *Journal of Comparative and Physiological Psychology*, 1958, **51**, 119–125.

Talland, G. A. *Deranged memory*. New York: Academic Press, 1965.

Warrington, E. K., & Weiskrantz. L. New method of testing long-term retention with special reference to amnesic patients. *Nature*, 1968, **217**, 972–974.(a)

Warrington, E. K., & Weiskrantz, L. A study of learning and retention in amnesic patients. *Neuropsychologia*, 1968, **6**, 283–291.(b)

Weiskrantz, L. Experimental studies of amnesia. In C. W. M. Whitty & O. L. Zangwill (Eds.), *Amnesia*. London: Butterworth, 1966. Pp. 1–35.

Weiskrantz, L. Central nervous system and organization of behavior. In D. P. Kimble (Ed.), *The organization of recall*. New York: New York Academy of Sciences, 1967.

Weiskrantz, L., & Cowey, A. Striate cortex lesions and visual acuity of the rhesus monkey. *Journal of Comparative and Physiological Psychology*, 1963, **56**, 225–231.

Weiskrantz, L., & Mingay, R. Patterns of selection by monkeys with lesions of the cerebral cortex. *Nature*, 1967, **213**, 573–574.

Wilson, W. A., Jr., & Mishkin, M. Comparison of the effects of inferotemporal and lateral occipital lesions on visually guided behavior in monkeys. *Journal of Comparative and Physiological Psychology*, 1959, **52**, 10–17.

THE BEHAVIOR OF HIPPOCAMPAL NEURONS DURING CONDITIONING EXPERIMENTS

J. OLDS
DEPARTMENT OF PSYCHOLOGY, UNIVERSITY OF MICHIGAN, ANN ARBOR, MICHIGAN

In the experiments which will be reported, action potentials were recorded from single neurons in the brains of awake and behaving animals. One group of experiments was aimed at analyzing the reward areas of lateral hypothalamus and their afferents and efferents. Another group of experiments was aimed at recording brain changes during conditioning in the hope of finding centers critically involved in the learning process. The experiments have not advanced far in the direction of the original goals but they have provided new information about the neural correlates of instrumental behavior and this information has initiated new theoretical interpretations of the rewarding process.

One goal of the first set of experiments was to find special projections to and from the "reward centers" (Olds, Mink, & Best, 1969). Another was the problem of interpreting the "mixed" effects of stimulation when several different responses were produced by applying relatively small stimulus currents to a single bipolar probe within the lateral hypothalamus. Often positive responses, negative responses, and instrumental and consummatory responses related to several different drives could be evoked by one and the same lateral hypothalamic stimulus. This caused us to wonder whether the lateral hypothalamus might not be a complicated network in which families of neurons

This research was supported by grants from the U.S. Public Health Service.

257

representing different drives and processes were interdigitated. It seemed possible that neurons related to positive and negative mechanisms might be brought into contact with one another to mediate integrative processes and reciprocal relations. And it seemed possible that neurons representing different and sometimes competing drives might also be brought into proximity and contact, again for the purpose of mediating integrative and reciprocally inhibitory relationships. If neighboring neurons were functionally different and often opposed, and if it were necessary for a brain stimulus to provoke activity in several members of a family of neurons in order for it to produce a behavioral output, then stimulation studies would not be able to resolve and clarify the relationships involved.

A relatively large, extracellular microelectrode can "see" the spiking activity of several different neurons simultaneously. Fortunately, the spikes of one neuron usually have a different amplitude and wave shape from those of another. Thus we can "see" and distinguish two or more neighboring responses with the same probe at the same time and thereby observe the relationships between them. With this method we hope to be able to test the hypothesis that opposing systems are often represented by neighboring neurons in lateral hypothalamus.

The simplest and perhaps best experiment would involve unit recordings during consummatory responses. Because such responses involve simultaneously both drive states and reward states, it seems they should most certainly involve lateral hypothalamic neurons if any of our current conceptions is accurate. When we first started our present series of experiments, we could not record during consummatory behavior because the relatively large movement artifact obscured the recorded neuron responses. It seemed at the time that the next best thing would be to record during the antecedent instrumental behaviors. If recordings could not be made during consummatory eating and drinking, it seemed that they might be made during pedal pressing responses while animals were waiting for food or water. If anticipatory "reward" responses occurred in the "reward" centers, then these might be observed.

I. The Quiet Waiting Experiment

Action potentials were recorded simultaneously from the reticular formation, from several points in the hypothalamic drive and reward systems, and from hippocampus.

The probes in the reticular formation were used in the hope that neural correlates of changes in arousal level might be observed during these periods when the motivated animals awaited rewards. Action potentials from hippo-

campus were recorded for three reasons. In the first place, during earlier
" unit reinforcement " experiments, action potentials from hippocampus often
appeared to be correlated with food-striving activities, suggesting perhaps an
a priori relation between hippocampus and food anticipatory behaviors.
Second, during the early "instrumental waiting" experiments, action potentials that seemed to come from areas related to descending hippocampal
fibers were the only ones to show interesting differences correlated with the
nature of the reward. Third, it seemed important to have some action potential recordings from cortical areas, and for a variety of reasons it turned
out to be much more convenient to make recordings from the hippocampal
portions of the paleocortex than from any other part of the cortical mantle.

It was fortunate that recordings were made from reticular formation and
hippocampus in these experiments because interesting neural correlates of
instrumental behavior were observed in both of these areas, but not in the
hypothalamic drive and reward areas.

The methods of the study permitted recordings to be made during pedal
pressing responses while the animals were waiting for food or water (Olds,
Mink, & Best, 1969). In order to enhance the quietness of behavior, animals
were trained to depress a pedal and then to remain motionless for a period
of time in order to obtain the reward. The reward was forfeited if even a
slight move occurred. Two pedals were provided, one for food and one for
water.

Fine wires of 60-μ diameter insulated at the factory and cut with scissors
were used as microelectrodes. These were more flexible, more constant from
probe to probe, and far more likely to yield good neuronal recordings for long
periods of time than either rigid etched metal or rigid pulled glass micro-
probes. Furthermore they were far easier to make and to handle. At the time
of surgery, probes were moved into the general area to be studied by use of
stereotaxic coordinates and then moved within that area until clear unit spikes
were recorded. Spikes of relatively constant amplitude (about 200–300 μV)
were often observed (see Fig. 1). The duration of these was very short, rarely
amounting to more than 400 μsec. When the microelectrodes were being
placed, these spikes would appear and disappear on movements of from
30 to 100 μ.

In chronic preparations, spikes which appeared to originate from the
same unit were observed often for periods of many days. Neuronal activity
was characterized by periods of firing alternated with relatively silent intervals
even in the course of brief observations (see Fig. 2).

Large neurons recorded in reticular formation (see Fig. 3) provided the
most interesting patterns during anticipatory periods. There were large increments in the firing rate of these neurons which often occurred during the last

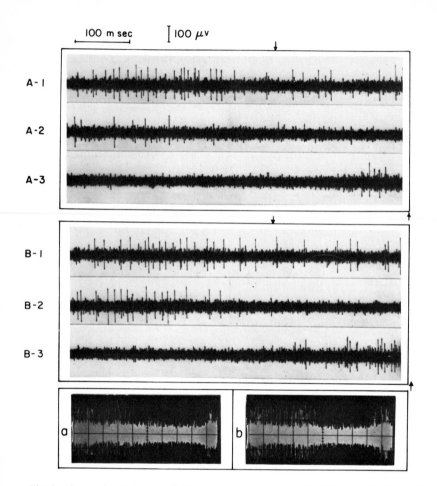

Fig. 1. *Neuronal activity recorded from a dorsal anterior part of the reticular formation near the posterior commissure.* A-1, A-2, and A-3 represent a continuous 2-sec waiting period terminated by a food reinforcement (at the upward-pointing arrow). Movement after the first 250 msec (the downward-pointing arrow) would have caused cancellation of the reward. B-1, B-2, and B-3 represent a similar waiting period a few minutes later. Below: same data (slower time base) from A in a, and from B in b. Note a burst of spikes just prior to reinforcement and one early in the waiting period.

part of a 2-sec waiting interval just before the reward was presented, and often this was preceded by a decline in neuronal activity even below baseline rates during the middle part of the waiting interval. A series of further tests suggested strongly that the large increments in firing rates of these neurons were correlated with the degree of expectancy on the one hand and with the moti-

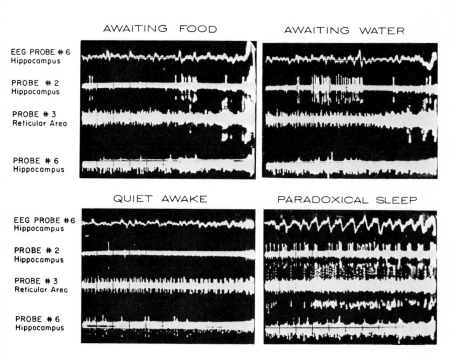

Fig. 2. *Neuron activity and EEG samples during food, water, and two control intervals in one animal.* These are single trials. The traces start as the animal depressed the pedal or at the beginning of a control trial. The reinforcement was presented near the end of the trace. The traces were photographed from the tube of a storage oscilloscope; they represented successful trials without any movement during the last 1.75 sec. Note a burst of hippocampal activity during the food and water waiting periods and theta in EEG and unit traces during paradoxical sleep. Also note an anticipatory burst of activity from the reticular area (Channel 3) just prior to reinforcement.

vational relevance of the goal on the other. The reticular neurons fired rapidly at the beginning of the waiting period when expectancy was initiated by the pedal response and at the end when expectancy was again high (see Fig. 4). The amount of firing was ordinarily more pronounced when the animal was working for food for which motivation was very high than when the animal was working for water for which motivation was lower. The intensity of motivation for the two incentives was judged both by the fact the animal worked for 400 food rewards daily and less than 100 water rewards, and by the greater intensity of the capture response when food rewards were presented. That the degree of motivation made the difference was proved in later studies where it was found that by feeding the animal on an *ad lib* basis

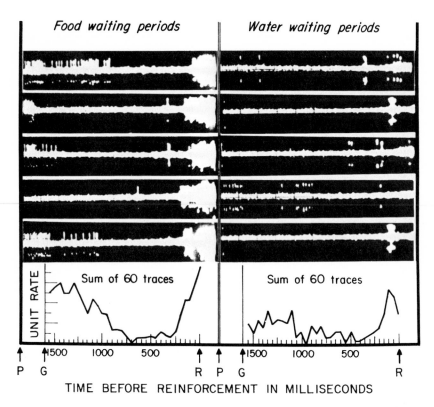

Fig. 3. *Photographic documentation of the computer curves.* For both food and water periods, five photographic samples of activity recorded from a reticular unit are shown and the computer sum of 60 such traces is shown below. In food traces a movement artifact after reinforcement obscures the terminal burst but there is no movement prior to the point marked R. *Symbols*: P, pedal depression; G, electronic gate open and counting begins; R, reinforcement applied and counting stopped.

so that there was no particular food motivation, the response could be made to occur for water but not for food.

In later studies (Phillips & Olds, 1969) it was also possible to separate the level of expectancy and the level of motivation from the mere response characteristics of holding the pedal and waiting (see Fig. 5). This was accomplished by having the animal press a single pedal without knowing what it would get. Then during the later half of the waiting period one of three auditory signals was presented, one announcing that food would be presented, another announcing that water would be presented, or a third announcing that there would be no reward. The firing rate of midbrain neurons would often become augmented just prior to the point in time when the auditory

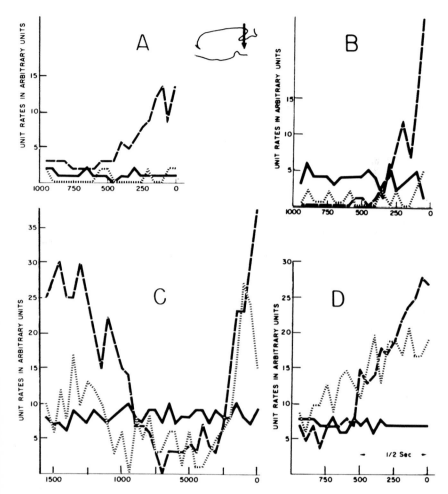

Fig. 4. *Slopes in reticular formation.* Each curve represents the averaged change of rate during the last part of the trials for a number of food, water, or control periods, plotting unit rates versus time (milliseconds) before reinforcement or end of trial. A, B, and C: data from the same reticular formation unit on three different days spread over the period of a month. Note a gradual increase in "anticipatory" neuronal activity prior to water reinforcement which did not, however, achieve the level of the food activity. D: data from a different reticular formation unit in a different animal. *Notation.* A and B: (– – –) 283 food waiting periods; (· · ·) 48 water waiting periods, (—) 378 control periods. C: (– – –) 60 food waiting periods; (· · ·) 60 water waiting periods; (—) 576 control periods. D: (– – –) 485 food waiting periods; (· · ·) 146 water waiting periods; (—) 1868 control periods.

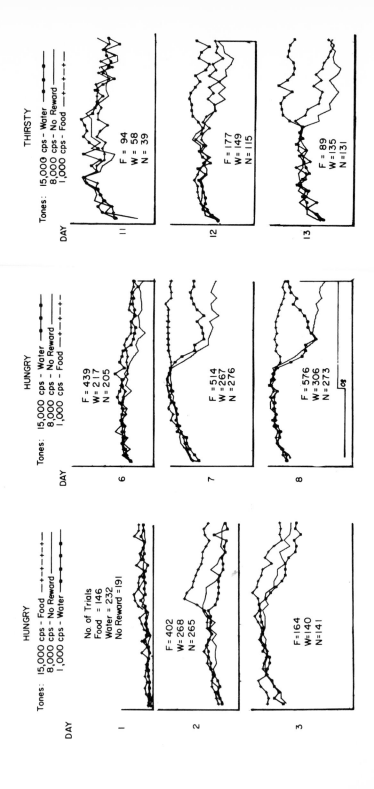

signal appeared, then the auditory signal would cause either an added or sustained increment if food was announced, a pronounced decrement in firing if no reward was announced, or a less pronounced decrement if water was announced.

In these experiments, the response to all three stimuli was quite similar before learning. Then a clear difference appeared favoring the food signal. Then when the significance was reversed so that the water signal became the food signal and vice versa, the difference first disappeared and then reappeared, again favoring food. Finally when the animal was given free food but remained thirsty, the difference gradually shifted and finally favored water; thus the high rate of firing did not depend on the quality of the goal but only on its motivational relevance.

In experiments completed to date, patterns from all of the 21 neurons recorded in reticular formation presented one feature in common, namely an increment in neuronal firing late in the last second just prior to reinforcement in the two-pedal experiment. Six animals have been transferred from the two-pedal experiment to the single-pedal experiment, and in all of these cases the neuronal firing rates have been highest in response to the tone which preannounced the goal with the most motivational relevance. Clearly all reticular neurons showed common features in their pattern of firing. By the same token, there was a lack of differentiation from neuron to neuron.

In hippocampus there were differences between neurons. There were some incremental patterns that were similar (superficially at least) to those of the reticular formation. But there was an equal number of decremental patterns (see Fig. 6).

Besides the incremental slopes and the decremental slopes which characterized hippocampal neuronal firing during the waiting periods, a third kind of response appeared quite often in the firing patterns of units in this area. This was a pattern of firing which appeared to be in some respects like repre-

---

Fig. 5. *Average response rate curves during an extended experiment lasting more than* 13 *days with a midbrain unit (Phillips and Olds,* 1969). In these tests, the animal depressed a pedal at the beginning of each trace. After the first period of about 1 sec, one of three auditory signals occurred, announcing that food, water, or no reward would be forthcoming after a 1-sec period. When the training commenced, the stimuli had no effect on unit rates. On Days 2 and 3 the food signal evoked a large excitatory response, and some suppression was caused by the other two signals. When the meaning of the food and water signals were reversed, on Day 6, the difference at first disappeared and then reappeared in favor of the food signal (which had previously been the water signal). Later on, Day 12, the animal was allowed to feed *ad lib* and was made thirsty. During the course of this modification of drives, the difference disappeared again and then reappeared, this time favoring the water signal.

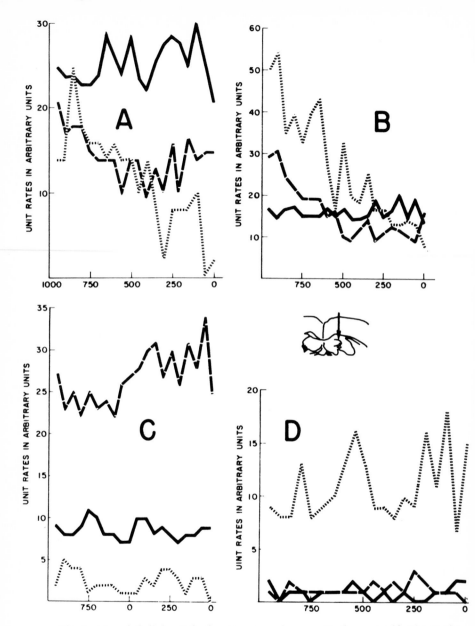

Fig. 6. *Mean daily "slope" for four hippocampal neurons (in three animals).* The graphs are plotted for unit rate versus time (milliseconds) before reinforcement or end of trial. These are samples indicating the kind of patterns obtained; they do not in all cases represent the full four days of data as there was sometimes considerable variability in hippocampus from day to day. Note, in A and B (CA4 and dentate gyrus, respectively), a decline in neuron rates prior to reinforcement, and in C and D (both in CA3) the neuron rates differed markedly depending on the incentive. *Notation.* A and B: (– – –) 283 food waiting periods; (· · ·) 48 water waiting periods; (—) 378 control periods. C: (– – –) 266 food waiting periods; (· · ·) 121 water waiting periods; (—) 621 control periods. D: (– – –) 256 food waiting periods; (· · ·) 92 water waiting periods; (—) 730 control periods.

sentation of the expected goal object. The pattern was relatively unrelated to the different temporal phases of the waiting period, and correlated instead with the nature of the goal object. In several cases, neurons were quite active while the animal awaited food but were relatively inactive while the animal waited for water or vice versa (see Figs. 6C and D). In some cases, neurons were even active far above control levels during the instrumental waiting related to one incentive and far below control levels during instrumental periods related to the other. Although these interesting differential activities were sporadically observed in recordings from other parts of the brain, and while about two-thirds of the hippocampal units did not exhibit them, there seemed to be a correlation of the differential unit patterns with one part of the hippocampus, namely in the "CA3 field" which is a set of large mid-hippocampal neurons with very well-known input and output connections. There was no similar correlation with any other part of the brain which has so far been explored.

In the one completed study of these phenomena (Olds *et al.* 1969) there were thirteen points with food–water differences amounting to 50% or more of the smaller value. Histological analysis showed seven of these to be in hippocampus, three in the preoptic area, and one apiece in medial hypothalamus, lateral hypothalamus, and ventral tegmentum. Five of the seven hippocampal points were in the CA3 field, or in the anterior-most tip of the hippocampus which is quite likely a part of the CA3 field. There were two probes in the CA3 field of hippocampus which did not yield these very large difference scores; these were cases having a kind of probe which did not hold units well anyway. There were also two hippocampal probes not in the CA3 field yielding very high difference scores. They were in the "anterior hippocampal commissure" region in front of hippocampus; this is an area of fibers from CA3 and other neurons and therefore the CA3 ones might have been involved. The phenomenon did not appear in the other fields of hippocampus. Decremental slopes during the waiting period were correlated to some degree with the dentate field which is often thought to be the input system of hippocampus, or with the CA4 field which stands between the dentate and CA3. The largest field of hippocampus, namely the CA1 system, yielded some units that were not affected by the experimental variables and some units that were quite similar to those recorded from the reticular formation.

Thus the hippocampus was found to be composed of three classes of units and the most interesting class occupied the middle, or CA3 field.

While these anticipatory responses were originally interpreted as suggesting that hippocampus might be innately wired to factors controlling food or water behavior, certain observations made it equally likely that temporary memories related to food or water behaviors might be stored in hippocampus. Two kinds of evidence made this likelihood seem reasonable. The first was that even though differential neuronal activity patterns favoring food or water behavior would often appear repeatedly for several days, they did not continue to be exhibited indefinitely. They would often disappear or be reversed even in cases where it appeared that the action potential was recorded from the same neuron before and after the change. Thus it seemed that the neuron firing was not a permanent anticipatory representor of food but only a temporary one which could be changed from week to week or day to day. The second thing which made the notion of temporary memory appealing was that the differential activity patterns favored food about three to five times as often as they favored water and this was about the proportion of the two kinds of activity in this experimental environment. The relative impermanence of these " representations " and the correlation of probabilities between brain events and behavior in an artificial environment converged in suggesting that this might be a relatively temporary neuronal reflection of recent behavioral events rather than an *a priori* correlate in instrumental food or water behavior.

At the end of the quiet waiting experiment it was not clear to what degree response and posture might have been responsible for the observed patterns. Was the large reticular formation response more related to the rising of the expectancy toward a critical point in time in which case it might appear equally if the animal were only expecting but not actively striving? Or was it somehow bound up with the striving or with the tense inhibitory and pedal holding behavior which occupied the animal from the beginning to the end of the pedal response? If so, it might be expected to disappear in an experiment which did not involve commitment and effortful behavior on the part of the animal. The same kind of question was relevant in the case of the hippocampal differences. Were they related to different postures or orientations which the animals assumed during their pedal responses but before they began to wait? If this were true the differences would not appear if we caught the animal off guard, taking it by surprise and requiring it to hold still in random postures and orientations for short periods during which movements would cause cancellation of reinforcements. If on the other hand these were mnemonic representations of the expected reward then the chance postures and orientations would still be accompanied by the differential neuron responses. Some of these questions were answered in our second series of experiments.

II. The Pavlovian Conditioning Experiments

Previous studies of neuron changes during conditioning have involved either surgical and paralytic restraints (Kamikawa, McIlwain, & Adey, 1964; Yoshii & Ogura, 1960) or free behavior in chronic animals (Buchwald, Halas, & Schramm, 1966; Ellison, Humphrey, & Feeney, 1968; Travis &

Sparks, 1967). The search for neural traces of critical changes in learning has thus been clouded by the surgical and paralytic procedures or confounded by the correlates of the new conditioned responses. There has also been confusion resulting from the sensitizing effects of the unconditioned stimulus (US) and from changes in attention level which occur as the conditioned stimulus (CS) becomes a sign of a more or less significant unconditioned stimulus. New techniques have permitted us (Hirano, Best, & Olds, 1970; Olds & Hirano, 1969) to study conditioned neuron responses that were not correlated with new skeletal movements or with changing states of sensitization or arousal in animals that were neither anesthetized nor paralyzed.

Our object was to obtain evidence which might implicate structures of the hypothalamo–hippocampal system in temporary information storage and in anticipatory or other internal responses divorced from immediate skeletal and arousal patterns. Interest in the hippocampus and its related subcortical structures stemmed partly from the experiments reported in the first half of the present paper and partly from several kinds of experiments which related hippocampus in one way or another to temporary information storage. These included first the observation indicating a failure of some information holding functions in humans after hippocampal damage (Milner, 1958). Second, there were difficulties (such as poor extinction, insufficient response variability, and excessive responding to the wrong stimulus) exhibited by animals with hippo-campal lesions (Isaacson & Wickelgren, 1962; Niki, 1967; Orbach, Milner, & Rasmussen, 1960). Third, there were observations of hippocampal "theta" rhythms during certain phases of learning but not in the very early period when the CS was entirely novel (Pickenhain & Klingberg, 1967) and not in the later period if at that time the response to the stimulus was fully deter-mined. Finally, there were stimulation studies implicating hippocampus and its related structures in the control of drives (MacLean, Denniston, Dua, & Ploog, 1962), and consummatory responses (Kawakami, Seto, Terasawa, & Yo-shida, 1967), and positive and negative reinforcements (Ursin, Ursin, & Olds, 1966). All of these motivational processes play a major role in marking information for storage or erasure. It seemed that if temporary information storage did occur in hippocampus then hippocampal neurons might display temporary responses in the course of conditioning; and if anticipatory re-sponses did occur in drive or reward "centers" then these might be observed during the period between the application of the CS and the application of the US.

Two sets of Pavlovian conditioning studies have been carried out. In the first set (Olds & Hirano, 1969) unit responses were observed during ali-mentary conditioning after habituation trials had been completed. The con-ditioning caused hippocampal and midbrain units to become more responsive to the CS. It remained to be determined, however, whether the augmented responses represented a return to the prehabituated state, that is whether the responses to conditioned stimuli were the same as the responses to novel stimuli. Other studies apparently indicated that while novel stimuli and conditioned stimuli might have similar effects on the reticular formation, they probably had different effects on the hippocampus (Adey, Dunlop, & Hendrix, 1960; Grastyan, 1959; Pickenhain & Klingberg, 1967).

We will dwell mainly on the second set of studies (Hirano *et al.* 1970) which confirmed and extended these findings. Long-run recordings were made of neuron responses in several limbic and midbrain structures during habituation, conditioning, and extinction. This permitted us to observe whether the responses that appeared in conditioning would be the same or different from the ones that disappeared during preceding pseudoconditioning, control periods. It also permitted us to observe whether the postextinction state would be similar to that which came before conditioning.

In order to accentuate the possibility of observing differences between the prehabituation responses and the conditioned responses, and in order to control for general changes in unit activity in individual cases, a discrimination procedure was used in which one auditory stimulus was a positive CS and a different one was a nonreinforced " control " stimulus.

Animals were prepared as in the quiet waiting study. Recordings were made simultaneously from four probes during 2-sec intervals which included a 1-sec prestimulus interval and a 1-sec interval of auditory stimulation.

Two auditory stimuli were used, 600 and 1000 Hz, respectively, applied for a full second. One was a reinforced CS (CS+) and the other was a nonreinforced control stimulus (CS−). The use of the high or low frequency tone for CS+ was alternated from rat to rat. The US was a 45 mg food pellet supplied by a noisy food magazine with which the animal was familiar.

During a 250-trial, 3-day preconditioning experiment, habituation and pseudoconditioning procedures were simultaneously employed. That is, the two tones and the US were presented separately on a random basis, each with an average intertrial interval of 4 min. Recordings were made prior to and during the auditory stimuli and movement prior to or during a tone caused its cancellation or termination. In such cases the data were discarded and the trial was not counted. There was no correlation between any of the three stimuli. If all trials had been completed and counted there would have been 360 trials daily with each stimulus. Because of movement only about one trial in four was completed and therefore 250 trials with a given stimulus occurred in three days.

During the following 200-trial, 2-day conditioning experiment, the conditions were the same in all respects except that the US was presented not on a schedule of its own but after completion of each 1-sec CS+ application. During this experiment, movement prior to or during the CS+ period caused not only cancellation or termination of the CS+ and discarding of the data but also cancellation of the US. During the final 150-trials, 1½-day extinction experiment, the habituation and pseudoconditioning procedures were reinstituted, and conditions were exactly the same as in the preconditioning experiment.

Experiments continued for 24 hr a day during the whole six- to seven-day series and animals received all their food from the magazine. During conditioning, the animal therefore had to learn to stand still in order to be fed.

Neuronal activity was discriminated and counted automatically as in the previous experiment.

In all areas there were increments in neuronal firing caused by the application of the auditory stimuli (see Fig. 7). Before conditioning these appeared during the first 50–100 msec and had run much of their course by the end of the first 300 msec. They were therefore called "on" responses and indexed by stating the neuronal response rate during the first 300-msec period as a percentage of the rate during the prestimulus, 1-sec control period. During the latter two-thirds of the 1-sec stimulus period the rate had stabilized in one of three states: (1) a sustained but greatly attenuated increment, or (2) a return to baseline, or (3) a subnormal firing rate. Because rates were quite constant during the last two-thirds of the stimulus period, they were called "stabilized" responses and indexed by stating the neuronal response rate during the last 300-msec period as a percentage of the rate during the prestimulus 1-sec control period.

The responses of the different units in a given brain area were sufficiently similar to one another at a given stage in the experiment so that means underwent reliable changes during habituation, conditioning, and extinction.

In the midbrain, the "on response" to the CS+ and CS− declined steadily during the pseudoconditioning, habituation series (see Fig. 8). The response started at a high of 200% of control during the first 25 habituation trials and fell to 130% during trials 275–300. The response rose back to 170% during the first 25 conditioning trials and remained at this level throughout the conditioning series. There was no difference between the midbrain "on response" to the CS+ and CS− during conditioning. During the first 75 trials of extinction a difference appeared: "on responses" to the CS+ rose to 200% during the first 50 trials of extinction, whereas those to the CS− fell toward the preconditioning levels. During the last 75 extinction trials the difference favoring the CS+ vanished, and the average "on response" to the CS+ and CS− was 140%, not significantly above the preconditioning level.

In the midbrain the "stabilized responses" (see Fig. 8) were very small at the beginning of habituation. They fell from 115% to zero during habituation. They rose to 140% early in the conditioning series and remained in this range all during that series. These responses then fell to zero again during extinc-

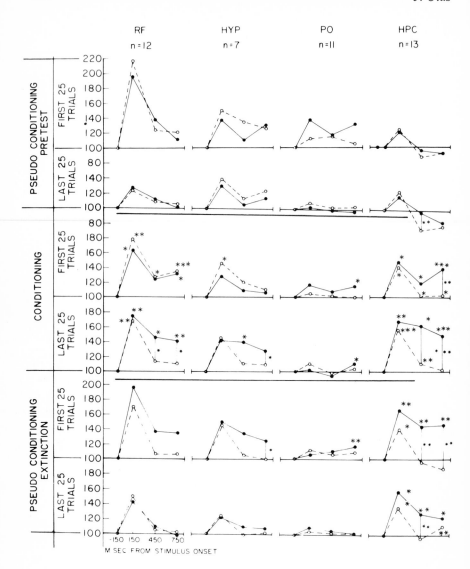

Fig. 7. *Grand average response curves for first and last 25 trials of habituation, con-ditioning, and extinction.* In this case, each point represents 333 msec, i.e., there is a single point for the first-third, second-third, and last-third of the stimulus interval. The first point represents the mean rate for the 333-msec prestimulus period. In Fig. 8, the data for the "on response" are taken from the first-third of the stimulus period, and the data for the "stabilized response" are taken from the last-third.

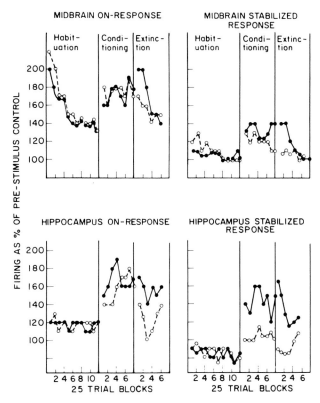

Fig. 8. The course of habituation, conditioning, and extinction in 25 trial blocks for the "on response" and the "stabilized response" recorded from the midbrain and the hippocampus. The data are taken from grand average plots as shown in Fig. 7. (O), CS−; (●) CS+.

tion. In this case a large difference between the responses to CS+ and CS− appeared during conditioning. It was not significant until after 100 to 150 conditioning trials. From this time onward the stabilized response to the CS− fell toward zero even during continued conditioning, while the response to the CS+ remained at 140%. The difference between the CS+ and CS− lasted during the first 75 extinction trials. Then during the last half of the extinction series, the response to the CS+ and CS− were the same again and were at or near the zero level.

In hippocampus, no change in the "on response" to either stimulus was observed during the course of the pseudoconditioning, habituation series (see Fig. 8). A change during the first 25 trials might have occurred and been unobserved; but there was no further change during successive 25 trials blocks. The response was 120% of control during the first 25 trials and the same during trials 275–300. The response to the CS+ then rose to 150% and the one to the CS— to 140% during the first 25 trials of conditioning. During the next three 25 trial blocks, the CS+ response rose to a maximum of 190%. The response to the CS— rose more slowly and there was a significant difference between the two responses during the two blocks from trials 25–75. Then during the last 100 conditioning trials, the responses to the two stimuli leveled off at 165% and the difference between time disappeared. During extinction, the response to the CS+ fell to about 135%. The difference between the two responses reappeared in extinction; it was significant during four of the six 25-trial blocks. The responses at the end of extinction were significantly above those at the end of habituation.

In hippocampus the "stabilized response" was consistently at 80 or 90% of control during pseudoconditioning and it was relatively unchanged in the course of the habituation series (see Fig. 8). During conditioning the response to the CS+ increased abruptly to 140% in the first 25 trials; it remained at about this level during the remainder of the conditioning series. The response to the CS— increased to only slightly above the 100% level, and there was a significant difference between the two responses during all eight 25-trial blocks of the conditioning series. During extinction the response to the CS+ declined to 120% during the first 74 trials and then remained at this level, 30 points above the preconditioning level. The response to the CS— leveled off at the 100% level, still significantly above its preconditioning level, and still significantly below the response to the CS+.

A substantial change between the first and last 25-trial blocks in the initial pseudoconditioning series was taken as indicating that a response underwent habituation. A large increase above the preconditioning levels during conditioning trials was taken as indicating that a response was modified by conditioning. A subsequent decline to preconditioning levels was taken as evidence of its extinction. Any large difference between CS+ and CS— responses during conditioning or extinction provided evidence that the response exhibited discrimination.

The midbrain "on response" exhibited habituation, conditioning, and extinction. There was discrimination only during the early part of the extinction series and this was not statistically reliable. The midbrain "stabilized response" also underwent habituation, conditioning, and extinction. In this case there was clear discrimination exhibited during conditioning. It did not appear until late in the conditioning series and it was statistically significant only during the last two blocks of conditioning (trials 150–200).

The hippocampal "on response" exhibited conditioning. There was no prior habituation because a large response in this area did not appear until after conditioning. Surprisingly there was no indication that extinction was complete or still underway at the end of the 150-trial extinction series; the response declined at first but then stabilized and gave no hint of further decline during the last 75-extinction trials. In the end it was far above and statistically above the preconditioning levels. Discrimination appeared and was statistically significant during the first part of the conditioning series; it disappeared during the latter half of conditioning and then reappeared in the subsequent extinction series.

The hippocampal "stabilized response" exhibited all the same features as the hippocampal "on response" but all of the effects were larger and more significant. There was no change during habituation; the response started out below control levels and stayed there. There was marked conditioning which appeared immediately and lasted through all eight 25-trial blocks. There was not complete extinction nor any sign that extinction was continuing beyond the 100th extinction trial. Most remarkable was the total discrimination which appeared in large and significant fashion during the first 25 conditioning trials and was then exhibited in all 25-trial blocks of conditioning and extinction.

There was a dramatic difference between the data from the midbrain and hippocampal units. The midbrain units showed clear and continuous habituation during the long series of preliminary trials, and a similar course of changes during the final extinction trials. The hippocampal units showed no particular change between the first 25 trials of habituation and trials 275–300; and the "new" response that appeared in the course of conditioning did not disappear in extinction. While there was some attenuation, this was complete by the end of the first 100 extinction trials, after which there was no further trend toward extinction of the still significantly augmented hippocampal response. It seemed as if the hippocampal firing rates were set in one steady state all during the habituation procedure, and had been shifted to a different steady state by the end of the extinction series. Perhaps a further series of extinction trials, or time alone would eventually have shifted the firing rate back to that which had been observed during habituation; but the last 50 extinction trials had no discernible effect. Correlated with this difference between midbrain and hippocampus in regard to habituation and extinction was a difference in discrimination: Discrimination appeared to be rapid and relatively stable in hippocampus and it did not extinguish; discrimination was slow in appearing in the midbrain and it disappeared readily in extinction.

For three reasons caution is required in comparing the hippocampal data reported here with that of previously reported experiments (Adey et al., 1950; Grastyan, 1959; Pickenhain & Klingberg, 1967). First, most of the older data were obtained by observation of hippocampal slow wave activity while the present data were obtained by observation of unit responses. As it is not clear whether a negative or positive relation exists between the two, they must not be uncritically considered as correlated indices of hippocampal activity. Second, most of the older reports involved a relatively small number of trials. In the present experiments the large number of trials in each block may have permitted an early and rapid habituation process in the hippocampus to occur without its being observed. Previous reports of Grastyan (1959) and Pickenhain and Klingberg (1967) have indicated that startle reactions and correlated hippocampal desynchronization occurred only during the first few trials and that thereafter, hippocampal slow waves occurred during orientation responses. This set of processes and even the later habituation of the orientation reactions and the associated hippocampal slow wave responses might have been completed during the first 25 trials in our experiment and it might, therefore, have escaped our observations. In fact, because our "conditioning" of hippocampal units was to all intents complete by the end of 25 trials, it seems particularly likely that habituation might have proceeded to completion with similar rapidity. Third, most of the older experiments involved overt and covert movements associated with startle and orienting reactions. The overt and even many of the covert movements would have caused our data-taking apparatus to reject the data and therefore the data in the present experiment were collected from trials during which such movements did not occur. Because it seems particularly likely that some hippocampal EEG changes, particularly the ones observed early in habituation, are associated with such movements, it should not be too surprising if these early changes did not appear in our data.

The failure of hippocampal neurons in our experiment to respond to novel stimuli and the response of these neurons to conditioned stimuli was superficially parallel to the findings of Grastyan (1959) and Pickenhain and Klingberg (1967) who observed hippocampal slow waves. However, because of the difference in number of trials between their experiments and ours and because of the difference in dependent variables there is no strong reason to believe that the processes they observed were related to the ones which we observed. Grastyan (1959) supposed that the hippocampal slow wave response was the concomitant of the overt orientation response, and Pickenhain and Klingberg (1967) supposed that an information "comparator" in hippo-campus served a mediating role in nonautomatic, purposive behavior. The latter view is also consistent with the experiments of Adey *et al.* (1960). The idea is that stimulus input is compared with remembered information in these nonautomatic behavior processes, and that hippocampus is involved in mediating the comparison. This view bears some similarity to the possibility which I have recently found to be attractive: namely, that the hippocampus might function as a temporary memory register participating in the control of operant behavior.

III. Résumé

Before elaborating on this possibility the significant features of our own data should be reviewed. In the first place we found a family of units in the anterior part of the midbrain whose firing rates were accelerated both prior to and subsequent to the onset of motivationally significant environmental events providing the animal was in a prepared and expectant state. The firing of these neurons did not appear to be "representational." That is, the neurons did not fire, especially during time periods related to food or water or during stimulation with one stimulus or another, except insofar as the different stimuli were related to the animal's motivational state. In the quiet waking experiments, these units fired rapidly at the beginning of the waiting period when the expectancy was initiated and just prior to reward when the expectancy was again high. In the experiments where animals pressed a pedal and waited for an informative auditory signal and then a reward, these units fired rapidly just prior to the presentation of the informative signal, and this high firing rate was then sustained or augmented if the signal initiated or sustained a motivationally relevant expectancy. In the Pavlovian conditioning experiments, these neurons fired rapidly at the onset of novel stimulation. This response habituated readily, however, both during the continuation of the stimulus, and in the couse of repeated stimulus presentations. When interest in the stimulus was revived during conditioning, the neuronal accelerated firing was also restored. And gradually in the course of conditioning, the response came to favor the more meaningful of two stimuli, particularly during the latter part of the 1-sec auditory stimulus, just prior to reinforcement, and in the latter part of the conditioning experiment after 100 or more conditioning trials. The response pattern then disappeared again during the extinction procedure at a time when the animal's interest in a stimulus appeared to wane. It is not unreasonable to suppose on the basis of these data that a relatively continuous but nonspecific motivational effect was involved.

In hippocampus we found a family of units with some similar characteristics but some differences. The most interesting differences all contributed to suggesting a discontinuous succession of steady states of the sort that characterizes an information-laden process. First, there was the fact that different neurons in hippocampus showed different responses while the response patterns of midbrain units were stereotyped. Second was the fact that there was a class of hippocampal units which did not change during momentary changes in the expectancy state even though they did appear to be reasonably stable correlates of the anticipated goal objects. That is, they often responded during the "expectancy" of one goal or the other but not both; while midbrain units were responding in anticipation of both. Third was the fact that in the Pavlovian experiments these neurons did not appear to respond to novel stimulation and held at a steady state all during habituation. Then they responded to stimuli which had been given motivationally significant meanings in the course of associative procedures. They showed clear and sudden discrimination between the CS+ and CS− . Finally, at a time when overt skeletal responses and accompanying emotional responses (indexed by the responses of the midbrain units) had disappeared, and at a time when the residual memory was "only informational" or only cognitive there was a new steady state but the effects of conditioning were still apparent in the firing patterns of hippocampal neurons. One might imagine that there was still a memory trace; and observation showed that there was still a hippocampal response. During further extinction or time alone this response might disappear (quite suddenly perhaps) but it did not disappear *pari passu* with the subsidence of skeletal and emotional reactions.

IV. The Hippocampus as a Processor

The well-known neuroanatomy and neurophysiology of hippocampus make it an appealing focal point for a discussion of interpretive schemes related to the problem of learning and reinforcement. The neuroanatomy of this older section of cortex is highly organized and the organization is well understood. Therefore if some aspects of the learning process occur in hippocampus or if it is only a guide to how other parts of the brain work it seems that a study of the hippocampus might make it a " Rosetta Stone " (to borrow a term from Evarts, 1967) to guide our unravelling of higher functions. Therefore, the conclusion will consist of showing how certain features of hippocampal organization might suit it for particular information handling functions.

In order to convey the author's view as to what might go on in one of the hippocampal registers, a brief discussion about an associational model for short-term learning and reinforcement would be appropriate. Imagine first a recording device having the form of a ladder, being similar in this respect to the DNA molecule which is supposed to carry the record of genetic information, but differing in several respects. Think of the rungs of the ladder as constituting the individual memories, and multiply them in your mind's eye so that there are as many hundreds of thousands as may be needed. Now again in your mind's eye, multiply the sides of the ladder so that instead of being two there are some 30 or 100 longitudinal elements contacting each rung, and let the messages coming into or going out of the memory be coded by the activation of permutations or combinations of these linear elements. Next, divide these longitudinal elements into three classes; and let the first class code the sensory environment, the second class code the on-going skeletal behavior, and the third class code the motivational or emotional state of the animal.

Let us think how it might work when recording a sequence of events. Remember that the rungs, or short elements represent the memories or traces or "words" in this apparatus; and the longitudinal elements carry the messages into or out of the store. We will speak of the longitudinal elements as the digit lines, using a convention which is common in the computer sciences (see Fig. 9). Suppose, now, that the first message, (that is, the record of the first instant) is inscribed on one of the memory elements. Then the record of the next instant is inscribed on its successor. And some clock or "program counter" steps down from rung to rung (memory to memory) as the instants go by so that the temporal array of events in the course of the recorded sequence becomes transformed into a spatial array of memories in the recording device (see Fig. 10). The clock might activate the short elements (memories) in succession. By activating them it might cause them to make a record. The message from the "sensory–motor–emotional" coding apparatuses might consist of an activation of a particular subset of the digit lines. Then the recording itself could consist simply in the establishment of a communications link, a bidirectional "synapse," between the two kinds of elements, the link being forged by the simultaneous activation of the two elements. This is approximately the way the random access memory of a computer works (see Fig. 11). If we imagine this as an erasable, temporary store, we must perhaps solve the problem of finding a starting place, but that could be easily handled by forming our ladder into an endless loop so that you might think of it now as a circular picket fence (see Fig. 12). Each inscription would be made on a succeeding picket, its older message being erased at this time.

Think next how it might work later, not as a recall device, which is fairly simple, but as a behavior control apparatus. Because each of the digit lines crosses each of the memories, a new message is not merely inscribed in its appropriate place at the end of the list but it also has access to all former memories (at least all of those still in the list). The pattern of a present moment would thus "scan" all of the memories (rungs) in the array. Any particular memory would be "reactivated" (in some fashion different from that occurring at the time of its inscription) if an input pattern in the digit lines had a sufficient similarity to the pattern recorded in that particular trace (see Fig. 13). The actual degree of similarity required would be preset for the recording device as a whole by means of some sort of "gain" control. A memory element on being reactivated in this fashion would have two kinds of effect. One would be for it to reactivate (in perhaps attenuated fashion) those digit lines with which it had been coupled at the time of its inscription but which were not involved in its reactivation this time. That is, some of the digits coupled to

MEMORY ELEMENTS = ADDRESSES

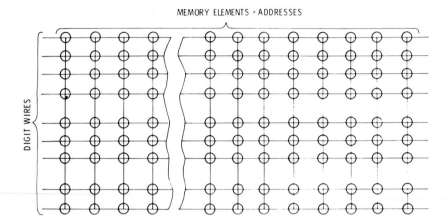

Fig. 9. *Schematic drawing of a random access computer memory.* The circular objects are "magnetic cores." They function as "labile, bidirectional synapses," being "set" by simultaneous activation of intersecting wires; once "set" they form a temporary communications link between the two wires.

MEMORY ELEMENTS

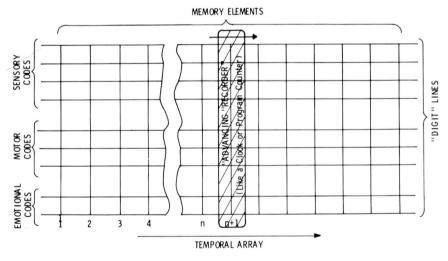

Fig. 10. Utilization of a random access memory as a sequential recorder by recording successive events on successive memory addresses.

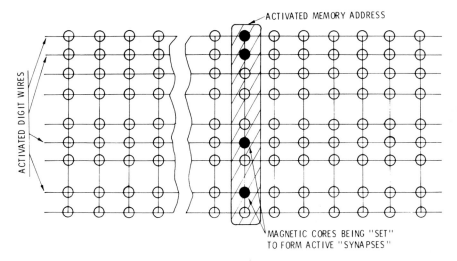

Fig. 11. *Storing a trace.* When currents of proper type flow simultaneously through the two wires that pass through a single magnetic core, they reset it in such a fashion that an appropriate current passed later through one of the wires will cause a pulse to occur in the other.

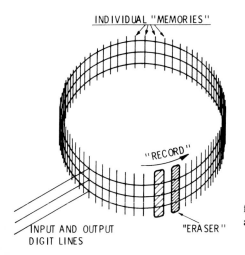

Fig. 12. A random access memory formed into a continuous loop to make a temporary memory register.

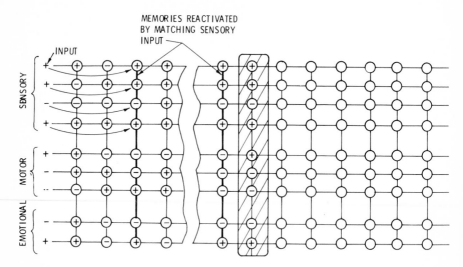

Fig. 13. *Scanning a random access memory with the digit wires.* Ordinarily a random access memory is "read" by passing an appropriate current through the word lines and recording the output from the digit lines. Technically it would be simple to scan it by passing appropriate currents through the digit lines and looking then to see which word lines were most activated (i.e., which ones had the most nearly matching patterns).

this memory would not be involved in its reactivation this time, and these would be the ones which, profiting from the reactivation, would now be activated by the memory itself, perhaps in an attenuated fashion as compared to the kind of activation induced by the sensory–motor–emotional coding apparatuses. Besides reactivating the missing pattern elements (digit lines), there might also be some mechanisms whereby the memory would impose a suppressing force on digit lines which were not part of its pattern. In addition to these effects on the digit lines, the reactivation of a memory would also cause a second kind of effect, namely to activate those memory traces (rungs) which constituted its successors, and thus a wave of activation would move forward along that dimension of the memory device which represented the temporal sequence of recorded events (see Fig. 14).

If we stop to think now of the forces acting on the digit lines we find several. There are the forces imposed by the codes representing the current state of the environment and the organism. There are the constraints imposed by all of the memory elements which have just been activated by the patterns contained in the digit lines, and there are the constraints imposed by the successors of those activated memories. There would often be many different initial memories or many different successor memories going at the same time, some with common patterns, others with diverse patterns. Since we must suppose that the digit lines form a single system, they would provide a matrix or

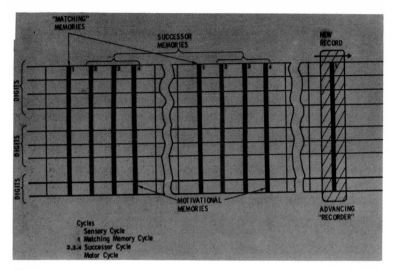

Fig. 14. *Repeated record of a recurring event sequence.* If sensory aspects matching the first element were applied, this might activate previous matching memories during a "matching memory cycle" and these in turn might activate their successors (2, 3, 4) during a "successor memory cycle"; finally, if one of the successors had a link to appropriate emotional digits, this might activate the motor components (of memory number 2 perhaps) during an ensuing "motor cycle." Using gating and timing hardware currently available it would be relatively easy to build an electronic equivalent of this device. The cycles are: sensory, matching memory (1), successor (2, 3, 4) and motor.

"field" mediating interaction among coding apparatus and the varied memory elements. We can imagine that a given digit line would be activated or not depending upon the number of initial memories acting upon it, or the number of successor memories acting upon it, and the amount of facilitation from coding apparatus, and perhaps also depending on the number of inhibitory processes acting against it. These might act all at once or there might be cycles succeeding one another in time: (1) coder control, (2) initial memory control, (3) successor memory control. And this might be followed by (4) a cycle in which the memory apparatus would control an output.

Let us suppose that these cycles did exist and that a given digit line during the memory cycles [(2) and (3)], would be activated or not, depending on the total sum of excitatory and suppressor forces acting on it during a given cycle. This required excitatory sum might be a variable controlled by a second gain control mechanism. In any event, a certain number of digit lines would be activated during the initial memory cycle, and during the several successor cycles that might follow.

If the principle of a firing period followed by a refractory period were imposed upon the reactivated memory elements, then each successor might be activated by its predecessor, and yet fire during a period when the predecessor would be silent. This would provide for a differentiation of the initial memory cycle from the various successor cycles, and for the differentiation of the successor cycles from one another. Depending on the ratio of the brief firing period to the longer refractory period, the succession would move forward from element to element for some number of steps before the originator would fire a second time, or perhaps before the sensory–motor–emotional coding apparatus would recycle the whole system.

If a recurring sequence had been recorded by the device, a group of "matching waves" of activity would advance simultaneously along the "time line"; there would be one for each time the repeated sequence had occurred. One might suppose that if there had been sufficient repetition, these matching waves would control a succession of patterns in the digit lines. Let us neglect for the moment what this might mean for those digit lines involved in representing sensory codes *as this might be relatively unimportant from a behavioral point of view.* Let us suppose that reactivation of digit lines involved in motor codes if followed by certain conditions could cause reperformance of the coded behaviors.

What would be the conditions? As the wave of activity progressed along the time line, it might set a motor buffer, i.e., prime a behavior, getting it ready to be released into action. It would perhaps be the behavior correlated with the first successor. If the wave of activity subsequently reached a memory element which contained a positive emotional record then the primed motor buffer might be triggered completely and the motor act correlated with the first successor might be caused to occur. In any event, the hypothesis supposes a rapid (and in the human being, unconscious) run-through of a series of successors until a positive emotional memory would be arrived at and then the actual performance of the first step in the formerly "rewarded" behavioral sequence.

The function of this mnemonic device, therefore, would be to guide behavior in the pursuit of positive reinforcements. During a particular cycle, a variety of events would occur. First, the input would be stored on a new word line for later use. At the same time, the input would scan all the previously stored word lines and would activate those with which it had a sufficient degree of pattern similarity. Each of these matching memories would then activate its successor; and that one would then activate its successor, and so on. The activation of successors by their antecedents would go on for several steps before recycling. All of the memories matching a given input pattern would be activated simultaneously, and during the next step of the cycle, all the first successors would be activated simultaneously, and then all the second successors and so on. During this kind of activation, each memory element would "tend" to reactivate those digit lines with which it had been connected by an earlier information storage process, but several such activated words would need to act in concert upon a digit in order to activate it. If motor digits were activated during this cycle, their output to actual behavioral processes would be gated and no behavior would occur. When positive emotional digits were activated (in sufficient number) during this cycle, they would activate an element which would open the output gate and cause the behaviors actually to occur. Therefore, if a familiar stimulus pattern were presented, and if it had been followed repeatedly by a sequence of behaviors terminating in reward, the stimulus would reactivate the matching memories (stored during previous instances of the behavior) and these would activate their successors. These would activate the memory of a reward; and this would release the succession of behaviors.

An electronic device with these functions could be fabricated with currently available hardware. Its main element would be a standard random access memory which has the form of a grid with a relatively small number of very long digit lines, and a much larger number of somewhat shorter word lines. The photographs and drawings of such grids which regularly appear in electronic treatises often have an appearance which is reminiscent of actual drawings, or schematic drawings made by Golgi, Cajal, and Lorente de Nó (see Lorente de Nó, 1934) in their interpretive anatomy of the hippocampus (see Figs. 15 and 16). An important difference is that the "synapses" of the random access memory are bidirectional and apparently need to be to perform the indicated functions. The accepted view is that the biological synapses in hippocampus are not.

Because the scheme is imaginative in any event, one might imagine bidirectional synapses in hippocampus even though these have not yet been demonstrated. Neurophysiologists, however, have generally found this suggestion obnoxious. Happily, I have recently found that the scheme itself (as a design for a mnemonic apparatus) and its match to hippocampus structure are improved if we accept the constraint of undirectional synapses.

In describing the properties of the mechanisms we bypassed the problem of what reactivation of the digit lines might mean in the case of those digit lines involved in representing sensory codes as this might be relatively unimportant from a behavioral point of view. It is this very unimportance that provides the clue. Bidirectional synapses are not needed because motor processes would be the only ones that would need to be efferent to the memory elements, and similarly sensory processes are the only ones that would need to be afferent. That is, sensory inputs would reactivate memories, and memories would reactivate motor processes. Each of the memory elements itself would have the unitary character of the single word line of a computer memory but it could have all the sensory digit lines crossing through its afferent side (its dendrites) and all of the motor digit lines crossing through its efferent side (its axons) (see Fig. 17). If such a grid existed in the brain, we

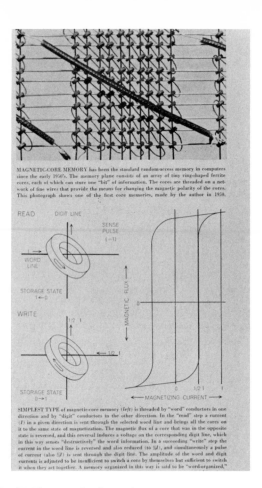

Fig. 15. Photograph of a random access computer memory.

might find that sensory axons would cross memory dendrites, and memory axons would cross motor dendrites. It might look like a double grid, with all A axons crossing through the B dendrites and all B axons crossing through the C dendrites.

Unlikely as it may seem we have only to substitute terms, and this is the structure of the hippocampus. In hippocampus, the input comes along the perforant pathway, across the hippocampal cleft, and innervates the dentate granule cells; the dentate cells might, therefore, be the sensory array. These give rise to large " mossy fibers."

So far as the eye can see, each large mossy fiber makes a very large number of "club-footed" synapses with all of the CA4 and CA3 dendrites in any given plane of section (see Fig. 18).

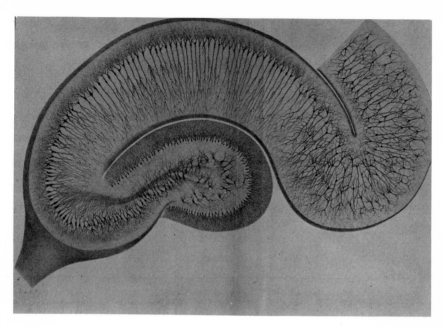

Fig. 16. *A drawing of mouse hippocampus made by Golgi in 1884.* Shown in fine grey lines are the "mossy" fibers. They originate in the very small "dentate granule" cells which are arrayed in the form of a horseshoe surrounding these fibers at their right-hand side. The mossy fibers pass through the dendrites of two sets of much larger neurons. One of these, scattered in disarray far inside the horseshoe is the CA4 field of the hippocampus. The other set, more orderly, half inside and half outside, is the CA3 field of hippocampus. Each mossy fiber makes a synapse "de passant" with many or all of the dendrites through which it passes. The very orderly arch extending from the end of the mossy fibers along the top of the picture is the CA1 field of hippocampus; through its dendrites pass axons (known as the Schaffer collaterals) from the CA3 and CA4 neurons. Beyond the CA1 field on the far right is a less orderly field, the "subiculum." It gives rise to fibers which innervate mainly the dentate granules, but also to a lesser degree the other fields of the hippocampus.

Finally, all of the CA4 and CA3 neurons give rise to the so-called Schaffer collaterals, and these cross all of the dendrites in the CA1 field (see Fig. 19).

It takes only redrawing to show that the hippocampus, for reasons the author cannot fathom, was organized in exactly the manner of our scheme (see Fig. 20).

Input from the dentate gyrus would carry in coded form the sensory patterns from the environment, memory elements in CA4 and CA3 would store these patterns by modified synaptic connections in their dendrites and would simultaneously monitor and store concomitant motor patterns by modified synaptic connections along their Schaffer collaterals. Patterns of CA1 activity would later carry the output codes of appropriate motor behaviors.

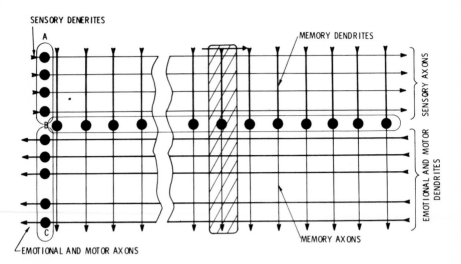

Fig. 17. *A random access memory device utilizing neurons and unidirectional labile synapses rather than wires and magnetic cores.* The black circles represent the neuron somata, the lines tipped with arrow heads pointing toward somata are dendrites, those tipped with arrow heads pointing away are axons. Sensory axons cross memory dendrites, memory axons cross motor and "emotional" dendrites. Functions would be the same as those in Fig. 14.

If it worked this way, then recordings from dentate should follow the sensory input, recordings from CA4 and CA3 should reveal patterns arbitrarily and temporarily related to significant and repeated features of an experimental environment, and recordings from CA1 would be related somehow to behaviors and therefore they might be conditionable by operant techniques. We are at present in a position to make the appropriate tests and to find out whether these things are so.

A reward stimulus might make a motivational inscription on both the afferent and the efferent sides of the memory elements. Therefore we might find some family of fibers which simultaneously innervated the dentate and the CA1 fields, and we might even find that its stimulation would be rewarding.

Both Cajal and Lorente de Nó made it clear that some parts of the perforant pathway bifurcate to go partly across the hippocampal cleft into dentate and partly along the cleft into the CA1 field (see Fig. 21). Recent self-stimulation studies of Mahut (personal communication) seem to indicate that self-stimulation can be obtained by stimulating some parts of this pathway in both of these areas and at its root in the subiculum.

In summary, it seems possible that sensory, motor, and motivational codes might project into gridlike structures such as those very orderly ones of hippocampus or the less orderly ones of other parts of paleo- and neocortex.

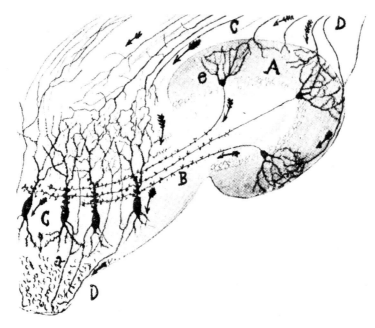

Fig. 18. Drawing by Cajal of dentate granule cells (marked A or e) in the horseshoe on the right, giving rise to mossy fibers (marked B) which then pass through the succession of CA4 and CA3 cells (marked C at the left) making large and interesting synapses with each of these neurons. The mossy fibers might be the "sensory axons"; and the CA4 and CA3 neurons might be "memory" neurons (at least for some temporary storage processes). A set of incoming fibers (marked C and D) at the top right is the "perforant pathway"; it comes from the "subiculum"; mainly to the dentate granules, but also through CA1 and on to the CA3 neurons.

Here they would have a function analogous to that of the digit lines in a random access memory. Certain other neurons within the gridlike structures would serve a function analogous to the word lines in such a memory. Along their dendritic arrays they would monitor sensory input and along their axonal arrays they would monitor motor processes. Emotional processes might have both sensory and motor aspects. High levels of excitation or repeated neuronal firing would characterize a memory element at the time of recording. Simultaneous firing in the sensory code elements passing through its dendrites and in the motor code elements passing through its axons would cause temporary synaptic modifications. In virtue of these, similar sensory inputs would later have appropriate connections to reactivate the memory elements and the memory elements would have appropriate connections to reactivate behavioral elements.

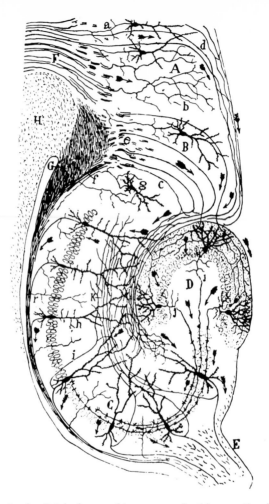

Fig. 19. *Drawing by Cajal of mouse hippocampus.* In this case, the dentate gyrus is just above D, the mossy fibers pass downward through the CA3 field which is marked C. Each CA3 neuron gives rise to a bifurcating axon; one part goes off and away at E, but the other part crosses upward to form the pathway marked K. These are the Schaffer collaterals and they pass through the CA3 dendrites. These might form the "memory axons," and the CA1 field might form the motor and emotional outflow aspects of a temporary memory system.

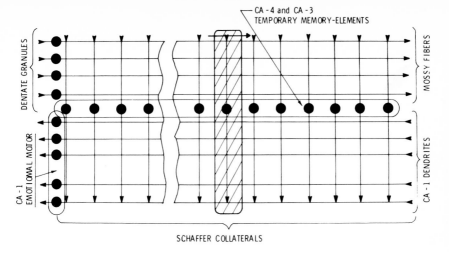

Fig. 20. A schematic drawing of the hippocampus, showing only the dentate granules sending mossy fibers through the CA4 and CA3 dendrites, and the CA4 and CA3 neurons sending Schaffer collaterals through CA1 dendrites.

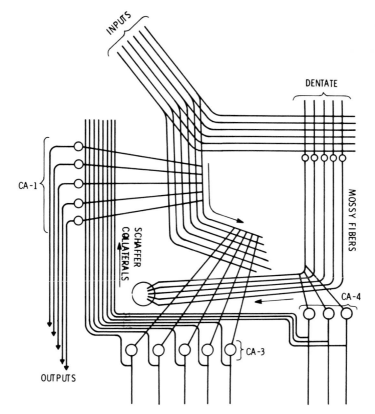

Fig. 21. *A more complicated schematic drawing of hippocampus.* This shows how the inputs (perforant pathway) sometimes bifurcate to innervate the dentate on one side of the "hippocampal cleft" and the CA1 and CA3 fields on the other side of the cleft.

ACKNOWLEDGMENTS

The author wishes to express his appreciation to his co-workers, Drs. P. J. Best, T. Hirano, W. D. Mink, and M. I. Phillips; and to W. Wetzel, G. Baldrighi, W. Allan, and J. Frey for instrumentation, surgical, experimental, and histological services, respectively.

REFERENCES

Adey, W. R., Dunlop, C. W., & Hendrix, C. E. Hippocampal slow waves. Distribution and phase relationships in the course of approach learning. *Archives Neurology*, 1960, **3**, 74–90.

Buchwald, J. S., Halas, E. S. & Schramm, S. Changes in cortical and subcortical unit activity during behavioral conditioning. *Physiology and Behavior*, 1966, **1**, 11–22.

Ellison, G. D., Humphrey, G. L., & Feeney, D. Some electrophysiological correlates of two behavioral states. *Journal of Comparative and Physiological Psychology*, 1968, **66**, 340–348.

Evarts, E. V. Internal workings of the brain. Review of Eccles, J. C., Ito, M., & Szentagothal, J. *The cerebellum as a neuronal machine*. *Science*, 1967, **158**, 1439–1440.

Grastyan, E. The hippocampus and higher nervous activities. In M. A. B Brazier (Ed.), *The central nervous system and behavior*. Transactions of the Second Conference. New York: Josiah Macy, Jr. Found., 1959. Pp. 119–205.

Hirano, R., Best, P. J., & Olds, J. Units during habituation, discrimination learning and extinction. *Electroencephalography and Clinical Neurophysiology*, 1970, **28**, 127–135.

Isaacson, R. L., & Wickelgren, W. O. Hippocampal ablation and passive avoidance. *Science*, 1962, **138**, 1104–1106.

Kamikawa, K., McIlwain, J. T., & Adey, W. R. Response patterns of thalamic neurons during classical conditioning. *Electroencephalography and Clinical Neurophysiology*, 1964, **17**, 485–496.

Kawakami, M., Seto, K., Terasawa, E., & Yoshida, K. Mechanisms in the limbic system controlling reproductive functions of the ovary with special reference to the positive feedback of progestin to the hippocampus. In W. R. Adey & T. Tokizane (Eds.), *Structure and function of the limbic system. Progress in brain research*. Vol. 27. Amsterdam: Elsevier, 1967. Pp. 69–102.

Lorente de Nó, R. Studies of the structure of the cerebral cortex. II. Continuation of the study of the ammonic system. *Journal für Psychologie und Neurologie*, 1934, **46**(2 & 3), 113–177.

MacLean, P. D., Denniston, R. H., Dua, S., & Ploog, D. W. Hippocampal changes with brain stimulation eliciting penile erection. In *Physiologie de l'hippocampe. Colloques Internationaux du Centre National de la Recherche Scientifique*, 1962, **107**, 492–510.

Milner, B. Psychological defects, produced by temporal lobe excision. *Research Publications, Association for Research in Nervous and Mental Diseases*, 1958, **36**, 244–257.

Niki, H. Effects of hippocampal ablation on learning in the rat. In W. R. Adey & T. Tokizane (Eds.), *Structure and function of the limbic system. Progress in brain research*. Vol. 27. Amsterdam: Elsevier, 1967. Pp. 305–317.

Olds, J., & Hirano, T. Conditioned responses of hippocampal and other neurons. *Electroencephalography and Clinical Neurophysiology*, 1969, **26**, 159–166.

Olds, J., Mink, W. D., & Best, P. J. Single unit patterns during anticipatory behavior. *Electroencephalography and Clinical Neurophysiology*, 1969, **26**, 144–158.

Orbach, J., Milner, B., & Rasmussen, T. Learning and retention in monkeys after amygdala-hippocampus resection. *Archives of Neurology*, 1960, **3**, 230–251.

Phillips, M. I., & Olds, J. Unit activity: motivation-dependent responses from midbrain neurons. *Science*, 1969, **165**, 1269–1271.

Pickenhain, L., & Klingberg, F. Hippocampal slow wave activity as a correlate of basic behavioral mechanisms in the rat. In W. R. Adey & T. Tokizane (Eds.), *Structure and function of the limbic system. Progress in brain research.* Vol. 27. Amsterdam: Elsevier, 1967. Pp. 218–227.

Travis, R. P., & Sparks, D. L. Changes in unit activity during stimuli associated with food and shock reinforcement. *Physiology and Behavior*, 1967, **2**, 171–177.

Ursin, R., Ursin, H., & Olds, J. Self-stimulation of hippocampus in rats. *Journal of Comparative and Physiological Psychology*, 1966, **61**, 353–359.

Yoshii, N., & Ogura, N. Studies on the unit discharge of brainstem reticular formation in the cat. *Medical Journal of Osaka University*, 1960, **11**, 1–17.

GENERAL DISCUSSION

E. ROY JOHN

Dr. Bureš and Dr. Weiskrantz have raised the question in their presentation of the spread of information and the possible diffuseness of storage in different brain areas. Dr. Olds just recently, still stored in your short-term memory, presented a model for how information might be stored and retrieved. I would like to discuss some data from our own laboratory which are relevant to some of these questions (see Figures 1 and 2). These data come from animals who were trained to discriminate between two frequencies of flicker for approach and avoidance. Let's call the two frequencies V-1 and V-2 for Visual-1 and -2. After these animals reached a very high criterion of discrimination they are challenged with V-3, which is a generalization stimulus located midway between V-1 and V-2. Sometimes the animal responds to V-3 by behaving as though it were V-1 (V_3CR) and sometimes he responds to V-3 by behaving as though it were V-2 (V_3CAR). We average the evoked responses caused by the same physical stimulus separately, depending on how the animal subsequently responds to it. The waveshape observed during V_3CR closely resembled the usual response to V_1, the conditioned approach stimulus (V_1CR), while during trials resulting in V_3CAR, the response closely resembled the usual response to V_2 in avoidance (V_2CAR). When we compare the evoked potential averages elicited by V-3, treated as though it were V-1 (V_3CR) with the evoked potential averages elicited by V-3 treated as though it were V-2, (V_3CAR), the differences are so significant that even the relatively small components exceed the .001 level. Thus, the evoked response waveshape is not determined by the physical stimulus. Only the early portion is.

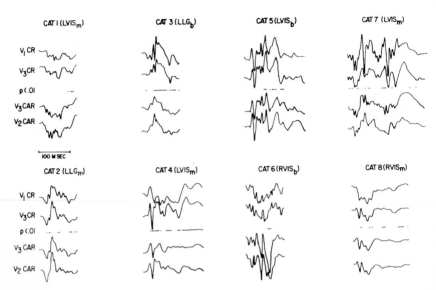

Fig. 1. Average response wave shapes recorded from one structure in each experimental animal, computed from last 4 seconds of trials resulting in correct performance of a lever-press for food during presentation of flicker at frequency 1 (V_1CR), correct performance of a lever-press to avoid shock during presentation of flicker at frequency 2 (V_2CAR), and during presentations of flicker at an intermediate frequency 3 resulting in generalized approach (V_3CR) or avoidance (V_3CAR). Interrupted line between the second and third wave shape in each group indicates those intervals during which the significance of the difference between V_3CR and V_3CAR exceeds the 0.1 level. LLG, Left lateral geniculate body; LVIS, left visual cortex; subscript m denotes monopolar derivation versus a frontal reference; subscript b indicates bipolar derivation taken between two electrodes 1 mm apart. Frequencies were as follows: Cats 1 and 2, $V_1 = 7.7$, $V_2 = 3.1$, $V_3 = 5.0$; cat 3, $V_1 = 3.1$, $V_2 = 7.7$, $V_3 = 5.0$; cats 4, 5, and 8, $V_1 = 5$, $V_2 = 2$, $V_3 = 3.1$; cat 6, $V_1 = 2.5$, $V_2 = 1.0$, $V_3 = 1.75$; cat 7, $V_1 = 1.0$, $V_2 = 2.5$, $V_3 = 1.75$. Sample size was variable, with an average of 56.

In addition you can observe widespread similarity in the responses of different regions of the brain to this stimulus. (The stimulus is a dim overhead flash, presented to an animal who is sitting in a cage in front of a work panel, which carries two levers. There is a dim light in the cage and the flicker, which is the cue to which he must respond, basically doubles the light level of the visual field. The stimulus is *not* a bright flash at a point in the visual field.) Regions as different as reticular formation, lateral geniculate, visual cortex, and hypothalamus show very similar waveshapes. I should stress that only some regions in the brain show this similarity of waveshape. Not all regions show similar responses and this similarity only occurs when the stimulus is familiar and the phenomenon is most marked in highly overtrained animals. It appears less markedly in animals who have just reached criterion than in

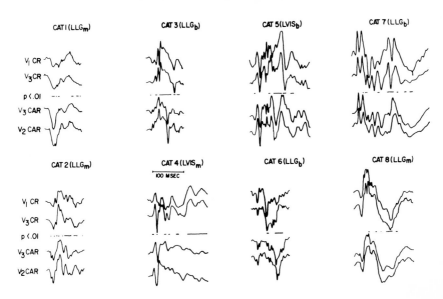

Fig. 2. Response wave shapes, as in Fig. 1, but with averages based upon sequences of evoked potentials selected by the experimenter from the last 4 seconds of multiple behavioral trials, Average sample size, 15.

animals who were trained in 1962 and have been working on various and sundry tasks for us in the last six years. Similarity diminishes if behavioral errors are committed. It is my belief that this similarity of waveshape represents the dynamic coupling between different brain regions. This coupling is not wired in and it is not immutable. Incidentally, this similarity phenomenon has been reported in about 8 or 10 other laboratories during the last 10 years.

After observing this kind of activity for a while we became very curious to find out what was happening on the unit level, because this evidence suggests that as an animal overlearns a response, there may be some kind of spread of the process mediating that response to other regions and a system capable of releasing a specified pattern of activity seems to become established.

To find out what was happening on the unit level we built a chronically implantable microdrive, which carries two microelectrodes to be moved a distance of about 12 mm at will. We compared the averaged evoked potentials and poststimulus time histograms when a differentially trained animal responded correctly to a 2-cps flash, which is the cue to press the right-hand bar on a two-bar work panel for food, with evoked potentials and unit activity caused when the animal generalized (pushed the same right-hand bar) to a 1/sec test stimulus which he had never seen before. The evoked response to the 1/sec test stimulus well reproduced the evoked response caused by the 2/sec conditioned differential stimulus. During such behavioral generalization to the 1/sec stimulus, the poststimulus unit histogram pattern was very closely similar to that which is normally elicited by the appropriate stimulus for that behavior (that is, the 2/sec stimulus to which the animal's interpretation would seem to correspond). Now suppose the animal makes no response to the 1/sec test stimulus. He simply sits there and says that, although he is motivated and working in a random sequence of stimuli, " I don't think this means anything and I'll ignore it." Marked differences in the histogram then occur after about 40 m/sec of latency. In our previous work on difference waveshapes, 40 msec was the time at which these different components, which we called " endogenous components," were produced.

How localized are these brain responses? We recorded the family of post-stimulus histograms generated as we moved the microdrive, over a period of about six months, a distance of 3000 μ. The electrodes were moved, about a week was spent looking at activity in the new position, and then the electrode was advanced to the next position.

We found a basically similar firing pattern throughout the region. Jim (Dr. Olds) mentioned in the talk he just finished that the gross characteristics of the neuronal response seem to have certain similarities from region to region. Any place in this region where we found cells responding to the stimulus, we could decide which stimulus was present by looking at the firing pattern. The report from one region was basically the same as the report from any of the other of the eight positions we studied. To me, what I have just described looks like evidence for diffuse participation of ensembles of cells in differential signaling. This is not a task which is an existential discrimination (a specified action must be performed if signal is detected); this is a differential discrimination that the animal cannot resolve by mere detection, he must decode the signal. The populations participating in decoding these signals seem to be very widespread. Now the question arises, what is the contribution of the discharge of a single cell to information processing. I would like to have heard before this symposium terminated a discussion of that question, because we have heard quite a lot of data about single cells and about information processing, be it in the hypothalamus or someplace else. I suggest that evidence of the sort that I have presented supports the idea that processing, by which I mean interpretation of the information being handled by an ensemble, may consist not in whether any particular cell fires or does not fire, but in the temporal patterning of the departure from baseline or random patterns of discharge in the ensemble. To restate this, the information in the ensemble may be defined by the time course of changes in entropy. I am not proposing that the whole brain might work in this fashion, because there is a discrete set of peripheral receptors which provide information that must be brought centrally by stipulated sense lines and there is a specific set of peripheral effectors for which there is a final common path. I am talking about what is in between. How the translation is made from the specific to the statistical and back to the specific I do not know, but I submit that regularities of the sort that I have described to you are unlikely to occur by chance. Thank you.

SUBJECT INDEX

THIS VOLUME MAY CIRCULATE FOR 1 WEEK.
RENEWALS MAY BE MADE IN PERSON OR BY
TELEPHONE - TR 9 - 9000   x 7332

DATE DUE	DATE RETURNED
FEB 1 1971	FEB 2 1971
FEB 9 1971	FEB 4 1971
FEB 16 1971	FEB 23 1971
FEB 23 1971	MAR 1 1971
MAR 29 1971	MAR 24 1971
JAN 5 1972	JAN 14 1972
JUN 8 1972	JUN 6 1972
APR 5 1973	APR 5 1973